Fourth NLP4 for Internet Freedom: Censorship, Disinformation, and Propaganda (NLP4IF 2021)

Online
6 June 2021

ISBN: 978-1-7138-3025-2

Printed from e-media with permission by:

Curran Associates, Inc.
57 Morehouse Lane
Red Hook, NY 12571

Some format issues inherent in the e-media version may also appear in this print version.

Association for Computational Linguistics
209 N. Eighth Street
Stroudsburg, Pennsylvania 18360

Phone: 1-570-476-8006
Fax: 1-570-476-0860

acl@aclweb.org

Additional copies of this publication are available from:

Curran Associates, Inc.
57 Morehouse Lane
Red Hook, NY 12571 USA
Phone: 845-758-0400
Fax: 845-758-2633
Email: curran@proceedings.com
Web: www.proceedings.com

NLP4IF 2021

NLP for Internet Freedom: Censorship, Disinformation, and Propaganda

Proceedings of the Fourth Workshop

June 6, 2021

Preface

Welcome to the fourth edition of the Workshop on NLP for Internet Freedom: Censorship, Disinformation, and Propaganda. This is the second time we are running the workshop virtually, due to the COVID-19 pandemic. The pandemic has had a profound effect on the lives of people around the globe and, as much cliché as it may sound, we are all in this together. COVID-19 is the first pandemic in history in which technology and social media are being used on a massive scale to help people stay safe, informed, productive and connected. At the same time, the same technology that we rely on to keep us connected and informed is enabling and amplifying an *infodemic* that continues to undermine the global response and is detrimental to the efforts to control the pandemic. In the context of the pandemic, we define an infodemic as deliberate attempts to disseminate false information to undermine the public health response and to advance alternative agendas promoted by groups or individuals. We also realize that there is a vicious cycle: the more content is produced, the more misinformation and disinformation expand. The Internet is overloaded with false cures, such as drinking bleach or colloidal silver, conspiracy theories about the virus' origin, false claims that the COVID-19 vaccine will change patient's DNA or will serve to implant in us a tracking microchip, misinformation about methods such masks and social distancing, myths about the dangers and the real-world consequences of COVID-19. The goal of our workshop is to explore how we can address these issues using natural language processing.

We accepted 20 papers: 11 for the regular track and 9 for the shared tasks. The work presented at the workshop ranges from hate speech detection (Lemmens et al., Markov et al., Bose et al.) to approaches to identify false information and to verify facts (Maronikolakis et al., Bekoulis et al., Weld et al., Hämäläinen et al., Kazemi et al., Alhindi et al., Zuo et al.). The authors focus on different aspects of misinformation and disinformation: misleading headlines vs. rumor detection vs. stance detection for fact-checking. Some work concentrates on detecting biases in news media (e.g., Li & Goldwasser), which in turn contributes to research on propaganda. They all present different technical approaches.

Our workshop featured two shared tasks: Task 1 on Fighting the COVID-19 Infodemic, and Task 2 on Online Censorship Detection. Task 1 asked to predict several binary properties of a tweet about COVID-19, such as whether the tweet contains a verifiable factual claim or to what extent it is harmful to the society/community/individuals; the task was offered in multiple languages: English, Bulgarian, and Arabic. The second task was to predict whether a Sina Weibo tweet will be censored; it was offered in Chinese.

We are also thrilled to be able to bring two invited speakers: 1) Filippo Menczer, a distinguished professor of informatics and computer science at Indiana University, Bloomington, and Director of the Observatory on Social Media; and 2) Margaret Roberts, an associate professor of political science at University of California San Diego.

We thank the authors and the task participants for their interest in the workshop. We would also like to thank the program committee for their help with reviewing the papers and with advertising the workshop.

This material is partly based upon work supported by the US National Science Foundation under Grants No. 1704113 and No. 1828199.

It is also part of the Tanbih mega-project, which is developed at the Qatar Computing Research Institute, HBKU, and aims to limit the impact of "fake news," propaganda, and media bias by making users aware of what they are reading, thus promoting media literacy and critical thinking.

The NLP4IF 2021 Organizers:

Anna Feldman, Giovanni Da San Martino, Chris Leberknight and Preslav Nakov

http://www.netcopia.net/nlp4if/

Organizing Committee

Anna Feldman, Montclair State University
Giovanni Da San Martino, University of Padova
Chris Leberknight, Montclair State University
Preslav Nakov, Qatar Computing Research Institute, HBKU

Program Committee

Firoj Alam, Qatar Computing Research Institute, HBKU
Tariq Alhindi, Columbia University
Jisun An, Singapore Management University
Chris Brew, LivePerson
Meghna Chaudhary, University of South Florida
Jedidah Crandall, Arizona State University
Anjalie Field, Carnegie-Mellon University
Parush Gera, University of South Florida
Yiqing Hua, Cornell University
Jeffrey Knockel, Citizen Lab
Haewoon Kwak, Singapore Management University
Verónica Pérez-Rosas, University of Michigan
Henrique Lopes Cardoso, University of Porto
Yelena Mejova, ISI Foundation
JIng Peng, Montclair State University
Marinella Petrocchi, IIT-CNR
Shaden Shaar, Qatar Computing Research Institute, HBKU
Matthew Sumpter, University of South Florida
Michele Tizzani, ISI Foundation
Brook Wu, New Jersey Institute of Technology

Table of Contents

Identifying Automatically Generated Headlines using Transformers
Antonis Maronikolakis, Hinrich Schütze and Mark Stevenson 1

Improving Hate Speech Type and Target Detection with Hateful Metaphor Features
Jens Lemmens, Ilia Markov and Walter Daelemans 7

Improving Cross-Domain Hate Speech Detection by Reducing the False Positive Rate
Ilia Markov and Walter Daelemans 17

Understanding the Impact of Evidence-Aware Sentence Selection for Fact Checking
Giannis Bekoulis, Christina Papagiannopoulou and Nikos Deligiannis 23

Leveraging Community and Author Context to Explain the Performance and Bias of Text-Based Deception Detection Models
Galen Weld, Ellyn Ayton, Tim Althoff and Maria Glenski 29

Never guess what I heard... Rumor Detection in Finnish News: a Dataset and a Baseline
Mika Hämäläinen, Khalid Alnajjar, Niko Partanen and Jack Rueter 39

Extractive and Abstractive Explanations for Fact-Checking and Evaluation of News
Ashkan Kazemi, Zehua Li, Verónica Pérez-Rosas and Rada Mihalcea 45

Generalisability of Topic Models in Cross-corpora Abusive Language Detection
Tulika Bose, Irina Illina and Dominique Fohr 51

AraStance: A Multi-Country and Multi-Domain Dataset of Arabic Stance Detection for Fact Checking
Tariq Alhindi, Amal Alabdulkarim, Ali Alshehri, Muhammad Abdul-Mageed and Preslav Nakov 57

MEAN: Multi-head Entity Aware Attention Networkfor Political Perspective Detection in News Media
Chang Li and Dan Goldwasser 66

An Empirical Assessment of the Qualitative Aspects of Misinformation in Health News
Chaoyuan Zuo, Qi Zhang and Ritwik Banerjee 76

Findings of the NLP4IF-2021 Shared Tasks on Fighting the COVID-19 Infodemic and Censorship Detection
Shaden Shaar, Firoj Alam, Giovanni Da San Martino, Alex Nikolov, Wajdi Zaghouani, Preslav Nakov and Anna Feldman 82

DamascusTeam at NLP4IF2021: Fighting the Arabic COVID-19 Infodemic on Twitter Using AraBERT
Ahmad Hussein, Nada Ghneim and Ammar Joukhadar 93

NARNIA at NLP4IF-2021: Identification of Misinformation in COVID-19 Tweets Using BERTweet
Ankit Kumar, Naman Jhunjhunwala, Raksha Agarwal and Niladri Chatterjee 99

R00 at NLP4IF-2021 Fighting COVID-19 Infodemic with Transformers and More Transformers
Ahmed Al-Qarqaz, Dia Abujaber and Malak Abdullah Abdullah 104

Multi Output Learning using Task Wise Attention for Predicting Binary Properties of Tweets : Shared-Task-On-Fighting the COVID-19 Infodemic
Ayush Suhane and Shreyas Kowshik 110

iCompass at NLP4IF-2021–Fighting the COVID-19 Infodemic
Wassim Henia, Oumayma Rjab, Hatem Haddad and Chayma Fourati 115

Fighting the COVID-19 Infodemic with a Holistic BERT Ensemble
Georgios Tziafas, Konstantinos Kogkalidis and Tommaso Caselli 119

Detecting Multilingual COVID-19 Misinformation on Social Media via Contextualized Embeddings
Subhadarshi Panda and Sarah Ita Levitan 125

Transformers to Fight the COVID-19 Infodemic
Lasitha Uyangodage, Tharindu Ranasinghe and Hansi Hettiarachchi 130

Classification of Censored Tweets in Chinese Language using XLNet
Shaikh Sahil Ahmed and Anand Kumar M. 136

Workshop Program

Identifying Automatically Generated Headlines using Transformers
Antonis Maronikolakis, Hinrich Schütze and Mark Stevenson

Improving Hate Speech Type and Target Detection with Hateful Metaphor Features
Jens Lemmens, Ilia Markov and Walter Daelemans

Improving Cross-Domain Hate Speech Detection by Reducing the False Positive Rate
Ilia Markov and Walter Daelemans

Understanding the Impact of Evidence-Aware Sentence Selection for Fact Checking
Giannis Bekoulis, Christina Papagiannopoulou and Nikos Deligiannis

Leveraging Community and Author Context to Explain the Performance and Bias of Text-Based Deception Detection Models
Galen Weld, Ellyn Ayton, Tim Althoff and Maria Glenski

Never guess what I heard... Rumor Detection in Finnish News: a Dataset and a Baseline
Mika Hämäläinen, Khalid Alnajjar, Niko Partanen and Jack Rueter

Extractive and Abstractive Explanations for Fact-Checking and Evaluation of News
Ashkan Kazemi, Zehua Li, Verónica Pérez-Rosas and Rada Mihalcea

Generalisability of Topic Models in Cross-corpora Abusive Language Detection
Tulika Bose, Irina Illina and Dominique Fohr

AraStance: A Multi-Country and Multi-Domain Dataset of Arabic Stance Detection for Fact Checking
Tariq Alhindi, Amal Alabdulkarim, Ali Alshehri, Muhammad Abdul-Mageed and Preslav Nakov

MEAN: Multi-head Entity Aware Attention Networkfor Political Perspective Detection in News Media
Chang Li and Dan Goldwasser

An Empirical Assessment of the Qualitative Aspects of Misinformation in Health News
Chaoyuan Zuo, Qi Zhang and Ritwik Banerjee

Findings of the NLP4IF-2021 Shared Tasks on Fighting the COVID-19 Infodemic and Censorship Detection
Shaden Shaar, Firoj Alam, Giovanni Da San Martino, Alex Nikolov, Wajdi Zaghouani, Preslav Nakov and Anna Feldman

No Day Set (continued)

DamascusTeam at NLP4IF2021: Fighting the Arabic COVID-19 Infodemic on Twitter Using AraBERT
Ahmad Hussein, Nada Ghneim and Ammar Joukhadar

NARNIA at NLP4IF-2021: Identification of Misinformation in COVID-19 Tweets Using BERTweet
Ankit Kumar, Naman Jhunjhunwala, Raksha Agarwal and Niladri Chatterjee

R00 at NLP4IF-2021 Fighting COVID-19 Infodemic with Transformers and More Transformers
Ahmed Al-Qarqaz, Dia Abujaber and Malak Abdullah Abdullah

Multi Output Learning using Task Wise Attention for Predicting Binary Properties of Tweets : Shared-Task-On-Fighting the COVID-19 Infodemic
Ayush Suhane and Shreyas Kowshik

iCompass at NLP4IF-2021–Fighting the COVID-19 Infodemic
Wassim Henia, Oumayma Rjab, Hatem Haddad and Chayma Fourati

Fighting the COVID-19 Infodemic with a Holistic BERT Ensemble
Georgios Tziafas, Konstantinos Kogkalidis and Tommaso Caselli

Detecting Multilingual COVID-19 Misinformation on Social Media via Contextualized Embeddings
Subhadarshi Panda and Sarah Ita Levitan

Transformers to Fight the COVID-19 Infodemic
Lasitha Uyangodage, Tharindu Ranasinghe and Hansi Hettiarachchi

Classification of Censored Tweets in Chinese Language using XLNet
Shaikh Sahil Ahmed and Anand Kumar M.

Identifying Automatically Generated Headlines using Transformers

Antonis Maronikolakis
CIS, LMU Munich
antmarakis@cis.lmu.de

Hinrich Schutze
CIS, LMU Munich

Mark Stevenson
University of Sheffield
mark.stevenson@sheffield.ac.uk

Abstract

False information spread via the internet and social media influences public opinion and user activity, while generative models enable fake content to be generated faster and more cheaply than had previously been possible. In the not so distant future, identifying fake content generated by deep learning models will play a key role in protecting users from misinformation. To this end, a dataset containing human and computer-generated headlines was created and a user study indicated that humans were only able to identify the fake headlines in 47.8% of the cases. However, the most accurate automatic approach, transformers, achieved an overall accuracy of 85.7%, indicating that content generated from language models can be filtered out accurately.

1 Introduction

Fake content has been rapidly spreading across the internet and social media, misinforming and affecting users' opinion (Kumar and Shah, 2018; Guo et al., 2020). Such content includes fake news articles[1] and truth obfuscation campaigns[2]. While much of this content is being written by paid writers (Luca and Zervas, 2013), content generated by automated systems is rising. Models can produce text on a far greater scale than it is possible to manually, with a corresponding increase in the potential to influence public opinion. There is therefore a need for methods that can distinguish between human and computer-generated text, to filter out deceiving content before it reaches a wider audience.

While text generation models have received consistent attention from the public as well as from the academic community (Dathathri et al., 2020; Subramanian et al., 2018), interest in the detection of automatically generated text has only arisen more recently (Jawahar et al., 2020). Generative models have several shortcomings and their output text has characteristics that distinguish it from human-written text, including lower variance and smaller vocabulary (Holtzman et al. (2020); Gehrmann et al. (2019)). These differences between real and generated text can be used by pattern recognition models to differentiate between the two. In this paper we test this hypothesis by training classifiers to detect headlines generated by a pretrained GPT-2 model (Radford et al., 2019). Headlines were chosen as it has been shown that shorter generated text is harder to identify than longer content (Ippolito et al., 2020).

The work described in this paper is split into two parts: the creation of a dataset containing headlines written by both humans and machines and training of classifiers to distinguish between them. The dataset is created using real headlines from the *Million Headlines* corpus[3] and headlines generated by a pretrained GPT-2. The training and development sets consist of headlines from 2015 while the testing set consists of 2016 and 2017 headlines. A series of baselines and deep learning models were tested. Neural methods were found to outperform humans, with transformers being almost 35% more accurate.

Our research highlights how difficult it is for humans to identify computer-generated content, but that the problem can ultimately be tackled using automated approaches. This suggests that automatic methods for content analysis could play an important role in supporting readers to understand the veracity of content. The main contributions of this work are the development of a novel fake content identification task based on news headlines[4] and analysis of human evaluation and machine learning approaches to the problem.

[1]For example, How a misleading post went from the fringes to Trump's Twitter.

[2]For example, Can fact-checkers save Taiwan from a flood of Chinese fake news?

[3]Accessed 25/01/2021.

[4]Code available at http://bit.ly/ant_headlines.

Proceedings of the 4th NLP4IF Workshop on NLP for Internet Freedom, pages 1–6
June 6, 2021.

2 Relevant Work

Kumar and Shah (2018) compiled a survey on fake content on the internet, providing an overview of how false information targets users and how automatic detection models operate. The sharing of false information is boosted by the natural susceptibility of humans to believe such information. Pérez-Rosas et al. (2018) and Ott et al. (2011) reported that humans are able to identify fake content with an accuracy between 50% and 75%. Information that is well presented, using long text with limited errors, was shown to deceive the majority of readers. The ability of humans to detect machine-generated text was evaluated by Dugan et al. (2020), showing that humans struggle at the task.

Holtzman et al. (2020) investigated the pitfalls of automatic text generation, showing that sampling methods such as Beam search can lead to low quality and repetitive text. Gehrmann et al. (2019) showed that automatic text generation models use a more limited vocabulary than humans, tending to avoid low-probability words more often. Consequently, text written by humans tends to exhibit more variation than that generated by models.

In Zellers et al. (2019), neural fake news detection and generation are jointly examined in an adversarial setting. Their model, called Grover, achieves an accuracy of 92% when identifying real from generated news articles. Human evaluation though is lacking, so the potential of Grover to fool human readers has not been thoroughly explored. In Brown et al. (2020), news articles generated by their largest model (175B parameters) managed to fool humans 48% of the time. The model, though, is prohibitively large to be applied at scale. Further, Ippolito et al. (2020) showed that shorter text is harder to detect, both for humans and machines. So even though news headlines are a very potent weapon in the hands of fake news spreaders, it has not been yet examined how difficult it is for humans and models to detect machine-generated headlines.

3 Dataset

3.1 Dataset Development

The dataset was created using Australian Broadcasting Corporation headlines and headlines generated from a model. A pretrained[5] GPT-2 model (Radford et al., 2019) was finetuned on the headlines data. Text was generated using sampling with temperature and continuously re-feeding words into the model until the end token is generated.

Data was split in two sets, 2015 and 2016/2017, denoting the sets a "defender" and an "attacker" would use. The goal of the attacker is to fool readers, whereas the defender wants to filter out the generated headlines of the attacker. Headlines were generated separately for each set and then merged with the corresponding real headlines.

The "defender" set contains $72,401$ real and $414,373$ generated headlines, while the "attacker" set contains $179,880$ real and $517,932$ generated.

3.2 Dataset Analysis

Comparison of the real and automatically generated headlines revealed broad similarities between the distribution of lexical terms, sentence length and POS tag distribution, as shown below. This indicates that the language models are indeed able to capture patterns in the original data.

Even though the number of words in the generated headlines is bound by the maximum number of words learned in the corresponding language model, the distribution of words is similar across real and generated headlines. In Figures 1 and 2 we indicatively show the 15 most frequent words in the real and generated headlines respectively. POS tag frequencies are shown in Table 1 for the top tags in each set. In real headlines, nouns are used more often, whereas in generated headlines the distribution is smoother, consistent with findings in Gehrmann et al. (2019). Furthermore, in generated headlines verbs appear more often in their base (VB) and third-person singular (VBZ) form while in real headlines verb tags are more uniformly distributed. Overall, GPT-2 has accurately learned the real distribution, with similarities across the board.

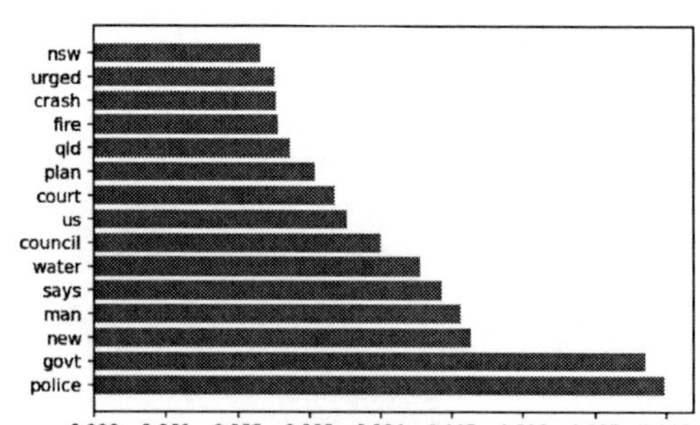

Figure 1: Top 15 Words for real headlines

Lastly, the real headlines are shorter than the generated ones, with 6.9 and 7.2 words respectively.

[5]As found in the HuggingFace library.

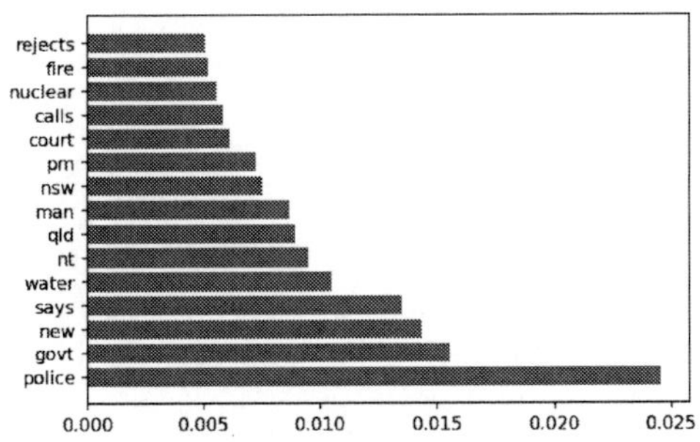

Figure 2: Top 15 Words for generated headlines

Real		Generated	
POS	freq	POS	freq
NN	0.372	NN	0.352
NNS	0.129	NNS	0.115
JJ	0.109	JJ	0.113
IN	0.108	IN	0.113
VB	0.045	VB	0.061
TO	0.040	TO	0.056
VBZ	0.033	VBZ	0.047
VBP	0.031	VBP	0.022
VBN	0.020	RB	0.017
VBG	0.020	VBG	0.015

Table 1: Frequencies for the top 10 part-of-speech tags in real and generated headlines

3.3 Survey

A crowd-sourced survey[6] was conducted to determine how realistic the generated text is. Participants (n=124) were presented with 93 headlines (three sets of 31) in a random order and asked to judge whether they were real or generated. The headlines were chosen at random from the "attacker" (2016/2017) headlines.

In total, there were 3435 answers to the 'real or generated' questions and 1731 (50.4%) were correct. When presented with a computer-generated headline, participants answered correctly in 1113 out of 2329 (47.8%) times. In total 45 generated headlines were presented and out of those, 23 were identified as computer-generated (based on average response). This is an indication that GPT-2 can indeed generate realistic-looking headlines that fool readers. When presented with actual headlines, participants answered correctly in 618 out of 1106 times (55.9%). In total 30 real headlines were presented and out of those, 20 were correctly identified as real (based on average response).

Of the 45 generated headlines, five were marked as real by over 80% of the participants, while for the real headlines, 2 out of 30 reached that threshold. The five generated headlines were:

Rumsfeld Talks Up Anti Terrorism Campaign
Cooper Rebounds From Olympic Disappointment
Jennifer Aniston Tops Celebrity Power Poll
Extra Surveillance Announced For WA Coast
Police Crack Down On Driving Offences

At the other end of the spectrum, there were seven generated headlines that over 80% of the participants correctly identified as being computer-generated:

Violence Restricting Rescue Of Australian
Scientists Discover Gene That May Halt Ovarian
All Ordinaries Finishes Day On Closing High
Waratahs Starting Spot Not A Mere Formality Sailor
Proposed Subdivision Wont Affect Recreational
Bangladesh To Play Three Tests Five Odis In
Minister Promises More Resources To Combat Child

Most of these examples contain grammatical errors, such as ending with an adjective, while some headlines contain absurd or nonsensical content. These deficiencies set these headlines apart from the rest. It is worth noting that participants appeared more likely to identify headlines containing grammatical errors as computer-generated than other types of errors.

4 Classification

For our classifier experiments, we used the three sets of data (2015, 2016 and 2017) we had previously compiled. Specifically, for training we only used the 2015 set, while the 2016 and 2017 sets were used for testing. Splitting the train and test data by the year of publication ensures that there is no overlap between the sets and there is some variability between the content of the headlines (for example, different topics/authors). Therefore, we can be confident that the classifiers generalize to unknown examples.

Furthermore, for hyperparameter tuning, the 2015 data was randomly split into training and development sets on a 80/20 ratio. In total, for training there are 129,610 headlines, for development there are 32,402 and for testing there are 303,965.

4.1 Experiments

Four types of classifiers were explored: baselines (Elastic Net and Naive Bayes), deep learning (CNN, Bi-LSTM and Bi-LSTM with Attention), transfer

[6]Participants were students and staff members in a mailing list from the University of Sheffield.

Method	Ovr. Acc.	Precision	Recall
Human	*50.4*	66.3	*52.2*
Naive Bayes	50.6	58.5	56.9
Elastic Net	73.3	*58.1*	62.3
CNN	81.7	75.3	76.2
BiLSTM	82.8	77.9	77.3
BiLSTM/Att.	82.5	76.9	77.2
ULMFit	83.3	79.1	78.5
BERT	**85.7**	**86.9**	**81.2**
DistilBERT	85.5	86.8	81.0

Table 2: Each run was executed three times with (macro) results averaged. Standard deviations are omitted for brevity and clarity (they were in all cases less than 0.5).

learning via ULMFit (Howard and Ruder, 2018) and Transformers (BERT (Devlin et al., 2019) and DistilBERT (Sanh et al., 2019)). The architecture and training details can be found in Appendix A.

Results are shown in Table 2. Overall accuracy is the accuracy in percentage over all headlines (real and generated), while (macro) precision and recall are calculated over the generated headlines. Precision is the percentage of correct classifications out of all the generated classifications, while recall is the percentage of generated headlines the model classified correctly out of all the actual generated headlines. High recall scores indicate that the models are able to identify a generated headline with high accuracy, while low precision scores show that models classify headlines mostly as generated.

We can observe from the results table that humans are overall less effective than all the examined models, including the baselines, scoring the lowest accuracy. They are also the least accurate on generated headlines, achieving the lowest recall. In general, human predictions are almost as bad as random guesses.

Deep learning models scored consistently higher than the baselines, while transfer learning outperformed all previous models, reaching an overall accuracy of around 83%. Transformer architectures though perform the best overall, with accuracy in the 85% region. BERT, the highest-scoring model, scores around 30% higher than humans in all metrics. The difference between the two BERT-based models is minimal.

Since training and testing data are separate (sampled from different years), this indicates that there are some traits in generated text that are not present in human text. Transformers are able to pick up on these traits to make highly-accurate classifications. For example, generated text shows lower variance than human text (Gehrmann et al., 2019), which means text without rarer words is more likely to be generated than being written by a human.

4.2 Error Analysis

We present the following two computer-generated headlines as indicative examples of those misclassified as real by BERT:

Extra Surveillance Announced For WA Coast

Violence Restricting Rescue Of Australian

The first headline is not only grammatically sound, but also semantically plausible. A specific region is also mentioned ("WA Coast"), which has low probability of occurring and possibly the model does not have representative embeddings for. This seems to be the case in general, with the mention of named entities increasing the chance of fooling the classifier. The task of predicting this headline is then quite challenging. Human evaluation was also low here, with only 19% of participants correctly identifying it.

In the second headline, the word "restricting" and the phrase "rescue of" are connected by their appearance in similar contexts. Furthermore, both "violence" and "restricting rescue" have negative connotations, so they also match in sentiment. These two facts seem to lead the model in believing the headline is real instead of computer-generated, even though it is quite flimsy both semantically (the mention of violence is too general and is not grounded) and pragmatically (some sort of violence restricting rescue is rare). In contrast, humans had little trouble recognising this as a computer-generated headline; 81% of participants labelled it as fake. This indicates that automated classifiers are still susceptible to reasoning fallacies.

5 Conclusion

This paper examined methods to detect headlines generated by a GPT-2 model. A dataset was created using headlines from ABC and a survey conducted asking participants to distinguish between real and generated headlines.

Real headlines were identified as such by 55.9% of the participants, while generated ones were identified with a 47.8% rate. Various models were trained, all of which were better at identifying generated headlines than humans. BERT scored 85.7%, an improvement of around 35% over human accuracy.

Our work shows that whereas humans cannot differentiate between real and generated headlines, automatic detectors are much better at the task and therefore do have a place in the information consumption pipeline.

Acknowledgments

This work was supported by ERCAdG #740516. We want to thank the anonymous reviewers for their insightful comments and questions, and the members from the University of Sheffield who participated in our survey.

References

Tom Brown, Benjamin Mann, Nick Ryder, Melanie Subbiah, Jared D Kaplan, Prafulla Dhariwal, Arvind Neelakantan, Pranav Shyam, Girish Sastry, Amanda Askell, Sandhini Agarwal, Ariel Herbert-Voss, Gretchen Krueger, Tom Henighan, Rewon Child, Aditya Ramesh, Daniel Ziegler, Jeffrey Wu, Clemens Winter, Chris Hesse, Mark Chen, Eric Sigler, Mateusz Litwin, Scott Gray, Benjamin Chess, Jack Clark, Christopher Berner, Sam McCandlish, Alec Radford, Ilya Sutskever, and Dario Amodei. 2020. Language models are few-shot learners. In *Advances in Neural Information Processing Systems*, volume 33, pages 1877–1901. Curran Associates, Inc.

Sumanth Dathathri, Andrea Madotto, Janice Lan, Jane Hung, Eric Frank, Piero Molino, Jason Yosinski, and Rosanne Liu. 2020. Plug and play language models: A simple approach to controlled text generation. In *International Conference on Learning Representations*.

Jacob Devlin, Ming-Wei Chang, Kenton Lee, and Kristina Toutanova. 2019. BERT: Pre-training of deep bidirectional transformers for language understanding. In *Proceedings of the 2019 Conference of the North American Chapter of the Association for Computational Linguistics: Human Language Technologies, Volume 1 (Long and Short Papers)*, pages 4171–4186, Minneapolis, Minnesota. Association for Computational Linguistics.

Liam Dugan, Daphne Ippolito, Arun Kirubarajan, and Chris Callison-Burch. 2020. RoFT: A tool for evaluating human detection of machine-generated text. In *Proceedings of the 2020 Conference on Empirical Methods in Natural Language Processing: System Demonstrations*, pages 189–196, Online. Association for Computational Linguistics.

Sebastian Gehrmann, Hendrik Strobelt, and Alexander Rush. 2019. GLTR: Statistical detection and visualization of generated text. In *Proceedings of the 57th Annual Meeting of the Association for Computational Linguistics: System Demonstrations*, pages 111–116, Florence, Italy. Association for Computational Linguistics.

Bin Guo, Yasan Ding, Lina Yao, Yunji Liang, and Zhiwen Yu. 2020. The future of false information detection on social media: New perspectives and trends. *ACM Comput. Surv.*, 53(4).

Ari Holtzman, Jan Buys, Li Du, Maxwell Forbes, and Yejin Choi. 2020. The curious case of neural text degeneration. In *International Conference on Learning Representations*.

Jeremy Howard and Sebastian Ruder. 2018. Universal language model fine-tuning for text classification. In *Proceedings of the 56th Annual Meeting of the Association for Computational Linguistics (Volume 1: Long Papers)*, pages 328–339, Melbourne, Australia. Association for Computational Linguistics.

Daphne Ippolito, Daniel Duckworth, Chris Callison-Burch, and Douglas Eck. 2020. Automatic detection of generated text is easiest when humans are fooled. In *Proceedings of the 58th Annual Meeting of the Association for Computational Linguistics*, pages 1808–1822, Online. Association for Computational Linguistics.

Ganesh Jawahar, Muhammad Abdul-Mageed, and Laks Lakshmanan, V.S. 2020. Automatic detection of machine generated text: A critical survey. In *Proceedings of the 28th International Conference on Computational Linguistics*, pages 2296–2309, Barcelona, Spain (Online). International Committee on Computational Linguistics.

Srijan Kumar and Neil Shah. 2018. False information on web and social media: A survey. *CoRR*, abs/1804.08559.

Michael Luca and Georgios Zervas. 2013. Fake it till you make it: Reputation, competition, and yelp review fraud. *SSRN Electronic Journal*.

Stephen Merity, Nitish Shirish Keskar, and Richard Socher. 2018. Regularizing and optimizing LSTM language models. In *6th International Conference on Learning Representations, ICLR 2018, Vancouver, BC, Canada, April 30 - May 3, 2018, Conference Track Proceedings*.

Myle Ott, Yejin Choi, Claire Cardie, and Jeffrey T. Hancock. 2011. Finding deceptive opinion spam by any stretch of the imagination. In *Proceedings of the 49th Annual Meeting of the Association for Computational Linguistics: Human Language Technologies*, pages 309–319, Portland, Oregon, USA. Association for Computational Linguistics.

Verónica Pérez-Rosas, Bennett Kleinberg, Alexandra Lefevre, and Rada Mihalcea. 2018. Automatic detection of fake news. In *Proceedings of the 27th International Conference on Computational Linguistics*, pages 3391–3401, Santa Fe, New Mexico, USA. Association for Computational Linguistics.

Alec Radford, Jeff Wu, Rewon Child, David Luan, Dario Amodei, and Ilya Sutskever. 2019. Language models are unsupervised multitask learners.

Victor Sanh, Lysandre Debut, Julien Chaumond, and Thomas Wolf. 2019. Distilbert, a distilled version of bert: smaller, faster, cheaper and lighter.

Sandeep Subramanian, Sai Rajeswar Mudumba, Alessandro Sordoni, Adam Trischler, Aaron C Courville, and Chris Pal. 2018. Towards text generation with adversarially learned neural outlines. In S. Bengio, H. Wallach, H. Larochelle, K. Grauman, N. Cesa-Bianchi, and R. Garnett, editors, *Advances in Neural Information Processing Systems 31*, pages 7551–7563. Curran Associates, Inc.

Ashish Vaswani, Noam Shazeer, Niki Parmar, Jakob Uszkoreit, Llion Jones, Aidan N Gomez, Ł ukasz Kaiser, and Illia Polosukhin. 2017. Attention is all you need. In *Advances in Neural Information Processing Systems*, volume 30. Curran Associates, Inc.

Rowan Zellers, Ari Holtzman, Hannah Rashkin, Yonatan Bisk, Ali Farhadi, Franziska Roesner, and Yejin Choi. 2019. Defending against neural fake news.

A Classifier Details

ULMFit and the Transformers require their own special tokenizers, but the rest of the models use the same method, a simple indexing over the most frequent tokens. No pretrained word vectors (for example, GloVe) were used for the Deep Learning models.

ULMFit uses pre-trained weights from the AWD-LSTM model (Merity et al., 2018). For fine-tuning, we first updated the LSTM weights with a learning rate of 0.01 for a single epoch. Then, we unfroze all the layers and trained the model with a learning rate of 7.5e-5 for an additional epoch. Finally, we trained the classifier head on its own for one more epoch with a learning rate of 0.05.

For the Transformers, we loaded pre-trained weights which we fine-tuned for a single epoch with a learning rate of 4e-5. Specifically, the models we used were base-BERT (12 layers, 110m parameters) and DistilBERT (6 layers, 66m parameters).

The CNN has two convolutional layers on top of each other with filter sizes 8 and 4 respectively, and kernel size of 3 for both. Embeddings have 75 dimensions and the model is trained for 5 epochs.

The LSTM-based models have one recurrent layer with 35 units, while the embeddings have 100. Bidirectionality is used alongside a spatial dropout of 0.33. After the recurrent layer, we concatenate average pooling and max pooling layers. We also experiment with a Bi-LSTM with self-attention (Vaswani et al., 2017). These models are trained for 5 epochs.

Improving Hate Speech Type and Target Detection with Hateful Metaphor Features

Jens Lemmens and **Ilia Markov** and **Walter Daelemans**
CLiPS, University of Antwerp
Lange Winkelstraat 40
2000, Antwerp (Belgium)
`firstname.lastname@uantwerpen.be`

Abstract

We study the usefulness of hateful metaphors as features for the identification of the type and target of hate speech in Dutch Facebook comments. For this purpose, all hateful metaphors in the Dutch LiLaH corpus were annotated and interpreted in line with Conceptual Metaphor Theory and Critical Metaphor Analysis. We provide SVM and BERT/RoBERTa results, and investigate the effect of different metaphor information encoding methods on hate speech type and target detection accuracy. The results of the conducted experiments show that hateful metaphor features improve model performance for the both tasks. To our knowledge, it is the first time that the effectiveness of hateful metaphors as an information source for hate speech classification is investigated.

1 Introduction

In this paper, the usefulness of hateful metaphors used as features for detecting the type and target of Dutch online hate speech comments is investigated. Although both hate speech and metaphor detection have been researched widely (e.g., MacAvaney et al., 2019; Basile et al., 2019; Leong et al., 2018, 2020), and figurative language used in hateful content has been identified as one of the main challenges in (implicit) hate speech detection (MacAvaney et al., 2019; van Aken et al., 2018), the question whether detecting (hateful) metaphors and using them as features improves hate speech detection models has remained unstudied in previous research. Therefore, it is the goal of the present paper to address this question.

In order to achieve this goal, we used the Dutch LiLaH[1] corpus which consists Facebook comments on online newspaper articles related to either migrants or the LGBT community. The comments were annotated for the type of hate speech and the target of hate speech, and for "hateful metaphors", i.e., metaphors that express hate towards a specific target (e.g., "het parlement is een circus!"; *the parliament is a circus*). We investigate whether features based on these manual annotations can improve Natural Language Processing (NLP) models that predict the type (e.g., violence, offense) and target (e.g., migrants, LGBT, journalist) of hateful content. Our experimental setup is therefore different from the commonly-used one in the sense that we are focusing only on the fine-grained hate speech categories and not on classification of hateful and non-hateful content. We hypothesize that hateful metaphors contain valuable information for type and target classification, especially in cases of implicit hate speech, and can therefore improve classification accuracy when used as features.

Prior to the classification experiments, a linguistic analysis of the annotated metaphors is conducted in the framework of Conceptual Metaphor Theory and Critical Metaphor Analysis. We would like to warn that for clarity of exposition, randomly chosen examples of hate speech from our corpus will be provided in this paper, and that some readers could find those offensive.

2 Related research

Hate speech detection Hate speech – frequently defined as a form of communication that disparages a person or a group on the basis of some characteristic such as race, color, ethnicity, gender, sexual orientation, nationality, religion, or other (Nockleby, 2000) – has been extensively researched in the field of NLP. Pretrained language models such as Bidirectional Encoder Representations from Transformers (BERT) and Robustly Optimized BERT Pretraining Approach (RoBERTa) (Devlin et al., 2019; Liu et al., 2019) provide the best results for hate speech detection, including type and target classification (Basile et al., 2019; Zampieri et al., 2019b, 2020), while shallow machine learning models (e.g., Support Vector Ma-

[1] `https://lilah.eu/`

Proceedings of the 4th NLP4IF Workshop on NLP for Internet Freedom, pages 7–16
June 6, 2021. ©2021 Association for Computational Linguistics

chines (SVM)) can achieve a near state-of-the-art performance (MacAvaney et al., 2019).

Examples of successful machine learning models include the winning teams of both subtasks A (binary hate speech detection) and B (binary target classification) of task 5 of SemEval 2019: multilingual detection of hate speech against women and immigrants on Twitter (Basile et al., 2019). These teams all used SVM-based approaches for both languages provided (English and Spanish) with the exception of the winner of task B for Spanish, who used various other classifiers and combined them by means of majority voting. For English, the winning teams obtained an F1-score of 65% for task A and an EMR score of 57% for task B.

Examples of effective neural approaches can be found in OffensEval 2020 (Zampieri et al., 2020). This shared task consisted of three subtasks: (A) offensive language identification, (B) categorization of offensive types and (C) target identification for multiple languages. For English, each of the top 10 teams for all three tasks used pretrained language models such as BERT and RoBERTa. The highest macro F1-scores obtained for task A, B, and C were 92%, 75% and 71%, respectively.

Figurative and implicit language in hate speech In their hate speech detection survey, MacAvaney et al. (2019) highlight current challenges in hate speech detection. One of the main challenges mentioned is the use of figurative and implicit language such as sarcasm and metaphors, which can lead to classification errors, as evidenced by their experiments. An SVM classifier with TF-IDF weighted character n-gram features was used to perform hate speech detection on the Stormfront, TRAC, HatEval and HatebaseTwitter datasets (de Gibert et al., 2018; Kumar et al., 2018; Basile et al., 2019; Davidson et al., 2017). An error analysis of the misclassified instances showed that sarcastic and metaphorical posts were the main causes of misclassifications, next to too little context (posts containing fewer than 6 tokens) and aggressive statements occurring in posts that were not annotated as "hateful".

Similar findings were observed by van Aken et al. (2018). An ensemble of machine learning and deep learning models was used for multi-class classification of toxic online comments and an error analysis of the incorrect predictions showed that metaphors can lead to classification errors because the models require significant world knowledge to process them.

To address the problem of implicit language in hate speech, more recent studies have used datasets that distinguish between implicit and explicit hate speech, such as AbuseEval v1.0 (Caselli et al., 2020). This dataset was created by annotating the OLID/OffensEval dataset (Zampieri et al., 2019a) for implicitness/explicitness. The authors of AbuseEval v1.0 provide results with BERT for binary classification (abusive, non-abusive) and multi-class classification (non-abusive, implicit abuse, explicit abuse) for the same train/test split and show that the binary classification task (71.6% macro F1-score) becomes substantially more complex when distinguishing between implicit and explicit abusive language (61.4% macro F1-score). Additionally, they show that the results for implicit hate speech detection (24% precision, 23% recall) are substantially lower than for explicit hate speech detection (64% precision, 51% recall).

Metaphors The foundations of the state-of-the-art way of thinking about metaphors is presented in "Metaphors We Live By" (Lakoff and Johnson, 1980), in which metaphors are defined as utterances that describe a target concept in terms of a source concept that is semantically distinct from the target concept, this includes idiomatic expressions and dead metaphors such as "the *body* of a paper" and "the *foot* of a mountain". The authors argue that specific metaphorical expressions can be traced back to more abstract metaphor schemes that overarch similar metaphors. This is what they call "Conceptual Metaphor Theory" (CMT). Examples are utterances such as "he *attacked* my arguments" and "I *destroyed* him during our discussion" which can be traced back to the conceptual metaphor *argument is war.*

In Charteris-Black (2004), Critical Metaphor Analysis (CMA), an integration of various linguistic disciplines such as cognitive linguistics, corpus linguistics and discourse analysis, is applied to CMT. According to CMA, metaphors highlight certain aspects of the target concept while hiding other aspects. At the same time, they uncover the speaker's thought patterns and ideological views. Therefore, metaphors – this includes dead metaphors used subconsciously – provide insights into how a speaker or community perceives the target domain. In short, metaphors reveal speaker bias. This is particularly valuable in the present study, since the toxicity that is spread through hateful metaphors resides in the source domains, more precisely in the aspect of the source domain that is highlighted by the metaphor.

Metaphor detection in NLP Recent advances in NLP-related metaphor studies can be found in the 2020 VUA and TOEFL metaphor detection shared task (Leong et al., 2020). The participating models showed substantial improvements compared to previous research, such as the 2018 VUA metaphor detection shared task (Leong et al., 2018), due to the effectiveness of (pretrained) transformer and language models. More than half of the participants used BERT (or related) models and all participating teams obtained higher F1-scores on the VUA metaphor corpus than the best-performing approach that participated in the 2018 shared task (65.1% F1-score). Further, the 2020 winning model, which consists of transformer stacks with linguistic features such as part-of-speech (PoS) tags, outperformed its predecessor of 2018 by more than 10% (76.9% F1-score, Su et al., 2020).

Contributions To our knowledge, we are the first to use hateful metaphor features for hate speech detection. We provide SVM and BERT/RoBERTa results and show the impact of using hateful metaphors as features on predicting the type and target of hateful content. In addition, the qualitative analysis of the annotated metaphors provide insights into what linguistic strategies are used to convey hate towards specific target groups.

3 Data

3.1 Corpus description

The Dutch LiLaH corpus consists of approximately 36,000 Facebook comments on online news articles related to migrants or the LGBT community mined from three popular Flemish newspaper pages (HLN, Het Nieuwsblad and VRT)[2]. The corpus, which has been used in several recent studies on hate speech detection in Dutch, e.g., (Markov et al., 2021; Ljubešić et al., 2020), was annotated for the type and target of hateful comments following the same procedure and annotation guidelines as presented in (Ljubešić et al., 2019), that is, with respect to the type of hate speech, the possible classes were violent speech and offensive speech (either triggered by the target's personal background, e.g., religion, gender, sexual orientation, nationality, etc., or on the basis of individual characteristics), inappropriate speech (without a specific target), and appropriate speech. The targets, on the other hand, were divided into migrants and the LGBT community, people related to either of these communities (e.g., people who support them), the journalist who wrote or medium that provided the article, another commenter, other targets and no target. The comments were labeled by two trained annotators (both Master's students and native speakers of Dutch) and the final labels were determined by a single expert annotator (PhD student and native speaker of Dutch).

As mentioned, our analysis deviates from the more "standard" experimental setup in hate speech research, namely classifying comments into hate speech or non-hate speech. In contrast, we consider only the fine-grained hate speech categories, i.e., discarding the non-hate speech classes (i.e., "inappropriate speech" and "appropriate speech" for the type class; "no target" for the target class) and focusing only the type and target of hateful content. Additionally, the four hate speech type categories (violent-background, violent-other, offensive-background, offensive-other) were converted to binary classes (violent, offensive).

The statistics of the hate speech comments used for our metaphor analyses are shown in Table 1. For the machine learning experiments, we selected a balanced subset in terms of the number of comments per class and the number of literal and non-literal comments per class (whenever possible). The statistics of the train/test partitions used for these machine learning experiments are shown in Table 2. In the subsets used, Cohen's Kappa equals 0.46 for the target classes and 0.54 for the type classes, indicating a "moderate" agreement between the two annotators for both the type and target annotations.

3.2 Hateful metaphor annotations

All hateful metaphors in our corpus were annotated by the same expert annotator mentioned above. For this task, the definition of a metaphor presented in Lakoff and Johnson (1980), described in Section 2, was adopted. More specifically, we define *hateful* metaphors as metaphorical utterances (including similes) that express hate towards a specific target, and therefore occur in hate speech comments, that

[2] https://www.facebook.com/hln.be; https://www.facebook.com/nieuwsblad.be; https://www.facebook.com/vrtnws

are not used to refer to someone else's opinion or previous comments, and that are written in Dutch.

We found that 2,758 (14.7%) out of all 18,770 hateful comments in our corpus contain at least one hateful metaphor. In those comments, 282 were LGBT-related, whereas all other 2,476 non-literal comments were related to migrants. In other words, 15.7% of all hate speech comments on LGBT-related news articles (1,797 in total) contain one or more hateful metaphor(s), whereas 14.6% of all hate speech comments on migrants-related news articles (16,973 in total) contain one or more hateful metaphor(s). See Table 1 for more fine-grained information on (non-)literal comments per type/target.

A qualitative analysis showed that many similar metaphors occurred in the corpus (in line with CMT). Therefore, we manually determined the source domains of the metaphors in a bottom-up fashion. If only one variation of a metaphor occurred for a certain source domain, it was added to the category "other". A list of the source domains, the number of comments in our corpus that contain them, a Dutch example, and its English translation can be found below together with a linguistic analysis in line with CMT and CMA.

- **Animals** (646), e.g., "migranten zijn bruine apen" (*migrants are brown apes*)
- **Dirt and personal hygiene** (529), e.g., "de EU is een beerput" (*the EU is a cesspool*)
- **Body parts** (299), e.g., "bij jouw geboorte hebben ze de baby weggegooid en de moederkoek gehouden" (*when you were born, they threw away the baby and kept the placenta*)
- **Disease and illness** (228), e.g., "jij bent vergif" (*you're poison*)
- **History** (192), e.g., "die minister is Hitler" (*that minister is Hitler*)
- **Food** (147), e.g., "bootvluchtelingen zijn vissoep" (*boat refugees are fish soup*)
- **Fiction** (139), e.g., "de Bijbel is een sprookjesboek" (*the Bible is a collection of fairy tales*)
- **Mental conditions** (119), e.g., "ik dacht dat het internetuurtje in het gekkenhuis al voorbij was" (*I thought that internet time in the madhouse was already over*)
- **Products** (107), e.g., "migranten zijn importbelgen" (*migrants are imported Belgians*)
- **Children** (80), e.g., "politici zijn kleuters" (*politicians are toddlers*)
- **Carnival and circus** (75), e.g., "politici zijn clowns" (*politicians are clowns*)
- **Home and kitchen linen** (68), e.g., "hoofddoeken zijn keukenhanddoeken" (*head scarfs are kitchen towls*)
- **Sight** (65), e.g., "je draagt paardenkleppen" (*you're wearing horse blinkers*)
- **Religious mythology** (44), e.g., "het paard van Troje is al binnen" (*the Trojan horse is already inside*, referring to migrants)
- **Sand** (24), e.g., "die migranten moeten terug naar hun zandbak" (*those migrants should return to their sand boxes*)
- **Tourism** (19), e.g., "oorlogsvluchtelingen zijn gewoon citytrippers" (*war refugees are just on a citytrip*)
- **Machines** (14), e.g., "IS strijders zijn moordmachines" (*IS warriors are murder machines*)
- **Physical conditions** (7), e.g., "trans-atleten zijn paralympiërs" (*trans-athletes are paralympians*)
- **Lottery** (4), e.g., "die migranten denken dat ze de Euromillions gewonnen hebben zeker?" (*those migrants must think that they've won Euromillions*)
- **Other** (349), e.g., "migranten zijn geleide projectielen" (*migrants are guided missiles*)

In our corpus, the source domains in metaphors that express hate towards migrants frequently refer to animals, especially pests (e.g., "parasites", "cockroaches") and primates (e.g. "apes"), commodities (e.g., "import Belgians/criminality") and food (e.g., "rotten apples", "boat refugees are fish soup"). These findings are in line with previous work on English and cross-lingual hate speech (Demjen and Hardaker, 2017; Dervinytė, 2009). Given the persuasive, ideological nature of metaphors (cf. CMA), the usage of these metaphors suggests that the speaker wishes for migrants and their "species" to be "exterminated", "kept in the zoo", "returned to sender", "thrown in the bin", and to stop "breeding".

Conversely, the source domains that were found in hateful metaphors that target the LGBT community often refer to diseases, and mental and physical conditions. This indicates that the user of these metaphors believes that the LGBT community should be "cured", "hospitalized"or "internalized". Other hateful metaphors that target the LGBT community highlight aspects such as appearance and therefore refer to carnival or the circus,

Task	Class	Literal	Non-literal	All
Type	Violence	394	80	474
	Offensive	15,618	2,678	18,296
Target	Migrants/LGBT	5,184	723	5,907
	Related	558	84	642
	Journalist/medium	544	90	634
	Commenter	2,946	574	3,520
	Other	6,780	1,287	8,067
Total		**16,012**	**2,758**	**18,770**

Table 1: Statistics of all hateful comments in our corpus, including the number of hateful comments per type/target class, and the number of literal and non-literal comments (in total and per class).

		Training set			Test set			
Task	Class	Literal	Non-literal	Both	Literal	Non-literal	Both	Total
Type	Violence	311	63	374	83	17	100	474
	Offensive	1,000	1,000	2,000	250	250	500	2,500
	All	1,311	1,063	**2,374**	333	267	**600**	**2,974**
Target	Migrants/LGBT	200	200	400	50	50	100	500
	Related	333	67	400	83	17	100	500
	Journalist/medium	328	72	400	82	18	100	500
	Commenter	200	200	400	50	50	100	500
	Other	200	200	400	50	50	100	500
	All	1,261	739	**2,000**	315	185	**500**	**2,500**

Table 2: Statistics of the subsets used in the type and target classification experiments, including the number of comments in the train/test splits for the type and target prediction tasks, the number of comments per class, and the number of literal and non-literal comments.

such as "de Antwerp Pride is een carnavalsstoet" (*the Antwerp Pride is a carnival parade*).

Journalists or newspapers, on the other hand, are often described as "linkse" (*left-wing*) or "rechtse" (*right-wing*) "ratten" (*rats*) that need to be "uitgeroeid" (*exteriminated*). Other metaphors often refer to dirt and personal hygiene such as "strontgazet" (literally *"excrement newspaper"*), "rioolgazet" (literally *"sewer newspaper"*), and "riooljournalist" (literally *"sewer journalist"*) highlighting the quality of journalism.

Other social media users and commenters are metaphorized in a variety of ways in our corpus, depending on the context and on what aspect the speaker wants to highlight. Examples are "vuile hond" (*dirty dog*), "domme geit" (*stupid goat*), "schaap" (*sheep*), "mongool" (*person with Down syndrome*), "kleuters" (*toddlers*), and "middeleeuwers" (*people who live in the middle ages*).

Finally, the "other" category is complex, due to its variety of target groups that it contains. Politicians, for example, are often metaphorized as left-wing or right-wing "rats", similar to how journalists, newspapers, other social media users, and the followers of those political parties are occasionally metaphorized as well. Further, religious institutions are often characterized as a circus or a hospital for the mentally ill, whereas religion itself is described as a fairytale or a disease.

4 Classification experiments

4.1 SVM

An SVM model was established with Sklearn (version 0.23.1, Pedregosa et al., 2011) by using token 1- and 2-grams with TF-IDF weights fed into a linear SVM, henceforth referred to as "SVM". Grid search under 10-fold cross-validation was conducted to determine the optimal settings for the "C", "loss", and "penalty" parameters[3]. Then, the following methods were used to integrate the hateful metaphor features:

Generic metaphor features which do not take into account the source domains of the metaphors.

- **N tokens** – the number of hateful metaphorical tokens was counted and appended to the feature vectors.
- **N expressions** – the number of hateful metaphorical expressions was counted and appended to the feature vectors.

[3]Since the classes are not distributed equally in the subset used for type classification, the "class weight" parameter was also optimized in the type prediction task.

- **Suffix** – a suffix in the form of the placeholder[4] "MET" was added at the end of all hateful metaphorical tokens before vectorization, e.g., "You're a pigMET." This way, the model distinguishes between a hateful, non-literal token and the same token used literally and in a non-hateful way (e.g., "That farmer bought a pig").
- **Tokens** – the token "MET" was added after all metaphorical tokens before vetorization, e.g., "You're a pig MET". This allows the model to see similarities between a word form used literally and the same word form used figuratively, yet distinguish between them because of the placeholder that follows.
- **Tags** – all subsequent metaphorical tokens were enclosed in tags, such as in "You're a MET dirty pig MET". This method allows the model to focus on the on- and offset tokens of the metaphorical expressions.
- **All features** – the combination of all feature sets described above. For example, this encoding method would transform the utterance "migrants are a Trojan Horse" into "migrants are a MET trojanMET MET horseMET MET" and append the numerical features ("2" and "1" in this case) to its feature vector after vectorization to represent the number of hateful metaphorical tokens and expressions in the text, respectively.

Source domain metaphor features Since the source domains of the hateful metaphors could contain useful information for the predictions of the type and target of hate speech, because they highlight certain aspects of the target domain and reflect the way that the speaker perceives it (as described in Section 2), all methods described above were also used to encode hateful metaphor information while considering the source domains of the metaphors. More specifically, when using in-text metaphor information encoding methods, the "MET" placeholder was replaced with the first three characters of the names of the source domain of the metaphor (e.g., "ANI" for animal, "HIS" for history, etc.). For the numerical features, on the other hand, 20-dimensional vectors were used to count the number of metaphorical tokens/expressions in each comment (each dimension representing one of the 20 source domains

[4]In order to ensure that the placeholders were not confused with actual text, all text was lowercased and all placeholders were uppercased before training.

	CV		Test set		
Approach	**F**	**Std**	**Pre**	**Rec**	**F**
SVM	55.9	2.5	56.6	56.5	56.4
+n tokens	56.9	2.8	58.0	57.9	57.5
+n expressions	**57.3**	2.9	56.6	56.4	56.1
+suffix	55.6	2.2	57.4	57.9	57.3
+tokens	56.9	2.1	56.6	56.6	56.3
+tags	57.0	2.2	57.2	57.3	57.0
+all	56.4	2.4	**59.0**	**58.9**	**58.8**
BERTje	-	-	**63.1**	**62.8**	**62.4**
+tags	-	-	61.2	61.2	61.1
RobBERT	-	-	**61.9**	**61.8**	**61.8**
+tags	-	-	60.9	60.8	60.8

Table 3: 10-fold cross-validation and test set performances (%) on the **target** prediction task with **generic** metaphor features (best results in bold).

	CV		Test set		
Approach	**F**	**Std**	**Pre**	**Rec**	**F**
SVM	71.5	3.5	68.8	79.9	72.3
+n tokens	73.8	3.2	74.0	81.6	**76.9**
+n expressions	**74.1**	3.2	**74.2**	80.4	76.7
+suffix	71.3	2.9	68.5	80.9	72.2
+tokens	73.4	3.4	71.0	**82.4**	74.8
+tags	73.1	3.1	71.2	81.0	74.6
+all	73.6	3.2	73.8	80.6	76.5
BERTje	-	-	80.2	78.5	79.3
+tags	-	-	**82.7**	**80.0**	**81.2**
RobBERT	-	-	81.1	74.8	77.4
+tags	-	-	**82.0**	**77.2**	**79.3**

Table 4: 10-fold cross-validation and test set performances (%) on the **type** prediction task with **generic** metaphor features (best results in bold).

that were observed in the linguistic analysis of the metaphors).

4.2 BERTje and RobBERT

Predictions for both tasks were made with BERTje and RobBERT (de Vries et al., 2019; Delobelle et al., 2020; the Dutch versions of BERT and RobBERTa) using HuggingFace 4.0.0 (Wolf et al., 2020). In an attempt to improve these models, the "tags" method described above was used, but with the "<met>" (onset) and "</met>" (offset) placeholders for generic features and the same more fine-grained placeholders as described above when using source domain features. This tagging method is frequently used to highlight textual features or external knowledge in sequence-to-sequence tasks such as machine translation and named entity recognition (e.g., Chatterjee et al., 2017; Li et al., 2018). Four epochs were used for training and all other parameters were set to default. The experiments were conducted five times with different seeds and we report the median of these runs.

5 Results

5.1 Quantitative results

The 10-fold cross-validation and test results of the SVM model[5], BERTje and RobBERT without additional features, with generic features or with source domain features for both tasks can be found in Table 3, 4, 5 and 6, respectively.

No additional features Without using additional features, it can be observed that BERTje performed best for both the target and type prediction tasks, closely followed by RobBERT and finally the SVM classifier. It can also be observed that target prediction accuracy is substantially lower than type prediction accuracy for all the models.

Generic features Regarding the SVM model, all proposed feature implementation methods improved the performance of the SVM classifier, with the exceptions of the token labels and number of metaphorical expressions for the target prediction task, and the suffix labels for the type prediction task. The best SVM-based approach for target predictions used the combination of all features, which showed a 2.4% F1-score improvement over the SVM classifier without additional features. For the type prediction task, the number of hateful metaphorical tokens used as feature improved the SVM baseline by 4.6% F1-score. Further, the performance of both BERTje and RobBERT improved by 1.9% when adding metaphor features to the text data for the type prediction task. Adding these labels before training on the target prediction task, however, did not improve the performance.

Source domain features With respect to the SVM approach, all feature implementation methods improved its performance for both the type and target prediction tasks, with the exception of the suffix features used for the type prediction task. Amongst the different types of source domain features, both numerical features (number of metaphorical tokens and number of metaphorical expressions) improved the SVM approach the most for type predictions (4% in F1-score). Conversely, adding the source domains after all hateful metaphors as tokens improved target prediction with SVM the most (1.6% in F1-score). On

	CV		Test set		
Approach	**F**	**Std**	**Pre**	**Rec**	**F**
SVM	55.9	2.5	56.6	56.5	56.4
+n tokens	**57.5**	2.7	57.8	57.6	57.4
+n expressions	57.3	2.9	58.2	58.0	57.8
+suffix	55.6	2.5	57.2	57.5	57.0
+tokens	56.9	2.0	**58.2**	**58.4**	**58.0**
+tags	57.0	1.7	57.6	57.9	57.4
+all	56.1	1.7	57.6	57.6	57.3
BERTje	-	-	**63.1**	**62.8**	**62.4**
+tags	-	-	61.2	61.4	61.2
RobBERT	-	-	**61.9**	**61.8**	**61.8**
+tags	-	-	61.2	61.7	61.4

Table 5: 10-fold cross-validation and test set performances (%) on the **target** prediction task with **source domain** metaphor features (best results in bold).

	CV		Test set		
Approach	**F**	**Std**	**Pre**	**Rec**	**F**
SVM	71.5	3.5	68.8	79.9	72.3
+n tokens	**74.3**	4.2	73.7	80.1	**76.3**
+n expressions	74.0	3.1	73.7	80.1	**76.3**
+suffix	71.0	3.3	68.4	80.2	72.0
+tokens	72.9	3.6	69.7	**82.9**	73.7
+tags	73.0	3.9	70.9	81.8	74.5
+all	73.3	4.1	**74.3**	77.2	75.6
BERTje	-	-	80.2	**78.5**	**79.3**
+tags	-	-	**81.6**	77.1	79.0
RobBERT	-	-	**81.1**	74.8	77.4
+tags	-	-	79.8	**75.8**	**77.5**

Table 6: 10-fold cross-validation and test set performances (%) on the **type** prediction task with **source domain** metaphor features (best results in bold).

the other hand, the performance of the language models could only be improved marginally: when adding in-text features before training RobBERT on the type prediction task, its performance increased by 0.1% in F1-score.

Overall Substantial improvements up to 4.6% and 2.4% could be observed in the type and target classification tasks, respectively. These results indicate that hateful metaphor features contribute to type and target classification of hate speech comments in the current experimental setting.

5.2 Qualitative results

In this section, individual instances that were classified correctly only after adding hateful metaphor features are discussed. We focus on two comparisons, namely between the model that showed the highest increase in performance after adding metaphor information and the same model without additional features (per task). For the target prediction task, these are SVM and SVM to which all generic features have been added. For the type prediction task, on the other hand, these are the

[5]The optimal SVM parameter settings for the target prediction task were {"C": 1, "loss": "squared_hinge", "penalty": "l2"} and {"C": 0.5, "loss": "hinge", "penalty": "l2", "class_weight": "balanced"} for the type prediction task.

baseline SVM classifier and the SVM classifier enriched with numerical features based on the number of hateful metaphorical tokens (regardless of their source domains). The confusion matrices of these models are provided in Figures 1, 2, 3 and 4, respectively.

Target prediction task For this task, it can be observed that the additional features improved the classification accuracy for all classes. The only exception was the "journalist/medium" class, which is the most accurately predicted class using the SVM baseline and is predicted equally accurately when using additional features. On a deeper level, we observed that 52.8% of all instances in the target prediction task that were classified correctly only after adding metaphor features to the SVM baseline contained at least one hateful metaphor. These metaphors were often implicit cases of hate speech, such as "nep Belgen" (*fake Belgians*), "soortgenoten" (*conspecifics*), and "die leven nog in de middeleeuwen" (*they still live in the Middle Ages*). Still, we also found less subtle hateful metaphors, e.g., "strontvretende kakkerlakken" (*shit eating cockroaches*).

Type prediction task As evidenced by Figures 3 and 4, adding hateful metaphor features to the SVM model drastically decreases the number of cases where violent comments are confused with offensive comments, while retaining high classification accuracy for the "offensive" class. More specifically, 36.4% of all instances that were classified correctly only after adding hateful metaphor features contained at least one hateful metaphor. Similar to the improvements in the target prediction task, these metaphors were often implicit forms of hate speech, such as "op [ANONIEM]'s gezicht kan je pannenkoeken bakken" (*"you could cook pancakes on* [ANONYMOUS]*'s face"*) and afschaffen da klubke (*abolish that little club*, referring to the Catholic Church).

6 Conclusion

In this paper, we investigated the usefulness of hateful metaphors as predictive features for two less studied hate speech detection subtasks (namely type and target prediction) and analyzed the annotated hateful metaphors in our corpus in line with Conceptual Metaphor Theory and Critical Metaphor Analysis.

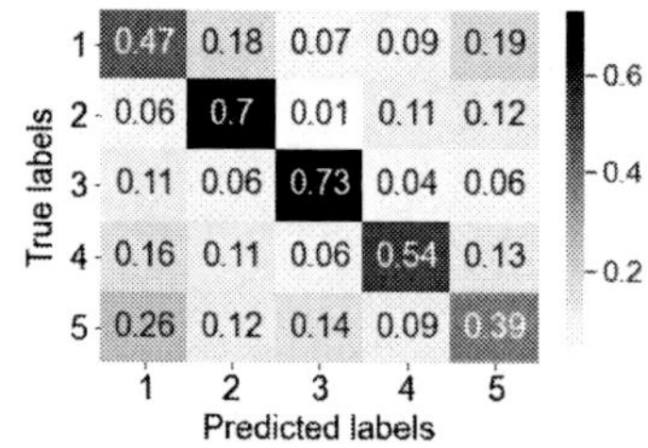

Figure 1: Confusion matrix for the **target** classification **SVM baseline** (1="migrants/LGBT", 2="related to migrants/LGBT", 3="journalist/medium", 4="commenter", 5="other").

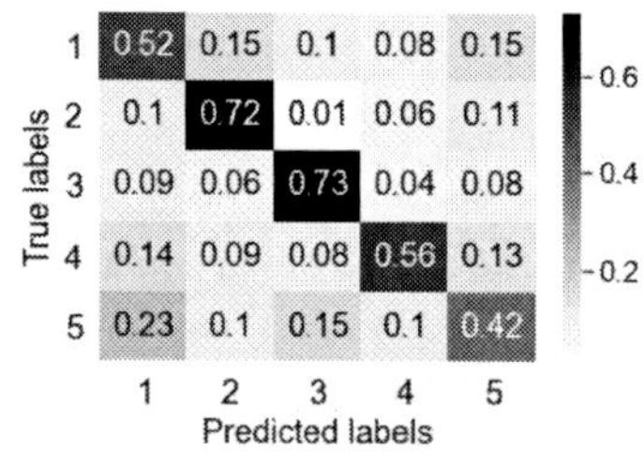

Figure 2: Confusion matrix for the **target** classification **SVM enriched with all generic features** (1="migrants/LGBT", 2="related to migrants/LGBT", 3="journalist/medium", 4="commenter", 5="other").

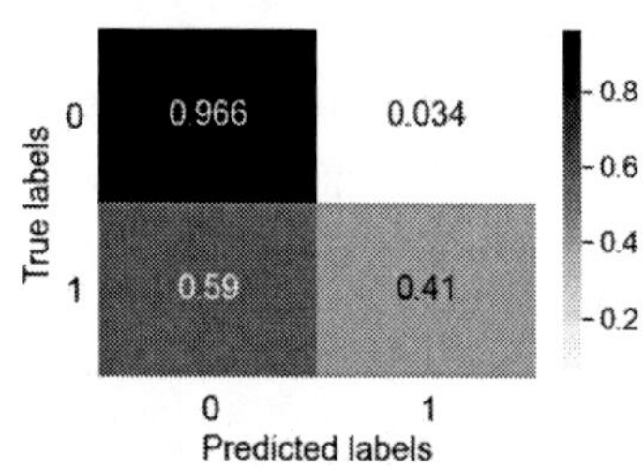

Figure 3: Confusion matrix for the **type** classification **SVM baseline** (1="violence", 0="offensive").

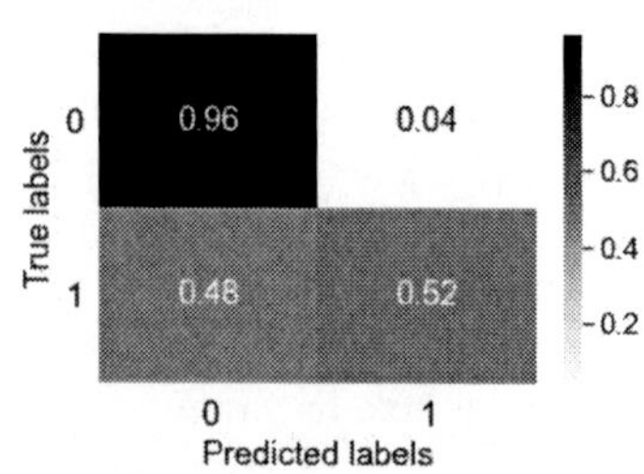

Figure 4: Confusion matrix for the **type** classification **SVM enriched with generic n tokens feature** (1="violence", 0="offensive").

Performances of SVM, BERTje and RobBERT were provided for both type and target prediction tasks and these models were then enriched with the hateful metaphor features in various ways to show their usefulness. The results show that the target SVM baseline improved by 2.4%. Conversely, BERTje and RobBERT could not be improved with additional features for this task. Regarding the type prediction task, an improvement up to 4.6% was observed for the SVM baseline, whereas the already high-performing BERTje and RobBERT baselines improved by 1.9% F1-score each. From the qualitative analysis that was conducted, it was observed that these improvements contained a large number of implicit forms of hate speech, which is considered to be one of the main challenges of hate speech detection at the moment.

This paper is a starting point for further research into the new area of (hateful) metaphors as predictive features for the hate speech classification tasks. Further research may include investigating whether the same results achieved with an upper-bound baseline in this paper (provided by our manually annotated features) can also be obtained when using labels predicted by models that have been trained to detect hateful metaphors. Other future research directions could include investigating more feature encoding methods and conducting ablation studies when combining multiple ways to encode hateful metaphors. In addition, it was observed that the SVM model cen be improved more strongly than BERTje and RobBERT, which suggest that the latter models already contain metaphorical information due to pretraining. Whether this is indeed the case is yet another subject worth investigating in future studies.

Acknowledgments

This research was supported by an IOF SEP project of the University of Antwerp. It also received funding from the Flemish Government (AI Research Program) and the Flemish Research Foundation through the bilateral research project FWO G070619N "The linguistic landscape of hate speech on social media".

References

Valerio Basile, Cristina Bosco, Elisabetta Fersini, Debora Nozza, Viviana Patti, Francisco Manuel Rangel Pardo, Paolo Rosso, and Manuela Sanguinetti. 2019. SemEval-2019 task 5: Multilingual detection of hate speech against immigrants and women in Twitter. In *Proceedings of the 13th International Workshop on Semantic Evaluation*, pages 54–63, Minneapolis (MN), USA. Association for Computational Linguistics.

Tommaso Caselli, Valerio Basile, Jelena Mitrović, Inga Kartoziya, and Michael Granitzer. 2020. I feel offended, don't be abusive! Implicit/explicit messages in offensive and abusive language. In *Proceedings of the 12th Language Resources and Evaluation Conference*, pages 6193–6202, Marseille, France. European Language Resources Association.

Jonathan Charteris-Black. 2004. *Corpus approaches to critical metaphor analysis*. Palgrave Macmillan.

Rajen Chatterjee, Matteo Negri, Marco Turchi, Marcello Federico, Lucia Specia, and Frédéric Blain. 2017. Guiding neural machine translation decoding with external knowledge. In *Proceedings of the Second Conference on Machine Translation*, pages 157–168, Copenhagen, Denmark. Association for Computational Linguistics.

Thomas Davidson, Dana Warmsley, Michael W. Macy, and Ingmar Weber. 2017. Automated hate speech detection and the problem of offensive language. *CoRR*, abs/1703.04009.

Ona de Gibert, Naiara Perez, Aitor García-Pablos, and Montse Cuadros. 2018. Hate speech dataset from a white supremacy forum. In *Proceedings of the 2nd Workshop on Abusive Language Online (ALW2)*, pages 11–20, Brussels, Belgium. Association for Computational Linguistics.

Wietse de Vries, Andreas van Cranenburgh, Arianna Bisazza, Tommaso Caselli, Gertjan van Noord, and Malvina Nissim. 2019. BERTje: A Dutch BERT Model. arXiv:1912.09582.

Pieter Delobelle, Thomas Winters, and Bettina Berendt. 2020. RobBERT: a dutch roBERTa-based language model.

Zsofia Demjen and Claire Hardaker. 2017. Metaphor, impoliteness, and offence in online communication. In *The Routledge Handbook of Metaphor and Language*, pages 353–367. Routledge.

Inga Dervinytė. 2009. Conceptual emigration and immigration metaphors in the language of the press: a contrastive analysis. *Studies about languages*, 14:49–55.

Jacob Devlin, Ming-Wei Chang, Kenton Lee, and Kristina Toutanova. 2019. BERT: Pre-training of deep bidirectional transformers for language understanding. In *Proceedings of the 2019 Conference of the North American Chapter of the Association for Computational Linguistics: Human Language Technologies, Volume 1 (Long and Short Papers)*, pages 4171–4186, Minneapolis (MN), USA. Association for Computational Linguistics.

Ritesh Kumar, Atul Kr. Ojha, Shervin Malmasi, and Marcos Zampieri. 2018. Benchmarking aggression identification in social media. In *Proceedings of the First Workshop on Trolling, Aggression and Cyberbullying (TRAC-2018)*, pages 1–11, Santa Fe (NM), USA. Association for Computational Linguistics.

George Lakoff and Mark Johnson. 1980. *Metaphors We Live By*. University of Chicago Press, Chicago (IL) USA.

Chee Wee (Ben) Leong, Beata Beigman Klebanov, Chris Hamill, Egon Stemle, Rutuja Ubale, and Xianyang Chen. 2020. A report on the 2020 VUA and TOEFL metaphor detection shared task. In *Proceedings of the Second Workshop on Figurative Language Processing*, pages 18–29, Online. Association for Computational Linguistics.

Chee Wee (Ben) Leong, Beata Beigman Klebanov, and Ekaterina Shutova. 2018. A report on the 2018 VUA metaphor detection shared task. In *Proceedings of the Workshop on Figurative Language Processing*, pages 56–66, New Orleans (LA), USA. Association for Computational Linguistics.

Zhongwei Li, Xuancong Wang, Ai Ti Aw, Eng Siong Chng, and Haizhou Li. 2018. Named-entity tagging and domain adaptation for better customized translation. In *Proceedings of the Seventh Named Entities Workshop*, pages 41–46, Melbourne, Australia. Association for Computational Linguistics.

Yinhan Liu, Myle Ott, Naman Goyal, Jingfei Du, Mandar Joshi, Danqi Chen, Omer Levy, Mike Lewis, Luke Zettlemoyer, and Veselin Stoyanov. 2019. RoBERTa: A robustly optimized BERT pretraining approach. *CoRR*, abs/1907.11692.

Nikola Ljubešić, Darja Fišer, and Tomaž Erjavec. 2019. The FRENK datasets of socially unacceptable discourse in slovene and english. In *Text, Speech, and Dialogue*, pages 103–114, Cham. Springer International Publishing.

Nikola Ljubešić, Ilia Markov, Darja Fišer, and Walter Daelemans. 2020. The LiLaH emotion lexicon of Croatian, Dutch and Slovene. In *Proceedings of the Third Workshop on Computational Modeling of People's Opinions, Personality, and Emotion's in Social Media*, pages 153–157, Barcelona, Spain (Online). Association for Computational Linguistics.

Sean MacAvaney, Hao-Ren Yao, Eugene Yang, Katina Russell, Nazli Goharian, and Ophir Frieder. 2019. Hate speech detection: Challenges and solutions. *PloS one*, 14(8):e0221152.

Ilia Markov, Nikola Ljubešić, Darja Fišer, and Walter Daelemans. 2021. Exploring stylometric and emotion-based features for multilingual cross-domain hate speech detection. In *Proceedings of the Eleventh Workshop on Computational Approaches to Subjectivity, Sentiment and Social Media Analysis*, pages 149–159, Kyiv, Ukraine (Online). Association for Computational Linguistics.

John T. Nockleby. 2000. Hate speech. In *Encyclopedia of the American Constitution*, pages 1277–1279. Macmillan, New York, USA.

F. Pedregosa, G. Varoquaux, A. Gramfort, V. Michel, B. Thirion, O. Grisel, M. Blondel, P. Prettenhofer, R. Weiss, V. Dubourg, J. Vanderplas, A. Passos, D. Cournapeau, M. Brucher, M. Perrot, and E. Duchesnay. 2011. Scikit-learn: Machine learning in Python. *Journal of Machine Learning Research*, 12:2825–2830.

Chuandong Su, Fumiyo Fukumoto, Xiaoxi Huang, Jiyi Li, Rongbo Wang, and Zhiqun Chen. 2020. DeepMet: A reading comprehension paradigm for token-level metaphor detection. In *Proceedings of the Second Workshop on Figurative Language Processing*, pages 30–39, Online. Association for Computational Linguistics.

Betty van Aken, Julian Risch, Ralf Krestel, and Alexander Löser. 2018. Challenges for toxic comment classification: An in-depth error analysis.

Thomas Wolf, Lysandre Debut, Victor Sanh, Julien Chaumond, Clement Delangue, Anthony Moi, Pierric Cistac, Tim Rault, Rémi Louf, Morgan Funtowicz, Joe Davison, Sam Shleifer, Patrick von Platen, Clara Ma, Yacine Jernite, Julien Plu, Canwen Xu, Teven Le Scao, Sylvain Gugger, Mariama Drame, Quentin Lhoest, and Alexander M. Rush. 2020. Transformers: State-of-the-art natural language processing. In *Proceedings of the 2020 Conference on Empirical Methods in Natural Language Processing: System Demonstrations*, pages 38–45, Online. Association for Computational Linguistics.

Marcos Zampieri, Shervin Malmasi, Preslav Nakov, Sara Rosenthal, Noura Farra, and Ritesh Kumar. 2019a. Predicting the type and target of offensive posts in social media.

Marcos Zampieri, Shervin Malmasi, Preslav Nakov, Sara Rosenthal, Noura Farra, and Ritesh Kumar. 2019b. Semeval-2019 task 6: Identifying and categorizing offensive language in social media (offenseval).

Marcos Zampieri, Preslav Nakov, Sara Rosenthal, Pepa Atanasova, Georgi Karadzhov, Hamdy Mubarak, Leon Derczynski, Zeses Pitenis, and Çağrı Çöltekin. 2020. Semeval-2020 task 12: Multilingual offensive language identification in social media (offenseval 2020).

Improving Cross-Domain Hate Speech Detection by Reducing the False Positive Rate

Ilia Markov
CLIPS Research Center
University of Antwerp, Belgium
ilia.markov@uantwerpen.be

Walter Daelemans
CLIPS Research Center
University of Antwerp, Belgium
walter.daelemans@uantwerpen.be

Abstract

Hate speech detection is an actively growing field of research with a variety of recently proposed approaches that allowed to push the state-of-the-art results. One of the challenges of such automated approaches – namely recent deep learning models – is a risk of false positives (i.e., false accusations), which may lead to over-blocking or removal of harmless social media content in applications with little moderator intervention. We evaluate deep learning models both under in-domain and cross-domain hate speech detection conditions, and introduce an SVM approach that allows to significantly improve the state-of-the-art results when combined with the deep learning models through a simple majority-voting ensemble. The improvement is mainly due to a reduction of the false positive rate.

1 Introduction

A commonly used definition of hate speech is a communication that disparages a person or a group on the basis of some characteristic such as race, color, ethnicity, gender, sexual orientation, nationality, religion, or other characteristics (Nockleby, 2000). The automated detection of hate speech online and related concepts, such as toxicity, cyberbullying, abusive and offensive language, has recently gained popularity within the Natural Language Processing (NLP) community. Robust hate speech detection systems may provide valuable information for police, security agencies, and social media platforms to effectively counter such effects in online discussions (Halevy et al., 2020).

Despite the recent advances in the field, mainly due to a large amount of available social media data and recent deep learning techniques, the task remains challenging from an NLP perspective, since on the one hand, hate speech, toxicity, or offensive language are often not explicitly expressed through the use of offensive words, while on the other hand, non-hateful content may contain such terms and the classifier may consider signals for an offensive word stronger than other signals from the context, leading to false positive predictions, and further removal of harmless content online (van Aken et al., 2018; Zhang and Luo, 2018).

Labelling non-hateful utterances as hate speech (false positives or type II errors) is a common error even for human annotators due to personal bias. Several studies showed that providing context, detailed annotation guidelines, or the background of the author of a message improves annotation quality by reducing the number of utterances erroneously annotated as hateful (de Gibert et al., 2018; Sap et al., 2019; Vidgen and Derczynski, 2020).

We assess the performance of deep learning models that currently provide state-of-the-art results for the hate speech detection task (Zampieri et al., 2019b, 2020) both under in-domain and cross-domain hate speech detection conditions, and introduce an SVM approach with a variety of engineered features (e.g., stylometric, emotion, hate speech lexicon features, described further in the paper) that significantly improves the results when combined with the deep learning models in an ensemble, mainly by reducing the false positive rate.

We target the use cases where messages are flagged automatically and can be mistakenly removed, without or with little moderator intervention. While existing optimization strategies (e.g., threshold variation) allow to minimize false positives with a negative effect on overall accuracy, our method reduces the false positive rate without decreasing overall performance.

2 Methodology

Hate speech detection is commonly framed as a binary supervised classification task (hate speech vs. non-hate speech) and has been addressed using both deep neural networks and methods based on manual feature engineering (Zampieri et al., 2019b,

Proceedings of the 4th NLP4IF Workshop on NLP for Internet Freedom, pages 17–22
June 6, 2021. ©2021 Association for Computational Linguistics

2020). Our work evaluates and exploits the advantages of deep neural networks as means for extracting discriminative features directly from text and of a conventional SVM approach taking the advantage of explicit feature engineering based on task and domain knowledge. In more detail, we focus on the approaches described below.

2.1 Baselines

Bag of words (BoW) We use a tf-weighted lowercased bag-of-words (BoW) approach with the liblinear Support Vector Machines (SVM) classifier. The optimal SVM parameters (penalty parameter (C), loss function (loss), and tolerance for stopping criteria (tol)) were selected based on grid search.

Convolutional neural networks (CNN) We use a convolutional neural networks (CNN) approach (Kim, 2014) to learn discriminative word-level hate speech features with the following architecture: to process the word embeddings (trained with fastText (Joulin et al., 2017)), we use a convolutional layer followed by a global average pooling layer and a dropout of 0.6. Then, a dense layer with a ReLU activation is applied, followed by a dropout of 0.6, and finally, a dense layer with a sigmoid activation to make the prediction for the binary classification.

Long short-term memory networks (LSTM) We use an LSTM model (Hochreiter and Schmidhuber, 1997), which takes a sequence of words as input and aims at capturing long-term dependencies. We process the sequence of word embeddings (trained with GloVe (Pennington et al., 2014)) with a unidirectional LSTM layer with 300 units, followed by a dropout of 0.2, and a dense layer with a sigmoid activation for predictions.

2.2 Models

BERT and RoBERTa Pretrained language models, i.e., Bidirectional Encoder Representations from Transformers, BERT (Devlin et al., 2019) and Robustly Optimized BERT Pretraining Approach, RoBERTa (Liu et al., 2019b), currently provide the best results for hate speech detection, as shown by several shared tasks in the field (Zampieri et al., 2019b; Mandl et al., 2019; Zampieri et al., 2020). We use the BERT-base-cased (12-layer, 768-hidden, 12-heads, 110 million parameters) and RoBERTa-base (12-layer, 768-hidden, 12-heads, 125 million parameters) models from the huggingface library[1] fine-tuning the models on the training data. The implementation was done in PyTorch (Paszke et al., 2019) using the simple transformers library[2].

Support Vector Machines (SVM) The Support Vector Machines (SVM) algorithm (Cortes and Vapnik, 1995) is commonly used for the hate speech detection task (Davidson et al., 2017; Salminen et al., 2018; MacAvaney et al., 2019; Del Vigna et al., 2017; Ljubešić et al., 2020).

Following Markov et al. (2021), we lemmatize the messages in our data and represent them through universal part-of-speech (POS) tags (obtained with the Stanford POS Tagger (Toutanova et al., 2003)), function words (words belonging to the closed syntactic classes)[3], and emotion-conveying words (from the NRC word-emotion association lexicon (Mohammad and Turney, 2013)) to capture stylometric and emotion-based peculiarities of hateful content. For example, the phrase *@USER all conservatives are bad people* [OLID id: 22902] is represented through POS, function words, and emotion-conveying words as 'PROPN', 'all', 'NOUN', 'be', 'bad', 'NOUN'. From this representation n-grams (with n = 1–3) are built.

We use the NRC lexicon emotion associations (e.g., *bad* = 'anger', 'disgust', 'fear', 'negative', 'sadness') and hate speech lexicon entries (De Smedt et al., 2020) as additional feature vectors, word unigrams, and character n-grams for the in-domain setting (with n = 1–6), considering only those n-grams that appear in ten training messages (min_df = 10).

We use tf-idf weighting scheme and the liblinear scikit-learn (Pedregosa et al., 2011) implementation of the SVM algorithm with optimized parameters (penalty parameter (C), loss function (loss), and tolerance for stopping criteria (tol)) selected based on grid search.

Ensemble We use a simple ensembling strategy, which consists in combining the predictions produced by the deep learning and machine learning approaches: BERT, RoBERTa, and SVM, through a hard majority-voting ensemble, i.e., selecting the label that is most often predicted.

[1] https://huggingface.co/
[2] https://simpletransformers.ai/
[3] https://universaldependencies.org/u/pos/

3 Experiments and Results

3.1 Data

To evaluate the approaches discussed in Section 2 we conducted experiments on two recent English social media datasets for hate speech detection:

FRENK (Ljubešić et al., 2019) The FRENK datasets consist of Facebook comments in English and Slovene covering LGBT and migrant topics. The datasets were manually annotated for fine-grained types of socially unacceptable discourse (e.g., violence, offensiveness, threat). We focus on the English dataset and use the coarse-grained (binary) hate speech classes: hate speech vs. non-hate speech. We select the messages for which more than four out of eight annotators agreed upon the class and use training and test partitions splitting the dataset by post boundaries in order to avoid comments from the same discussion thread to appear in both training and test sets, that is, to avoid within-post bias.

OLID (Zampieri et al., 2019a) The OLID dataset has been introduced in the context of the SemEval 2019 shared task on offensive language identification (Zampieri et al., 2019b). The dataset is a collection of English tweets annotated for the type and target of offensive language. We focus on whether a message is offensive or not and use the same training and test partitions as in the OffensEval 2019 shared task (Zampieri et al., 2019b).

The statistics of the datasets used are shown in Table 1. For cross-domain experiments, we train (merging the training and test subsets) on FRENK and test on OLID, and vice versa.

		FRENK		OLID	
		# messages	%	# messages	%
Train	HS	2,848	35.9	4,400	33.2
	non-HS	5,091	64.1	8,840	66.8
Test	HS	744	35.5	240	27.9
	non-HS	1,351	64.5	620	72.1
Total		10,034		14,100	

Table 1: Statistics of the datasets used.

3.2 Results

The performance of the models described in Section 2 in terms of precision, recall, and F1-score (macro-averaged) in the in-domain and cross-domain settings is shown in Table 2. Statistically significant gains of the ensemble approach (BERT, RoBERTa, and SVM) over the best-performing individual model for each of the settings according to McNemar's statistical significance test (McNemar, 1947) with $\alpha < 0.05$ are marked with '*'.

We can observe that the in-domain trends are similar across the two datasets: BERT and RoBERTa achieve the highest results, outperforming the baseline methods and the SVM approach. The results on the OLID test set are in line with the previous research on this data (Zampieri et al., 2019a) and are similar to the best-performing shared task systems when the same types of models are used (i.e., 80.0% F1-score with CNN, 75.0% with LSTM, and 82.9% with BERT (Zampieri et al., 2019b)), while the results on the FRENK test set are higher than the results reported in (Markov et al., 2021) for all the reported models.[4] We can also note that the SVM approach achieves competitive results compared to the deep learning models. A near state-of-the-art SVM performance (compared to BERT) was also observed in other studies on hate speech detection, e.g., (MacAvaney et al., 2019), where tf-idf weighted word and character n-gram features were used. The results for SVM on the OLID test set are higher than the results obtained by the machine learning approaches in the OffensEval 2019 shared task (i.e., 69.0% F1-score (Zampieri et al., 2019b)). Combining the SVM predictions with the predictions produced by BERT and RoBERTa through the majority-voting ensemble further improves the results on the both datasets. We also note that the F1-score obtained by the ensemble approach on the OLID test set is higher than the result of the winning approach of the OffensEval 2019 shared task (Liu et al., 2019a): 83.2% and 82.9% F1-score, respectively.

The cross-domain results indicate that using out-of-domain data for testing leads to a substantial drop in performance by around 5–10 F1 points for all the evaluated models. BERT and RoBERTa remain the best-performing individual models in the cross-domain setting, while the SVM approach shows a smaller drop than the baseline CNN and LSTM models, outperforming these models in the cross-domain setup, and contributes to the ensemble approach.

Both in the in-domain and cross-domain settings, combining the predictions produced by BERT and RoBERTa with SVM through the majority-voting

[4] Markov et al. (2021) used multilingual BERT and did not used pretrained embedding for CNN and LSTM to address multiple language covered in the paper.

	In-domain					
	FRENK			OLID		
Model	Precision	Recall	F1	Precision	Recall	F1
BoW	71.0	70.8	70.9	75.9	70.9	72.5
CNN	76.8	76.6	76.7	81.8	77.8	79.4
LSTM	73.3	72.5	72.8	78.2	75.1	76.4
BERT	78.3	78.4	78.3	82.3	82.0	82.2
RoBERTa	78.4	78.7	78.5	80.2	79.7	80.0
SVM	77.8	76.4	77.0	82.3	76.1	78.3
Ensemble	**80.0**	**79.5**	**79.7***	**84.7**	**82.0**	**83.2**

	Cross-domain					
	OLID – FRENK			FRENK – OLID		
Model	Precision	Recall	F1	Precision	Recall	F1
BoW	70.3	64.9	65.5	66.3	63.1	63.8
CNN	70.8	65.6	66.3	65.9	67.6	66.0
LSTM	68.0	66.1	66.6	67.5	65.9	66.5
BERT	70.5	68.8	69.4	71.7	72.7	72.1
RoBERTa	**73.9**	68.2	69.2	71.9	73.6	72.4
SVM	70.2	67.0	67.7	70.2	68.4	69.0
Ensemble	73.1	**68.8**	**69.7***	**73.5**	**73.9**	**73.6***

Table 2: In-domain and cross-domain results for the baselines, individual models and the ensemble.

	In-domain				Cross-domain			
	FRENK		OLID		OLID – FRENK		FRENK – OLID	
Model	FPR	PPV	FPR	PPV	FPR	PPV	FPR	PPV
CNN	15.8	70.6	7.3	77.0	11.0	68.2	31.2	51.0
LSTM	17.0	66.7	9.4	71.1	17.2	61.5	17.3	58.2
BERT	15.6	71.8	9.7	74.7	16.8	64.3	21.1	60.7
RoBERTa	16.0	71.7	10.6	71.8	**9.5**	**72.8**	23.7	59.5
SVM	**13.2**	73.3	**5.8**	79.4	14.0	65.6	**15.7**	62.1
Ensemble	13.3	**74.9**	6.8	**80.2**	11.4	70.5	18.3	**63.9**

Table 3: False positive rate (FPR) and positive predictive value (PPV) for the examined models.

ensemble approach improves the results over the individual models incorporated into the ensemble.[5] This improvement is significant in all cases, except for the OLID in-domain setting, where only 860 messages are used for testing. A more detailed analysis presented below provides deeper insights into the nature of these improvements.

4 Error Analysis

We performed a quantitative analysis of the obtained results focusing on the false positive rate: $FPR = FP/(FP + TN)$, the probability that a positive label is assigned to a negative instance; we additionally report positive predictive value: $PPV = TP/(TP + FP)$, the probability a predicted positive is a true positive, for the examined models in the in-domain and cross-domain settings (Table 3).

We note that the SVM approach shows the lowest FPR and the highest PPV in all the considered settings, except when training on the OLID dataset and testing on the FRENK dataset. Combining BERT and RoBERTa with SVM through the ensemble approach reduces the false positive rate in three out of four settings, when compared to BERT and RoBERTa in isolation, and contributes to the overall improvement of the results in all the considered settings. The improvement brought by combining BERT and RoBERTa with SVM is higher in the majority of cases than combining BERT and RoBERTa with either CNN or LSTM. Measuring the correlation of the predictions of different models using the Pearson correlation coefficient revealed that SVM produces highly uncorrelated predictions when compared to BERT and RoBERTa. An analogous effect for deep learning and shallow approaches was observed in (van Aken et al., 2018).

The majority of the erroneous false positive predictions produced by the SVM approach contain

[5] We also examined other ensemble approaches, e.g., Gradient Boosting, AdaBoost, soft majority voting, achieving similar results and trends under the cross-domain conditions.

offensive words used in a non-hateful context (avg. 78.8% messages over the four settings), while for BERT and RoBERTa this percentage is lower in all the settings (avg. 68.7% and 69.7%, respectively), indicating that BERT and RoBERTa tend to classify an instance as belonging to the hate speech class even if it is not explicitly contains offensive terms.

Our findings suggest that the SVM approach improves the results mainly by reducing the false positive rate when combined with BERT and RoBERTa. This strategy can be used to address one of the challenges that social media platforms are facing: removal of content that does not violate community guidelines.

5 Conclusions

We showed that one of the challenges in hate speech detection: erroneous false positive decisions, can be addressed by combining deep learning models with a robust feature-engineered SVM approach. The results are consistent within the in-domain and cross-domain settings. This simple strategy provides a significant boost to the state-of-the-art hate speech detection results.

Acknowledgements

This research has been supported by the Flemish Research Foundation through the bilateral research project FWO G070619N "The linguistic landscape of hate speech on social media". The research also received funding from the Flemish Government (AI Research Program).

References

Corinna Cortes and Vladimir Vapnik. 1995. Support-vector networks. *Machine learning*, 20(3):273–297.

Thomas Davidson, Dana Warmsley, Michael W. Macy, and Ingmar Weber. 2017. Automated hate speech detection and the problem of offensive language. In *Proceedings of the Eleventh International AAAI Conference on Web and Social Media*, pages 512–515, Montreal, QC, Canada. AAAI Press.

Ona de Gibert, Naiara Perez, Aitor García-Pablos, and Montse Cuadros. 2018. Hate speech dataset from a white supremacy forum. In *Proceedings of the 2nd Workshop on Abusive Language Online*, pages 11–20, Brussels, Belgium. ACL.

Tom De Smedt, Pierre Voué, Sylvia Jaki, Melina Röttcher, and Guy De Pauw. 2020. Profanity & offensive words (POW): Multilingual fine-grained lexicons for hate speech. Technical report, TextGain.

Fabio Del Vigna, Andrea Cimino, Felice Dell'Orletta, Marinella Petrocchi, and Maurizio Tesconi. 2017. Hate me, hate me not: Hate speech detection on Facebook. In *Proceedings of the First Italian Conference on Cybersecurity*, pages 86–95, Venice, Italy. CEUR-WS.org.

Jacob Devlin, Ming-Wei Chang, Kenton Lee, and Kristina Toutanova. 2019. BERT: Pre-training of deep bidirectional transformers for language understanding. In *Proceedings of the 2019 Conference of the North American Chapter of the Association for Computational Linguistics: Human Language Technologies)*, pages 4171–4186, Minneapolis, MN, USA. ACL.

Alon Halevy, Cristian Canton Ferrer, Hao Ma, Umut Ozertem, Patrick Pantel, Marzieh Saeidi, Fabrizio Silvestri, and Ves Stoyanov. 2020. Preserving integrity in online social networks. *CoRR*, abs/2009.10311.

Sepp Hochreiter and Jürgen Schmidhuber. 1997. Long short-term memory. *Neural Computation*, 9(8):1735–1780.

Armand Joulin, Edouard Grave, Piotr Bojanowski, and Tomas Mikolov. 2017. Bag of tricks for efficient text classification. In *Proceedings of the 15th Conference of the European Chapter of the Association for Computational Linguistics: Volume 2, Short Papers*, pages 427–431, Valencia, Spain. ACL.

Yoon Kim. 2014. Convolutional neural networks for sentence classification. In *Proceedings of the 2014 Conference on Empirical Methods in Natural Language Processing*, pages 1746–1751, Doha, Qatar. ACL.

Ping Liu, Wen Li, and Liang Zou. 2019a. NULI at SemEval-2019 task 6: Transfer learning for offensive language detection using bidirectional transformers. In *Proceedings of the 13th International Workshop on Semantic Evaluation*, pages 87–91, Minneapolis, Minnesota, USA. ACL.

Yinhan Liu, Myle Ott, Naman Goyal, Jingfei Du, Mandar Joshi, Danqi Chen, Omer Levy, Mike Lewis, Luke Zettlemoyer, and Veselin Stoyanov. 2019b. RoBERTa: A robustly optimized BERT pretraining approach. *ArXiv*, abs/1907.11692.

Nikola Ljubešić, Darja Fišer, and Tomaž Erjavec. 2019. The FRENK datasets of socially unacceptable discourse in Slovene and English. In *Proceedings of the 22nd International Conference on Text, Speech, and Dialogue*, pages 103–114, Ljubljana, Slovenia. Springer.

Nikola Ljubešić, Ilia Markov, Darja Fišer, and Walter Daelemans. 2020. The LiLaH emotion lexicon of Croatian, Dutch and Slovene. In *Proceedings of the Third Workshop on Computational Modeling of People's Opinions, Personality, and Emotion's in Social Media*, pages 153–157, Barcelona, Spain (Online). ACL.

Sean MacAvaney, Hao-Ren Yao, Eugene Yang, Katina Russell, Nazli Goharian, and Ophir Frieder. 2019. Hate speech detection: Challenges and solutions. *PLOS ONE*, 14(8):1–16.

Thomas Mandl, Sandip Modha, Prasenjit Majumder, Daksh Patel, Mohana Dave, Chintak Mandlia, and Aditya Patel. 2019. Overview of the HASOC track at FIRE 2019: Hate speech and offensive content identification in Indo-European languages. In *Proceedings of the 11th Forum for Information Retrieval Evaluation*, pages 14–17, New York, NY, USA. ACM.

Ilia Markov, Nikola Ljubešić, Darja Fišer, and Walter Daelemans. 2021. Exploring stylometric and emotion-based features for multilingual cross-domain hate speech detection. In *Proceedings of the Eleventh Workshop on Computational Approaches to Subjectivity, Sentiment and Social Media Analysis*, pages 149–159, Kyiv, Ukraine (Online). ACL.

Quinn McNemar. 1947. Note on the sampling error of the difference between correlated proportions or percentages. *Psychometrika*, 12(2):153–157.

Saif Mohammad and Peter Turney. 2013. Crowdsourcing a word-emotion association lexicon. *Computational Intelligence*, 29:436–465.

John Nockleby. 2000. Hate speech. *Encyclopedia of the American Constitution*, pages 1277–1279.

Adam Paszke, Sam Gross, Francisco Massa, Adam Lerer, James Bradbury, Gregory Chanan, Trevor Killeen, Zeming Lin, Natalia Gimelshein, Luca Antiga, Alban Desmaison, Andreas Kopf, Edward Yang, Zachary DeVito, Martin Raison, Alykhan Tejani, Sasank Chilamkurthy, Benoit Steiner, Lu Fang, Junjie Bai, and Soumith Chintala. 2019. Pytorch: An imperative style, high-performance deep learning library. In *Advances in Neural Information Processing Systems 32*, pages 8026–8037. Curran Associates, Inc.

Fabian Pedregosa, Gaël Varoquaux, Alexandre Gramfort, Vincent Michel, Bertrand Thirion, Olivier Grisel, Mathieu Blondel, Peter Prettenhofer, Ron Weiss, Vincent Dubourg, Jake Vanderplas, Alexandre Passos, David Cournapeau, Matthieu Brucher, Matthieu Perrot, and Édouard Duchesnay. 2011. Scikit-learn: Machine learning in Python. *Journal of Machine Learning Research*, 12:2825–2830.

Jeffrey Pennington, Richard Socher, and Christopher Manning. 2014. GloVe: Global vectors for word representation. In *Proceedings of the 2014 Conference on Empirical Methods in Natural Language Processing (EMNLP)*, pages 1532–1543, Doha, Qatar. CL.

Joni Salminen, Hind Almerekhi, Milica Milenković, Soon Gyo Jung, Jisun An, Haewoon Kwak, and Bernard J. Jansen. 2018. Anatomy of online hate: Developing a taxonomy and machine learning models for identifying and classifying hate in online news media. In *Proceedings of the Twelfth International AAAI Conference on Web and Social Media*, pages 330–339, Palo Alto, California, USA. AAAI press.

Maarten Sap, Dallas Card, Saadia Gabriel, Yejin Choi, and Noah A. Smith. 2019. The risk of racial bias in hate speech detection. In *Proceedings of the 57th Annual Meeting of the Association for Computational Linguistics*, pages 1668–1678, Florence, Italy. ACL.

Kristina Toutanova, Dan Klein, Christopher Manning, and Yoram Singer. 2003. Feature-rich part-of-speech tagging with a cyclic dependency network. In *Proceedings of the 2003 Human Language Technology Conference of the North American Chapter of the Association for Computational Linguistics*, pages 252–259, Edmonton, Canada. ACL.

Betty van Aken, Julian Risch, Ralf Krestel, and Alexander Löser. 2018. Challenges for toxic comment classification: An in-depth error analysis. *CoRR*, abs/1809.07572.

Bertie Vidgen and Leon Derczynski. 2020. Directions in abusive language training data: Garbage in, garbage out. *CoRR*, abs/2004.01670.

Marcos Zampieri, Shervin Malmasi, Preslav Nakov, Sara Rosenthal, Noura Farra, and Ritesh Kumar. 2019a. Predicting the type and target of offensive posts in social media. In *Proceedings of the 2019 Conference of the North American Chapter of the Association for Computational Linguistics: Human Language Technologies*, pages 1415–1420. ACL.

Marcos Zampieri, Shervin Malmasi, Preslav Nakov, Sara Rosenthal, Noura Farra, and Ritesh Kumar. 2019b. SemEval-2019 task 6: Identifying and categorizing offensive language in social media (OffensEval). In *Proceedings of the 13th International Workshop on Semantic Evaluation*, pages 75–86, Minneapolis, Minnesota, USA. ACL.

Marcos Zampieri, Preslav Nakov, Sara Rosenthal, Pepa Atanasova, Georgi Karadzhov, Hamdy Mubarak, Leon Derczynski, Zeses Pitenis, and Çağrı Çöltekin. 2020. Semeval-2020 task 12: Multilingual offensive language identification in social media (offenseval 2020). *CoRR*, abs/2006.07235.

Ziqi Zhang and Lei Luo. 2018. Hate speech detection: A solved problem? The challenging case of long tail on Twitter. *CoRR*, abs/1803.03662.

Understanding the Impact of Evidence-Aware Sentence Selection for Fact Checking

Giannis Bekoulis[1,2] **Christina Papagiannopoulou**[3] **Nikos Deligiannis**[1,2]
[1]ETRO, Vrije Universiteit Brussel, 1050 Brussels, Belgium
[2]imec, Kapeldreef 75, 3001 Leuven, Belgium
{gbekouli,ndeligia}@etrovub.be
[3]cppapagi@gmail.com

Abstract

Fact Extraction and VERification (FEVER) is a recently introduced task that consists of the following subtasks (i) document retrieval, (ii) sentence retrieval, and (iii) claim verification. In this work, we focus on the subtask of sentence retrieval. Specifically, we propose an evidence-aware transformer-based model that outperforms all other models in terms of FEVER score by using a subset of training instances. In addition, we conduct a large experimental study to get a better understanding of the problem, while we summarize our findings by presenting future research challenges[1]

1 Introduction

Recently a lot of research in the NLP community has been focused on the problem of automated fact checking (Liu et al., 2020; Zhong et al., 2020). In this work, we focus on the FEVER dataset that is the largest fact checking dataset (Thorne et al., 2018). The goal of the task is to identify the veracity of a given claim based on Wikipedia documents. The problem is traditionally approached as a series of three subtasks, namely (i) document retrieval (select the most relevant documents to the claim), (ii) sentence retrieval (select the most relevant sentences to the claim from the retrieved documents), and (iii) claim verification (validate the veracity of the claim based on the relevant sentences).

Several models have been proposed for the FEVER dataset (Hanselowski et al., 2018; Nie et al., 2019a; Soleimani et al., 2020). Most of the existing literature (Liu et al., 2020; Zhong et al., 2020) focuses on the task of claim verification, while little work has been done on the tasks of document retrieval and sentence retrieval. We suspect that this is because it is more straightforward for researchers to focus only on the improvement in terms of performance of the last component (i.e., claim verification) instead of experimenting with the whole pipeline of the three subtasks. In addition, the performance in the first two components is already quite high (i.e., >90% in terms of document accuracy for the document retrieval step and >87% in terms of sentence recall).

Unlike the aforementioned studies, in this work, we focus on the task of sentence retrieval on the FEVER dataset. Specifically, inspired by studies that investigate the impact of loss functions and sampling on other domains (e.g., computer vision (Wu et al., 2017; Wang et al., 2017), information retrieval (Pobrotyn et al., 2020)), this paper – to the best of our knowledge – is the first attempt to shed some light on the sentence retrieval task by performing the largest experimental study to date and investigating the performance of a model that is able to take into account the relations between all potential evidences in a given list of evidences. The contributions of our work are as follows: (i) we propose a simple yet effective evidence-aware transformer-based model that is able to outperform all other models in terms of the FEVER score (i.e., metric of the claim verification subtask) and improve a baseline model by 0.7% even by using a small subset of training instances; (ii) we conduct an extensive experimental study on various settings (i.e., loss functions, sampling instances) showcasing the effect in performance of each architectural choice on the sentence retrieval and the claim verification subtasks; (iii) the results of our study point researchers to certain directions in order to improve the overall performance of the task.

2 Models

We frame the sentence selection subtask, where the input is a claim sentence and a list of candidate evidence sentences (i.e., as retrieved from the document retrieval step, for that we used the same input as in the work of Liu et al. (2020)), as an NLI problem. Specifically, the claim is the "hypothesis"

[1]https://github.com/bekou/evidence_aware_nlp4if

Proceedings of the 4th NLP4IF Workshop on NLP for Internet Freedom, pages 23–28
June 6, 2021. ©2021 Association for Computational Linguistics

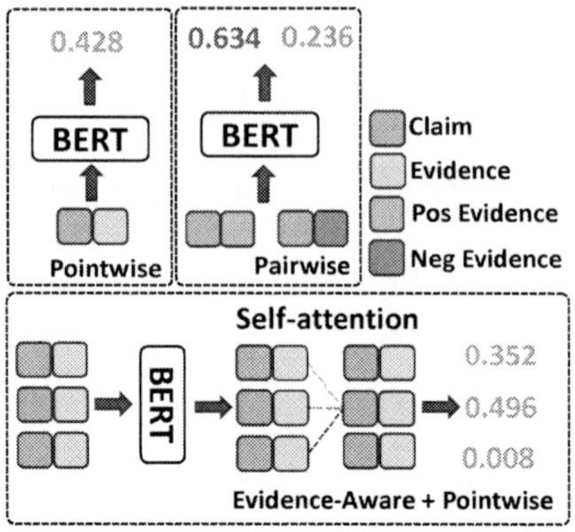

Figure 1: The architectures used for the sentence retrieval subtask. The pointwise loss considers each potential evidence independently. The pairwise loss considers the potential evidences in pairs (positive, negative). The proposed evidence-aware selection model uses self-attention to consider all the potential evidences in the evidence set simultaneously.

sentence and the potential evidence sentence is a "premise" sentence. In Fig. 1, we present the various architectures that we used in our experiments.

2.1 Baseline

Pointwise: Our model is similar to the one described in the work of Soleimani et al. (2020). We use a BERT-based model (Devlin et al., 2019) to obtain the representation of the input sentences. For training, we use the cross-entropy loss and the input to our model is the claim along with an evidence sentence. The goal of the sentence retrieval component paired with the pointwise loss is to predict whether a candidate evidence sentence is an evidence or not for a given claim. Thus, the problem of sentence retrieval is framed as a binary classification task.

2.2 Distance-based

Pairwise: In our work, we also exploit the pairwise loss, where the goal is to maximize the margin between the positive and the negative examples. Specifically, we use the pairwise loss that is similar to the margin based loss presented in the work of Wu et al. (2017). The pairwise loss is:

$$\mathcal{L}^{pairwise}(p,n) = [-y_{ij}(f(x_p) - f(x_n)) + m]_+ \quad (1)$$

In Eq. (1), $y_{ij} \in \{-1, 1\}$, $f(x)$ is the representation that we obtain from the BERT-based model, m is the margin and the indices p and n indicate a pair of a positive and a negative example. In order to obtain a claim aware representation of the (positive-negative) instances, we concatenate the claim with the corresponding evidence.

Triplet: Unlike the pairwise loss that considers only pairs of positive and negative examples, the triplet loss (Wu et al., 2017) uses triplets of training instances. Specifically, given an anchor sample a (i.e., claim), the goal is the distance $D_{ij} = \|f(x_i) - f(x_j)\|_2$ to be greater between the anchor and a negative example than the distance between the anchor and a positive example. The triplet loss is depicted in:

$$\mathcal{L}^{triplet}(a,p,n) = [D_{ap}^2 - D_{an}^2 + m]_+ \quad (2)$$

Similar to the previous equation, in Eq. (2), m is the margin and the indices a, p and n indicate the triplet of the anchor, a positive and a negative example. As anchor we use the claim, while similar to the pairwise loss, we concatenate the claim with the corresponding evidence for the positive and the negative examples.

Cosine: We have also experimented with the cosine loss. Specifically, we exploit positive and negative samples using the following formula:

$$\mathcal{L}^{cos}(p,n) = y_{ij}(1 - \cos(f(x_p), f(x_n))) + (1 - y_{ij})[(\cos(f(x_p), f(x_n)) - m)]_+ \quad (3)$$

In Eq. (3), $y_{ij} \in \{0, 1\}$ and cos indicates the cosine distance between the positive and the negative samples.

Angular: The angular loss (Wang et al., 2017) uses triplets of instances (i.e., similar to the triplet loss) while imposing angular constraints between the examples of the triplet. The formula is given by:

$$\mathcal{L}^{ang}(a,p,n) = [D_{ap}^2 - 4\tan^2 r D_{nc}^2]_+ \quad (4)$$

In Eq. (4), $f(x_c) = (f(x_a) - f(x_p))/2$ and r is a fixed margin (angle).

2.3 Evidence-Aware Selection

Unlike the aforementioned loss functions, the proposed model relies on a transformer-based model, similar to the retrieval model proposed in the work of Pobrotyn et al. (2020). This model exploits the use of self-attention over the potential evidence sentences in the evidence set. Unlike (i) the pointwise

Loss	# Negative Examples	# Max Instances	Dev P@5	Dev R@5	Dev F_1@5	Dev LA	Dev FEVER	Test P@5	Test R@5	Test F_1@5	Test LA	Test FEVER
Angular	✓	✓	26.90	93.93	41.82	77.22	74.81	24.36	86.14	37.98	72.30	68.30
Cosine	✓	✓	27.02	93.85	41.96	77.50	75.10	**24.83**	86.73	**38.61**	72.49	68.81
Triplet	✓	✓	26.99	94.24	41.96	77.51	75.32	24.74	**86.86**	38.51	72.76	69.31
Pairwise	✓	✓	26.88	93.90	41.79	78.05	75.61	24.44	86.17	38.08	72.92	69.34
	5	✓	26.76	93.23	41.58	77.21	74.74	24.53	85.90	38.17	72.05	68.22
	10	✓	26.77	92.99	41.57	77.58	75.04	24.62	86.15	38.29	72.65	68.93
	5	20	27.11	94.13	42.10	77.53	75.37	24.75	86.67	38.51	72.87	69.25
	10	20	27.09	94.40	42.10	78.05	75.79	24.74	86.84	38.51	**73.02**	69.38
Pointwise	✓	✓	25.77	91.96	40.26	77.94	75.12	22.28	82.61	35.01	71.63	67.63
	5	✓	27.74	95.93	43.04	78.43	76.71	23.99	85.67	37.48	72.54	68.71
	5	20	27.39	95.25	42.54	78.49	76.58	23.79	85.24	37.19	72.55	68.64
Evidence-Aware	5	20	**28.52**	**97.16**	**44.09**	**78.67**	**77.38**	24.70	86.81	38.46	72.93	**69.40**
	10	20	28.50	96.82	44.04	78.26	76.78	24.76	86.83	38.53	72.70	68.46

Table 1: Results of the (i) sentence retrieval task in terms of Precision (P), Recall (R), and F_1 scores and (ii) claim verification task in terms of the label accuracy (LA) and the FEVER score evaluation metrics in the dev and the test sets. The best performing models per column are highlighted in bold font. For more details, see Section 3.3.

loss that does not take into account the relations between the evidence sentences, and (ii) the distance-based losses (e.g., triplet) that considers only pairs of sentences, the transformer model considers subsets of evidence sentences simultaneously at the training phase. Specifically, the input to the transformer is a list of BERT-based representations of the evidence sentences. Despite its simplicity, the model is able to reason and rank the evidence sentences by taking into account all the other evidence sentences in the list. On top of the transformer, we exploit a binary cross-entropy loss similar to the one presented in the case of the pointwise loss.

3 Experimental Study

3.1 Setup

For the conducted experiments in the sentence retrieval task, in all the loss functions except for the evidence-aware one, we present results using all the potential evidence sentences (retrieved from document retrieval). For the evidence-aware model, we conduct experiments using either 5 or 10 negative examples per positive instance during training. In addition, the overall (positive and negative) maximum number of instances that are kept is 20. This is because unlike the other models that the evidences are considered individually or in pairs, in the evidence-aware model, we cannot consider all the evidences simultaneously. We experiment also with a limited number of instances in the other settings to have a fair comparison among the different setups. Note that for the distance-based losses, we conduct additional experiments only in the best performing model when all instances are included (i.e., pairwise). We also present results on the claim verification task with all of the examined architectures. For the claim verification step, we use the model of Liu et al. (2020). We evaluate the performance of our models using the official evaluation metrics for sentence retrieval (precision, recall and F_1 using the 5 highly ranked evidence sentences) and claim verification (label accuracy and FEVER score) in the dev and test sets.

3.2 Evaluation Metrics

We use the official evaluation metrics of the FEVER task for the sentence retrieval and the claim verification subtasks.

Sentence Retrieval: The organizers of the shared task suggested the precision to count the number of the correct evidences retrieved by the sentence retrieval component with respect to the number of the predicted evidences. The recall has also been exploited. Note that a claim is considered correct in the case that at least a complete evidence group is identified. Finally, the F_1 score is calculated based on the aforementioned metrics.

Claim Verification: The evaluation of the claim verification subtask is based on the *label accuracy* and the *FEVER score* metrics. The label accuracy measures the accuracy of the label predictions without taking the retrieved evidences into account. On the other hand, the FEVER score counts a claim as correct if a complete evidence group has been correctly identified as well as the corresponding label. Thus, the FEVER score is considered as a strict evaluation metric and it was the primary metric for ranking the systems on the leaderboard of the shared task.

3.3 Results

In Table 1, we present our results on the sentence retrieval and claim verification tasks. The "# Negative Examples" column indicates the number of negative evidences that are randomly sampled for each positive instance during training, while the "# Max Instances" column indicates the maximum number of instances that we keep for each claim. The ✓ symbol denotes that we keep all the instances from this category (i.e., "# Negative Examples" or "# Max Instances"). Note that for the number of maximum instances, we keep as many as possible from the positive samples, and then we randomly sample from the negative instances.

Benefit of Evidence-Aware Model: The evidence-aware model (see the setting with 5 negative examples and 20 maximum instances denoted as (5, 20)) is the best performing one both in dev and test set in terms of FEVER score. The pairwise loss performs best in terms of label accuracy on the test set. However, the most important evaluation metric is the FEVER score, since it takes into account both the label accuracy and the predicted evidence sentences. The pointwise loss is the worst performing one when using all the evidence sentences. This is because in the case that we use all the potential evidences, the number of negative samples is too large and we have a highly imbalance problem leading to low recall and FEVER score in both the dev and test set. Note that the evidence-aware model relies on the pointwise loss (i.e., the worst performing one). However, a benefit of the evidence-aware model (0.7% in terms of FEVER score) is reported (see pointwise (5, 20)). This showcases the important effect of ranking potential evidences simultaneously using self-attention. From the distance-based loss functions (e.g., triplet) except for the pairwise, we observe that the angular and the cosine loss have worst performance compared to the pairwise and the triplet loss when using all the instances. We hypothesize that this is because the norm-based distance measures fit best for scoring pairs using the BERT-based representations.

Performance Gain: Most recent research works (e.g., Zhao et al. (2020); Liu et al. (2020)) focus on creating complex models for claim verification. We conducted a small scale experiment (that is not present in Table 1), where we replaced our model for claim verification (recall that we rely on the method of Liu et al. (2020)) with a BERT-based classifier. We observed that when using the model of the Liu et al. (2020) instead of the BERT-classifier (in our early experiments on the dev set), the benefit for the pointwise loss was 0.2 percentage points, a benefit of 0.1 percentage points for the triplet loss and a drop of 1 percentage point in the performance of the cosine loss. Therefore, the seemingly small performance increase in our model (i.e., a benefit of 0.7% in terms of FEVER score) is in line with the performance benefit of complex architectures for the claim verification task. In our paper, we do not claim state-of-the-art performance on the task, but rather showcase the benefit of our proposed methodology over a strong baseline model that relies on BERT_{base}.

Number of Samples Matters: The evidence-aware model is the best performing one (5, 20), while using only a small fraction of the overall training instances. This is because the evidence-aware model is able to take into account all possible combinations of the sampled evidences while computing attention weights. However, the same model in the (10, 20) setting showcases a reduced performance. This is due to the fact that the pointwise loss affects the model in a similar way as in the pointwise setting leading to a lower performance (due to class imbalance). For the pairwise loss, we observe that the performance of the model when sampling constrained evidence sentences (see (5, 20), (10, 20) settings) is similar to the performance of the model when we do not sample evidence sentences. In addition, it seems that when one constrains the number of negative samples should also constrain the overall number of instances in order to achieve the same performance as in the non-sampling setting. We hypothesize that this is due to that fact that when we have a limited number of instances it is better to have a more balanced version of the dataset.

Outcome: Therefore, we conclude that the evidence-aware model achieves high performance by using few examples, and thus it can be used even in the case that we have a small amount of training instances. In the case of the pairwise loss is important to sample instances, otherwise it becomes computationally intensive when we take all the possible combinations between the positive and negative training instances into account. In addition, it is crucial to sample negative sentences to control: (i) the computational complexity in the case of the distance-based loss functions, (ii) the memory constraints in the case of the evidence-aware model and (iii) the imbalance issue in the case of the pointwise loss. However, more sophisticated techniques than random sampling should be investigated to select examples that are more informative. Finally, as indicated by our performance gain, we motivate future researchers to work also on the sentence retrieval subtask, as the improvement in this subtask leads to similar improvements with architectures proposed for the claim verification subtask.

4 Related Work

An extensive review on the task of fact extraction and verification can be found in Bekoulis et al. (2020). For the sentence retrieval task, several pipeline methods (Chernyavskiy and Ilvovsky, 2019; Portelli et al., 2020) rely on the sentence retrieval component of Thorne et al. (2018) that use TF-IDF representations. An important line of research (Hanselowski et al., 2018; Nie et al., 2019a; Zhou et al., 2019) includes the use of ESIM-based models (Chen et al. (2017). Those works formulate the sentence selection subtask as an NLI problem where the claim is the "premise" sentence and the potential evidence sentence is a "hypothesis" sentence. Similar to the ESIM-based methods, language model based methods (Nie et al., 2019b; Zhong et al., 2020; Soleimani et al., 2020; Liu et al., 2020; Zhao et al., 2020) transform the sentence retrieval task to an NLI problem using pre-trained language models. For the language model based sentence retrieval two types of losses have been exploited (i) pointwise loss, and (ii) pairwise loss, as presented also in Section 2. Unlike the aforementioned studies that rely only on losses of type (i) and (ii), we conduct the largest experimental study to date by using various functions on the sentence retrieval subtask of the FEVER task. In addition, we propose a new evidence-aware model that is able to outperform all other methods using a limited number of training instances.

5 Conclusion

In this paper, we focus on the subtask of sentence retrieval of the FEVER task. In particular, we propose a simple and effective evidence-aware model that outperforms all other models in which each potential evidence takes into account information about other potential evidences. The model uses only a few training instances and improves a simple pointwise loss by 0.7% percentage points in terms of FEVER score. In addition, we conduct a large experimental study, compare the pros and cons of the studied architectures and discuss the results in a comprehensive way, while pointing researchers to future research directions.

References

Giannis Bekoulis, Christina Papagiannopoulou, and Nikos Deligiannis. 2020. A review on fact extraction and verification. *arXiv preprint arXiv:2010.03001*.

Qian Chen, Xiaodan Zhu, Zhen-Hua Ling, Si Wei, Hui Jiang, and Diana Inkpen. 2017. Enhanced LSTM for natural language inference. In *Proceedings of the 55th Annual Meeting of the Association for Computational Linguistics (Volume 1: Long Papers)*, pages 1657–1668, Vancouver, Canada. Association for Computational Linguistics.

Anton Chernyavskiy and Dmitry Ilvovsky. 2019. Extract and aggregate: A novel domain-independent approach to factual data verification. In *Proceedings of the Second Workshop on Fact Extraction and VERification (FEVER)*, pages 69–78, Hong Kong, China. Association for Computational Linguistics.

Jacob Devlin, Ming-Wei Chang, Kenton Lee, and Kristina Toutanova. 2019. BERT: Pre-training of deep bidirectional transformers for language understanding. In *Proceedings of the 2019 Conference of the North American Chapter of the Association for Computational Linguistics: Human Language Technologies, Volume 1 (Long and Short Papers)*, pages 4171–4186, Minneapolis, Minnesota. Association for Computational Linguistics.

Andreas Hanselowski, Hao Zhang, Zile Li, Daniil Sorokin, Benjamin Schiller, Claudia Schulz, and Iryna Gurevych. 2018. UKP-athene: Multi-sentence textual entailment for claim verification. In *Proceedings of the First Workshop on Fact Extraction and VERification (FEVER)*, pages 103–108, Brussels, Belgium. Association for Computational Linguistics.

Zhenghao Liu, Chenyan Xiong, Maosong Sun, and Zhiyuan Liu. 2020. Fine-grained fact verification with kernel graph attention network. In *Proceedings of the 58th Annual Meeting of the Association for*

Computational Linguistics, pages 7342–7351, Online. Association for Computational Linguistics.

Yixin Nie, Haonan Chen, and Mohit Bansal. 2019a. Combining fact extraction and verification with neural semantic matching networks. In *Proceedings of the AAAI Conference on Artificial Intelligence*, volume 33, pages 6859–6866, Honolulu, Hawai. AAAI Press.

Yixin Nie, Songhe Wang, and Mohit Bansal. 2019b. Revealing the importance of semantic retrieval for machine reading at scale. In *Proceedings of the 2019 Conference on Empirical Methods in Natural Language Processing and the 9th International Joint Conference on Natural Language Processing (EMNLP-IJCNLP)*, pages 2553–2566, Hong Kong, China. Association for Computational Linguistics.

Przemysław Pobrotyn, Tomasz Bartczak, Mikołaj Synowiec, Radosław Białobrzeski, and Jarosław Bojar. 2020. Context-aware learning to rank with self-attention. In *Proceedings of the ECOM'20: The SIGIR 2020 Workshop on eCommerce*, Online. Association for Computing Machinery.

Beatrice Portelli, Jason Zhao, Tal Schuster, Giuseppe Serra, and Enrico Santus. 2020. Distilling the evidence to augment fact verification models. In *Proceedings of the Third Workshop on Fact Extraction and VERification (FEVER)*, pages 47–51, Online. Association for Computational Linguistics.

Amir Soleimani, Christof Monz, and Marcel Worring. 2020. Bert for evidence retrieval and claim verification. In *Advances in Information Retrieval*, pages 359–366, Cham. Springer International Publishing.

James Thorne, Andreas Vlachos, Christos Christodoulopoulos, and Arpit Mittal. 2018. FEVER: a large-scale dataset for fact extraction and VERification. In *Proceedings of the 2018 Conference of the North American Chapter of the Association for Computational Linguistics: Human Language Technologies, Volume 1 (Long Papers)*, pages 809–819, New Orleans, Louisiana. Association for Computational Linguistics.

Jian Wang, Feng Zhou, Shilei Wen, Xiao Liu, and Yuanqing Lin. 2017. Deep metric learning with angular loss. In *Proceedings of the IEEE International Conference on Computer Vision*, pages 2593–2601, Venice, Italy. IEEE.

Chao-Yuan Wu, R Manmatha, Alexander J Smola, and Philipp Krahenbuhl. 2017. Sampling matters in deep embedding learning. In *Proceedings of the IEEE International Conference on Computer Vision*, pages 2840–2848, Venice, Italy. IEEE.

Chen Zhao, Chenyan Xiong, Corby Rosset, Xia Song, Paul Bennett, and Saurabh Tiwary. 2020. Transformer-xh: Multi-evidence reasoning with extra hop attention. In *International Conference on Learning Representations*, Online.

Wanjun Zhong, Jingjing Xu, Duyu Tang, Zenan Xu, Nan Duan, Ming Zhou, Jiahai Wang, and Jian Yin. 2020. Reasoning over semantic-level graph for fact checking. In *Proceedings of the 58th Annual Meeting of the Association for Computational Linguistics*, pages 6170–6180, Online. Association for Computational Linguistics.

Jie Zhou, Xu Han, Cheng Yang, Zhiyuan Liu, Lifeng Wang, Changcheng Li, and Maosong Sun. 2019. GEAR: Graph-based evidence aggregating and reasoning for fact verification. In *Proceedings of the 57th Annual Meeting of the Association for Computational Linguistics*, pages 892–901, Florence, Italy. Association for Computational Linguistics.

Leveraging Community and Author Context to Explain the Performance and Bias of Text-Based Deception Detection Models

Galen Weld[1], Ellyn Ayton[2], Tim Althoff[1], Maria Glenski[2]
[1]Paul G. Allen School of Computer Science and Engineering, University of Washington
[2]National Security Directorate, Pacific Northwest National Laboratory
{gweld, althoff}@cs.washington.edu, first.last@pnnl.gov

Abstract

Deceptive news posts shared in online communities can be detected with NLP models, and much recent research has focused on the development of such models. In this work, we use characteristics of online communities and authors — the context of how and where content is posted — to explain the performance of a neural network deception detection model and identify sub-populations who are disproportionately affected by model accuracy or failure. We examine *who* is posting the content, and *where* the content is posted to. We find that while author characteristics are better predictors of deceptive content than community characteristics, both characteristics are strongly correlated with model performance. Traditional performance metrics such as F1 score may fail to capture poor model performance on isolated sub-populations such as specific authors, and as such, more nuanced evaluation of deception detection models is critical.

1 Introduction

The spread of deceptive news content in online communities significantly erodes public trust in the media (Barthel et al., 2016). Most social media users use these platforms as a means to consume news – 71% of Twitter users and 62% of Reddit users – and in general, 55% of Americans get news from online communities such as Facebook, Twitter, and reddit (Shearer and Grieco, 2019). The scale and speed with which new content is submitted to social media platforms are two key factors that increase the difficulty of how to respond to the spread of misinformation or deceptive news content online, and the appeal of automated or semi-automated defenses or interventions.

Natural language processing (NLP) models that identify deceptive content offer a path towards fortifying online communities, and a significant body of work (§ 2) has produced countless such models for deception detection tasks (Rubin et al., 2016; Mitra et al., 2017; Volkova et al., 2017; Rashkin et al., 2017; Karadzhov et al., 2018; Shu et al., 2020). However, evaluation of model performance is typically done in aggregate, across multiple communities, using traditional performance measurements like micro and macro F1-scores. We argue that it is critical to understand model behavior at a finer granularity, and we evaluate nuanced behavior and failure in the context of the populations that may be affected by predictive outcomes.

In this work, we seek to characterize and explain deception detection model performance and biases using the *context* of social media posts—*who* posted the content and *what* community it was posted to. To do so, we compute hundreds of *community* and *author* characteristics using information from two fact checking sources.

For a given post, community characteristics detail *where* a post was submitted to, *e.g., How many links to satirical news sources were submitted to the community this post was submitted to?* Author characteristics detail *who* submitted a post, *e.g., How many links to satirical news sources has the author recently submitted?* Our nuanced evaluation leverages these author and community characteristics to highlight differences in behavior within varying communities or sub-populations, to determine whether the model is reliable in general, or if model failures disproportionately impact sub-populations.

We make use of data from reddit, a popular social news aggregation platform. Reddit is widely used for research (Medvedev et al., 2019) due to its large size and public content (Baumgartner et al., 2020), and is ideally suited for studying author and community characteristics due to its explicit segmentation into many diverse communities, called "subreddits", with different sizes, topics, and userbases.[1]

[1]Although our analyses focus exclusively on posts, our approach can easily be extended to include comments in future work. We chose to focus on posts in the current work as they are the primary point of entry for news links submitted to the platform, with many users simply browsing the ranked previews (Glenski et al., 2017) as is consistent with social media platforms where a small subset of users typically contribute most new content (van Mierlo, 2014; Hargittai and Walejko, 2008).

Proceedings of the 4th NLP4IF Workshop on NLP for Internet Freedom, pages 29–38
June 6, 2021. ©2021 Association for Computational Linguistics

We use post context (community and author characteristics) and content (text features) to address two research questions focused around (1) *who* posts deceptive news links and (2) *where* they post differ:

1. What characteristics of post authors are associated with high and low model performance?
2. How does model performance vary across different communities, and does this correlate with characteristics of those communities?

We find that author characteristics are a stronger predictor of high model performance, with the model we evaluate performing especially well on authors who have a history of submitting low factual or deceptive content. We also find that the model performs especially well on posts that are highly accepted by the community, as measured by the community's votes on those posts.

To our knowledge, we are the first to present a fine-grained evaluation of deception detection model performance in the context of author and community characteristics.

2 Related Work

In the last several years, users have seen a tremendous increase in the amount of misinformation, disinformation, and falsified news in circulation on social media platforms. This seemingly ubiquitous digital deception is in part due to the ease of information dissemination and access on these platforms. Many researchers have focused on different areas of detecting deceptive online content. Glenski and Weninger (2018); Kumar et al. (2017, 2018) examine the behaviors and activities of malicious users and bots on different social media platforms. While others have worked to develop systems to identify fraudulent posts at varying degrees of deception such as broadly classifying suspicious and non-suspicious news (Volkova et al., 2017) to further separating into finer-grained deceptive classes (*e.g.,* propaganda, hoax) (Rashkin et al., 2017).

Common amongst recent detection methods is the mixed use of machine learning approaches, *e.g.*, Random Forest and state-of-the-art deep learning models, *e.g.,* Hierarchical Propagation Networks (Shu et al., 2020). Of the most prevalent are convolutional neural networks (CNNs) (Ajao et al., 2018; Wang, 2017; Volkova et al., 2017), Long Short Term Memory (LSTM) neural networks (Ma et al., 2016; Chen et al., 2018; Rath et al., 2017; Zubiaga et al., 2018; Zhang et al., 2019), and other variants with attention mechanisms (Guo et al., 2018; Li et al., 2019). Designing the right model architecture for a task can be very subjective and laborsome. Therefore, we implement the binary classification LSTM model from (Volkova et al., 2019) which reported an F1 score of 0.73 when distinguishing deceptive news from credible.

As artificial intelligence or machine learning models are developed or investigated as potential responses to the issue of misinformation and digital deception online, it is key to understand how models treat the individuals and groups who are impacted by the predictions or recommendations of the models or automated systems. For example, the European Union's GDPR directly addresses the "right of citizens to receive an explanation for algorithmic decisions" (Goodman and Flaxman, 2017) that requires an explanation to be available for individuals impacted by a model decision. Domains outside of deception detection have shown clear evidence of disproportionate biases against certain sub-populations of impacted individuals, *e.g.,* predictive policing (Ensign et al., 2018), recidivism prediction (Chouldechova, 2017; Dressel and Farid, 2018), and hate speech and abusive language identification online (Park et al., 2018; Davidson et al., 2019; Sap et al., 2019). The realm of deception detection is another clear area where disparate performance across communities or certain user groups may have significant negative downstream effects both online and offline. In this work, we seek to go beyond traditional, aggregate performance metrics to consider the differing behavior and outcomes of automated deception detection within and across communities and user characteristics.

3 Deception Detection Model

In this work, we focus on a binary classification task to identify posts which link to *Deceptive* or *Credible* news sources. We evaluate an existing, LSTM-based model architecture previously published by Volkova et al. (2019) that relies only on text and lexical features. As such, we refer to this model as the "*ContentOnly* model."

3.1 Train and Test Data

To replicate the *ContentOnly* model for our evaluations, we leverage the previously used list of annotated news sources from Volkova et al. (2017) as ground truth. The Volkova annotations consist of two classes: "Credible[2]" and "Deceptive." To label individual social media postings linked to these news sources, we propagate annotations of each source to all posts linked to the source. Therefore

[2]This class is denoted "Verified" in Volkova et al. (2017).

Credible posts are posts which link (via a URL or as posted by the source's official account) to a Credible news source and *Deceptive posts* are posts that link to a news source annotated as Deceptive.

In preliminary experiments, we find that model performance improves when Twitter examples are included in training, even when testing exclusively on reddit content. A model trained and tested exclusively on reddit data achieves a test set F1 of 0.577 and we observe a dramatic increase (F1 = 0.725), when we include the Twitter training data. As a result, we focus our analyses using the more robust *ContentOnly* model trained on both Twitter and reddit examples. As Twitter has no explicit communities equivalent to reddit subreddits, it is not possible to compute the same community characteristics for Twitter content. As such, in the analyses presented in this paper, we focus exclusively on content posted to reddit in the test set.

To gather train and test data, we collect social media posts from Twitter and reddit from the same 2016 time period as annotated by Volkova et al. (2017). For Twitter posts, this resulted in 54.4k Tweets from the official Twitter accounts for news sources that appear in the Volkova annotations. For reddit content, we collected all link-posts that link to domains associated with the labelled news sources from the Pushshift monthly archives of reddit posts[3] (Baumgartner et al., 2020), and randomly sample approximately the same number ($\sim$ 54k) of link-posts as Twitter posts collected.

In order to mitigate the bias of class imbalance on our analyses, these posts were then randomly down-sampled to include an approximately equal number of posts from/linking to deceptive and credible news sources. We divided the resulting data using a random, stratified 80%/20% split to create train and test sets, respectively.

4 Community & Author Characteristics

To evaluate fine-grained model performance and biases, we first quantify the *context* in which posts are submitted, using community and author characteristics.

4.1 Data for Context Annotations

We compute community and author characteristics by examining the entire post history on reddit for each community and author in the test set. We use annotations from Volkova *et al.* (described above, § 3.1) and from Media Bias/Fact Check (MBFC), an independent news source classifier. These annotations were compiled by Weld et al. (2021) and made publicly available[4].

The Volkova *et al.* annotations provide links to news sources with a categorical label: verified, propaganda, satire, clickbait, conspiracy, and hoax. The MBFC annotations provide links to news sources with a ordinal label for the factualness of the news source (very low, low, mixed, mostly, high, very high) as well as the political bias (extreme left, left, center left, center, center right, right, extreme right). In addition, the MBFC also include a few categorical labels applicable to a subset of news sources: questionable, satire, conspiracy.

4.2 Data Validation

Before using these annotations to compute community and author characteristics, we would like to validate that they represent meaningful and accurate aspects of communities and authors, respectively, and are not strongly influenced by noise in the annotation sources. To do so, we assess the coverage of our context annotations, — *i.e.,* the fraction of potential news links that we were able to label.

In order to consider the coverage relative to the *potential* news links, we identify a set of domains for which links are definitively not news sources. We identified these non-news links by examining the top 1,000 most frequently linked-to domains across all of reddit and iteratively classified them as non-news based on their domain (*e.g.,* reddit-based content hosting domains such as `v.redd.it` and `i.redd.it`, external content hosts such as `imgur.com`, social sites such as `facebook.com` and `instagram.com`, search engines, shopping platforms, music platforms, *etc.*). Websites which were not in English, were not clearly non-news domains, or which did not fit into a clear category, were included in the set of potential news sources. We imposed these restrictions to mitigate potential downward bias from overestimating non-news links. Although we do not claim to have an exhaustive coverage of non-news links, non-news links included in the set of potential news links at best underrepresents the coverage which is preferable to overrepresentation.

Encouragingly, coverage for both are fairly stable over time, suggesting that there are no significant influxes of additional, unlabelled news sources (or disappearances of retired news sources) that might be biasing our approach. As the MBFC set contains more news sources, the coverage is greater

[3]Pushshift archives of reddit data were collected from `https://files.pushshift.io/reddit/`

[4]`https://behavioral-data.github.io/news_labeling_reddit/`

($\sim$ 18% on average) than the Volkova set ($\sim$ 10%).

4.3 Community and Author Characteristics

Using the author and community history collection of posts and the associated MBFC and Volkova *et al.* annotations, we compute context characteristics for each subreddit community and author that is present in the test set described in § 3.

First, we compute the general activity of each community and author. These characteristics include the total number of posts by each community or author, the total number of removed posts, and similar overall counts that do not consider the nature of the content submitted.

Second, for each of the MBFC and Volkova *et al.* labels (*e.g.,* 'Satire' from Volkova *et al.* or 'Right Bias' from MBFC) we compute absolute and normalized counts of links of each category for each community and author. Normalized counts for each category are computed by dividing the number of links in the category submitted to each subreddit or by each author by the total number of links submitted in any category. This gives, for example, the fraction of links submitted by a author to MBFC High Factual news sources.

Third, for communities, we compute the equality of contributor activity (number of links submitted per contributor) using the Gini coefficient. A community with a Gini coefficient close to 1 would indicate almost all links in that community were submitted by a small fraction of users. On the other hand, a coefficient close to 0 would indicate that all users of the community who submit links submit approximately the same number of links each.

Last, again for communities, we approximate the community acceptance by normalizing the score (upvotes - downvotes) of each post relative to the median score of all posts submitted to the subreddit. A post with a normalized score of 1 received a typical score for the community it was submitted to, whereas a post with a normalized score of 100 received 100$\times$ as many upvotes as a typical post and was more widely or strongly positively received by the community.

Each of the community characteristics are computed separately for each month, maximizing temporal detail. However, as the typical reddit user submits far less content each month than the typical subreddit receives, most users' counts for specific link types (*e.g.,* MBFC Satire) for any individual month will be 0. To reduce sparsity in the data, we use a rolling sum of all posts submitted by the author in the specified month and the five preceding months to compute author characteristics.

5 Evaluation Methodology

Before our evaluation of model performance across different community or author characteristics and settings, we examine the overall performance of the model on aggregate, using macro F1 score, and the variance of performance within communities. A model with strong aggregate performance may have significant variability within subcommunities, especially those which are underrepresented. We also consider the variability of individual predictive outcomes, such as the confidence of predictions, across each class (deceptive and credible news) to examine the differences in model behavior across classes overall. We aim to discover if the model treats all posts, communities, and authors equally, or if there are differences in performance for certain groups that would bias the negative impacts of model error.

5.1 Comparison to Baselines

Next, we frame the performance of the *ContentOnly* model that classifies posts based on text and linguistic signals relative to naive baselines that randomly classify posts or classify posts based on the typical behavior of authors or communities. To this end, we consider three baseline models.

The **Author History Baseline** considers the author's history over the previous 6 months (as was used to calculate author characteristics) and computes the fraction of their links to news sources which are deceptive, as defined by the Volkova *et al.* annotations. It then predicts if a new submission is deceptive or credible with a biased random coin flip, with a probability of predicting deceptive equal to the author's recent tendency to submit deceptive news links (*i.e.,* the fraction of news links submitted by the author in the last six months that were linked to deceptive sources).

The **Community History Baseline** is similar except that it considers the *community's* tendency to receive deceptive news. This baseline predicts 'deceptive' with a probability equal to the fraction of news links submitted to a given subreddit in the last month that were linked to deceptive sources.

The **50/50 Baseline** predicts credible/deceptive with an unbiased 50/50 coinflip. No consideration is placed on the content, community, or author.

We compare the performance of these baselines with that of the *ContentOnly* model, providing a reference for its performance as well as an indication of the degree to which community and author characteristics alone are predictive of deceptive content.

Figure 1: Communities within each F1 score quartile, represented as wordclouds (size of the community name indicates its volume in test set and the color indicates fine-grained model performance using F1 score).

5.2 Community and Author Context

To better understand how community and author characteristics explain model performance, we compute the Pearson correlation between the value of each characteristic, and the model's confidence in predicting the true class for each post. We compute these correlations across the all test posts, and across deceptive and credible posts (based on true class value) separately. We also examine factors that explain the model's performance on entire authors or communities. To do so, we compute similar correlations for author and community characteristics with aggregated author or community F1 scores, respectively.

5.3 Popularity and Community Acceptance

We also examine the relationship between a community's acceptance of a post, and model performance. We measure community acceptance by normalizing each post's score (# upvotes - # downvotes) by the median score of a post in that community for the month of submission, to control for the larger number of votes in larger communities. We then compute Pearson's correlations between normalized score and the *ContentOnly* model's confidence that a post belongs to its annotated class – here we use not the models prediction confidence but the confidence for the "true class" given the groundtruth labels. As before, we use Pearson correlations and a significance threshold of 0.05.

6 Results

Although the *ContentOnly* model achieves an overall F1 score on the test set of 0.79, we see that the model performs much better on content from some communities than others (see Figure 2). Figure 1 presents the communities within the test set, partitioned by levels of model performance using the quartiles for the F1 scores. We find that 20% of the communities represented in our test set have F1 < 0.40, despite an overall test set F1 of almost 0.8.

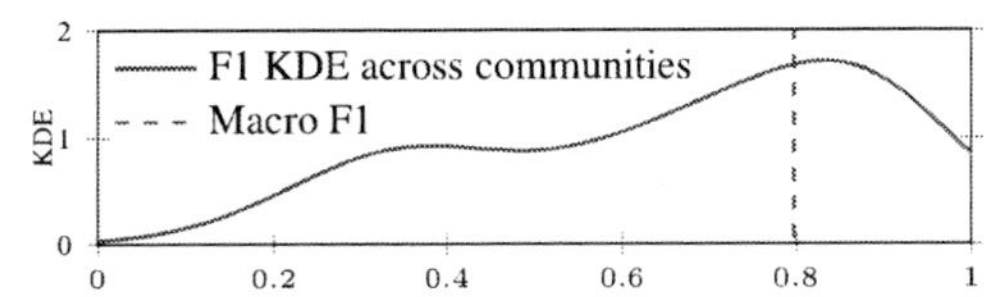

Figure 2: Macro F1 and the kernel density estimation (KDE) of F1 score over communities. While overall deception detection model performance is high, there is significant variability in performance across different online communities.

In the following subsections, we examine how the model's performance can be explained by community and author characteristics, post popularity, and community acceptance as we seek to understand *why* the model performs far better on content from some communities than others.

6.1 Comparison to Baselines

We use the community and author history baselines, as well as the 50/50 baseline described in §5.1 to contextualize the performance of the *ContentOnly* model. Figure 3 presents the distributions of performance across communities for each metric (solid lines) and the overall performance of each model (indicated by the dashed, vertical lines) using three traditional performance metrics: precision, recall, and F1 score. As expected, the *ContentOnly* model (in blue) dramatically outperforms the 50/50 baseline (in red) on all metrics, and achieves the best performance overall for F1 score (a significant difference in performance, p-value $\leq 1.5 \times 10^{-4}$).

However, the community and author history baselines have very high precision, offset by very poor recall. In comparing the two, the author baseline significantly outperforms the community baseline on precision, recall, and F1 (p-value $< .02$). This suggests that an author's previous activity is a better predictor of whether an author will submit deceptive content in the future than a community's previous behavior is of whether deceptive content will be submitted to the community in the future. This may be a result of a greater consistency in the behavior of an individual compared to a community where membership may vary over time, if not community attitudes.

6.2 Community and Author Context

In our next analyses, we investigate how community and author characteristics correlate with model confidence. We compute these correlations across the entire test set, as well as for just credible and deceptive posts separately.

We summarize the strongest, significant correlations between community or author context and model confidence in Table 1, using a threshold of at least 0.25 for inclusion. When we examine the author and community characteristics of posts from all classes, the strongest correlation coefficients are all positive, and suggest moderate correlations with stronger model confidence. The four strongest correlations from the author characteristics pertain to the author's tendency to submit posts linked to questionable or low factual news sources. In contrast, the author's tendency to link to *high* factual content is relatively correlated ($r = -0.21$) with *weaker* model confidence. It is easier for the model to identify *deceptive* posts submitted by authors who typically submit links to low-quality or deceptive news sources. Similarly, we see moderate correlation between increasing presence of deceptive or low factual news media in the community and model performance. Looking at each class individually, we see the strongest relationships for deceptive posts, with little to no correlation for credible posts.

To examine factors that explain the model's performance *in aggregate*, we consider performance across individual authors and communities. First, compute performance metrics (precision, recall, and F1 score) for the post across posts by every author, and then correlate these metrics with authors' characteristics. We repeat this process for communities, as well. Characteristics with at least moderate correlation ($r \geq 0.3$) are presented in Table 2. Compared to post-level correlations with model confidence, we immediately notice that both aggregated community- and author-level correlations are much stronger, *e.g.,* a maximum correlation value of 0.70 for features derived from all-reddit data, compared to a maximum correlation value of 0.37 for individual posts. This observation suggests that model performance is more strongly correlated with characteristics across entire communities or authors rather than individual posts.

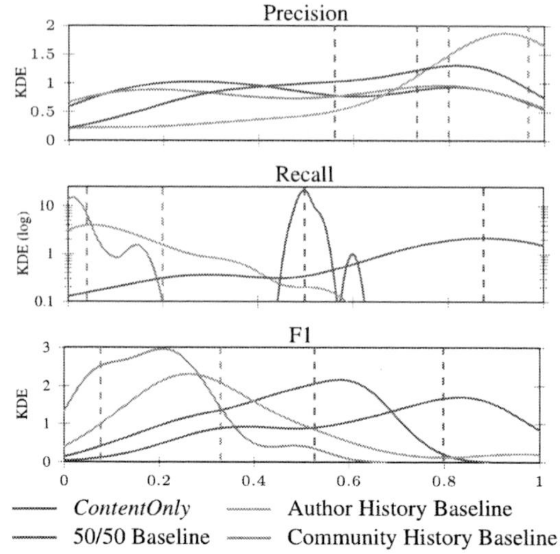

Figure 3: KDE plots illustrating performance metric distributions across communities for the *ContentOnly* and baseline models. Vertical dashed lines indicate the aggregate metric for each model across the full test set. While the *ContentOnly* model achieves the best overall performance and recall, the author and community characteristic baselines have higher precision.

		All	C Posts	D Posts
Author's Links	*Bias*			
	% Center Right Bias	**+0.25‡**	-0.00	**+0.27‡**
	Categorical			
	% Propaganda (Volkova)	**+0.35‡**	+0.08‡	+0.20‡
	% Questionable (MBFC)	**+0.37‡**	+0.10‡	+0.20‡
	Factualness			
	% Very Low Factual	**+0.33‡**	+0.07‡	**+0.29‡**
Community's Links	*Bias*			
	# Right Bias	**+0.25‡**	+0.18‡	+0.08‡
	Categorical			
	# Clickbait (Volkova)	**+0.25‡**	+0.17‡	+0.06‡
	# Questionable (MBFC)	**+0.26‡**	+0.18‡	+0.08‡
	Factualness			
	# Very Low Factual	**+0.31‡**	+0.15‡	+0.17‡
	# Low Factual	**+0.25‡**	+0.16‡	+0.07‡
	Inequality			
	Gini Coefficient (# Links)	**+0.32‡**	+0.18‡	+0.13‡
	Post Score	+0.12‡	-0.08‡	**+0.27‡**

Table 1: Correlations between community and author characteristics and true class confidence across the entire test set (All), credible posts (C posts), or deceptive posts (D posts). Characteristics are included when correlation $|r| \geq .25$ (in bold) in at least one column. † denotes a p-value $< .05$, ‡ denotes a p-value $< .01$.

For both authors and communities, the characteristics most strongly correlated with a higher F1 score is the fraction of deceptive content submitted in that community or by that author. These correlations are strongest (0.80 for communities, 0.85 for

Features Positively Correlated with Metric				Features Negatively Correlated with Metric			
Community Feature	r	Author Feature	r	Community Feature	r	Author Feature	r
F1-Score							
■ $(\%_T)$ Deceptive	0.80‡	■ $(\%_T)$ Deceptive	0.85‡	■ $(\%_L)$ High Factual	-0.43‡	■ $(\%_L)$ Mostly Factual	-0.70†
■ $(\%_L)$ Deceptive	0.40‡					■ $(\%_L)$ High Factual	-0.42‡
■ $(\%_L)$ Low Factual	0.39‡					■ $(\%_L)$ Center Bias	-0.36†
■ $(\%_L)$ V. Low Factual	0.37†						
■ $(\%_L)$ Extr. Right Bias	0.36†						
■ $(\%_L)$ Mixed Factual	0.33†						
Precision							
■ $(\%_T)$ Deceptive	0.89‡	■ $(\%_T)$ Deceptive	0.89‡	■ $(\%_L)$ High Factual	-0.33†	■ $(\%_L)$ V. High Factual	-0.48†
■ $(\%_L)$ Low Factual	0.48‡	■ $(\%_L)$ Deceptive	0.33‡			■ $(\%_L)$ High Factual	-0.46†
■ $(\%_L)$ Extr. Right Bias	0.45‡					■ $(\%_L)$ Center Left Bias	-0.45†
■ $(\%_L)$ Mixed Factual	0.44‡					■ $(\%_L)$ Center Bias	-0.40†
■ $(\%_L)$ V. Low Factual	0.43‡						
■ $(\%_L)$ Deceptive	0.42‡						
Recall							
		■ $(\%_T)$ Deceptive	0.35†				

Table 2: Characteristics with at least moderate correlation (Pearson $|r| > 0.3$) with model performance metrics across Communities or Authors. † denotes a p-value $< .05$, ‡ denotes a p-value $< .01$. "$\%_T$" refers to links in the test set and "$\%_L$" refers to links submitted to communities (Community characteristics) or by authors (Author characteristics) considering all posts submitted to reddit. Colored squares correspond to color used in Figure 4.

authors) when we examine just content from the test set, but are still substantial (0.42 and 0.33, respectively) when considering content across all of reddit. Computing the fraction of deceptive posts in the test set for each community/author results in larger fractions than when considering all of reddit, as the test set contains a greater proportion of deceptive posts than reddit in general. We also note that while the characteristics most strongly correlated with F1-Score and Precision are quite similar to one another, there are almost no features which are at least moderately (*i.e.,* $> \pm .3$) correlated with recall. This aligns with our findings when comparing the *ContentOnly* model to baseline performance (§3), where we found that author and community characteristics are more useful for achieving high precision than high recall.

Grouping the characteristics from Table 2 and displaying them visually, as in Figure 4 allows us to easily distinguish the differences between ordinal characteristics such as bias (extreme left to extreme right) and factualness (very low to very high). Across both communities and authors, greater fractions of left bias posts are correlated with *weaker* model performance, whereas greater fractions of right bias posts are correlated with *stronger* model performance. Similarly, greater fractions of high factual posts are correlated with *weaker* performance, while more low factual posts are correlated with *stronger* model performance.

6.3 Popularity and Community Acceptance

Next, we consider whether our model performs equitably across posts that do and do not gain community acceptance, and across varying levels of popularity. We examine the correlation of each post's community-normalized score[5] and the *ContentOnly* model's confidence when predicting the true class annotation of the post. For the test set overall, this correlation is +0.094, but is higher for deceptive posts (+0.104) than for credible posts (+0.083). We found that all correlations are significant (p-values $< 10^{-5}$) but the effect is small.

In Table 3, we see that there are no significant correlations greater than .2 for posts with low to moderate community acceptance. However, for the posts most highly accepted by the community (*i.e.,* those in the 9th and 10th deciles), the correlations are both significant and relatively strong. This suggests that in general, the model is more confident on posts that are more accepted by the community, but only for posts that are highly accepted by the community. We also compute the same correlation coefficients for posts linking to credible and deceptive news sources separately, and find the trend is magnified: For posts linking to deceptive sources that are most widely accepted within their given community, community acceptance is highly (+0.51 and +0.4) correlated with greater model confidence. In contrast, for posts linking to credible

[5]Normalized by the median score for all posts from the same month in the same subreddit.

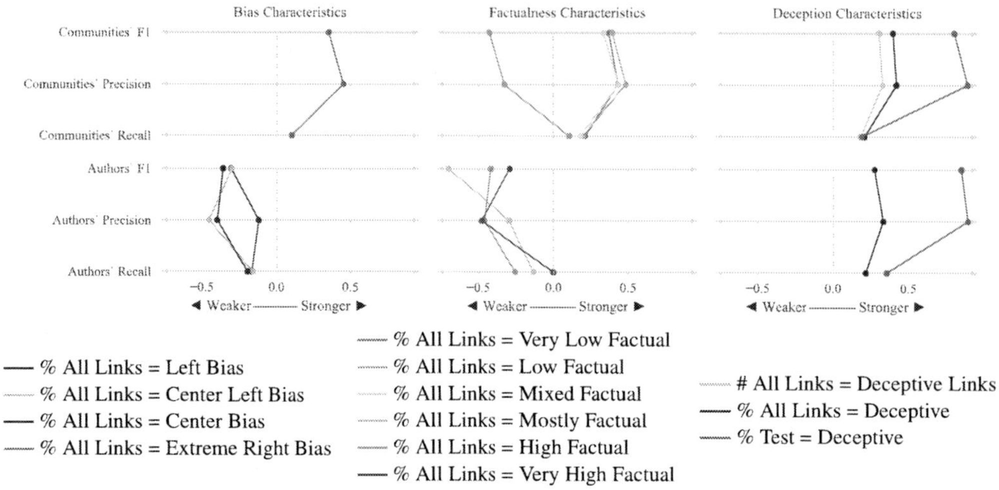

Figure 4: Correlation coefficients between characteristics and aggregated community/author performance metrics: F1, precision, and recall. All characteristics with an absolute Pearson's r correlation coefficient greater than 0.3 for at least one metric are included. Generally, stronger model performance is correlated with more right bias, low factual, and deceptive content, while weaker performance is correlated with more left bias and high factual content.

Community Acceptance (← More / Less →)	All	Credible	Deceptive
Decile 1	−0.05	+0.07	+0.01
Decile 2	+0.02	−0.05	+0.03
Decile 3	−0.02	−0.06	+0.04
Decile 4	−0.04	−0.03	−0.03
Decile 5	−0.02	−0.04	+0.01
Decile 6	+0.06	+0.01	+0.07
Decile 7	+0.10‡	+0.15	+0.14‡
Decile 8	−0.11‡	−0.11	+0.19‡
Decile 9	+0.47‡	−0.17‡	+0.51‡
Decile 10	+0.15‡	+0.02	+0.40‡

Table 3: Correlations between community acceptance, by decile, and the *ContentOnly* model confidence (true class). † denotes a p-value $< .05$, ‡ for p-value $< .01$.

news sources that are strongly positively received or promoted by the community, the model is actually slightly *less* confident (correlation coefficient of -.017). This is an important distinction in behavior, particularly for deception detection models that may be leveraged as automated systems to flag deceptive content to investigate or intervene against or as a gate-keeping mechanism to slow the spread of misinformation online.

7 Discussion and Conclusions

In summary, we quantify the context of deceptive and credible posts by computing community and author characteristics and use these characteristics, to explain and characterize the performance of an LSTM-based model for deception detection, examining performance variance across communities or users to identify characteristics of sub-populations where the model disproportionately underperforms.

We find that in general, sub-population characteristics are more strongly correlated with aggregate performance, and that, for both communities and authors, the model is more effective at identifying deceptive posts (higher F1 and precision) when the author/community has a greater tendency to submit or receive posts linked to deceptive, low factual, and right biased news sources. In contrast, a greater tendency to submit or receive posts linked to high factual and center biased content are correlated with weaker F1 and precision – the model is more likely to fail when identifying posts submitted to communities or users that engage with more trustworthy news sources.

We also investigate the impact that community acceptance has on model performance, using community-normalized scores to quantify acceptance. We find that, for posts with low to moderator community acceptance, correlations with the model's confidence that a post belongs to its groundtruth annotation class are small, but for posts that are strongly accepted by the community they are submitted to, acceptance is strongly correlated with increased model confidence for deceptive content, but only moderately correlated with *decreased* model confidence for credible content. It is important to consider what kinds of failures are most impactful given the specific application of a model. For example, if considering a deception detection model for use as an intervention strategy, it may be more important for a model to have greater reliability when identifying content that gains widespread community acceptance or popularity as we find our *ContentOnly* model does — this is an important direction of evaluation for researchers in the deception detection domain to consider.

We encourage NLP researchers working in the deception detection space to look beyond overall test-set performance metrics such as F1 score. Although many models achieve high overall F1 score, the performance of these models varies dramatically from community to community. Decisions about model design and training should not be made without considering the intended application of the model. For example, a model tasked with flagging posts for human review may be optimized with a very different precision-recall tradeoff than a model tasked with automatically taking entire enforcement actions, such as removing content.

Acknowledgements

This research was supported by the Laboratory Directed Research and Development Program at Pacific Northwest National Laboratory, a multi-program national laboratory operated by Battelle for the U.S. Department of Energy.

References

Oluwaseun Ajao, Deepayan Bhowmik, and Shahrzad Zargari. 2018. Fake news identification on twitter with hybrid cnn and rnn models. In *Proceedings of the 9th International Conference on Social Media and Society*, pages 226–230. ACM.

Michael Barthel, Amy Mitchell, and Jesse Holcomb. 2016. Many americans believe fake news is sowing confusion.

Jason Baumgartner, Savvas Zannettou, Brian Keegan, Megan Squire, and Jeremy Blackburn. 2020. The pushshift reddit dataset.

Weiling Chen, Yan Zhang, Chai Kiat Yeo, Chiew Tong Lau, and Bu Sung Lee. 2018. Unsupervised rumor detection based on users' behaviors using neural networks. *Pattern Recognition Letters*, 105:226–233.

Alexandra Chouldechova. 2017. Fair prediction with disparate impact: a study of bias in recidivism prediction instruments. *Big data*, 5(2):153–163.

Thomas Davidson, Debasmita Bhattacharya, and Ingmar Weber. 2019. Racial bias in hate speech and abusive language detection datasets. In *Proceedings of the Third Workshop on Abusive Language Online*, pages 25–35.

Julia Dressel and Hany Farid. 2018. The accuracy, fairness, and limits of predicting recidivism. *Science advances*, 4(1):eaao5580.

Danielle Ensign, Sorelle A Friedler, Scott Neville, Carlos Scheidegger, and Suresh Venkatasubramanian. 2018. Runaway feedback loops in predictive policing. In *Conference on Fairness, Accountability and Transparency*, pages 160–171.

Maria Glenski, Corey Pennycuff, and Tim Weninger. 2017. Consumers and curators: Browsing and voting patterns on reddit. *IEEE Transactions on Computational Social Systems*, 4(4):196–206.

Maria Glenski and Tim Weninger. 2018. How humans versus bots react to deceptive and trusted news sources: A case study of active users. In *Proceedings of the IEEE/ACM International Conference on Advances in Social Networks Analysis and Mining (ASONAM)*. IEEE/ACM.

Bryce Goodman and Seth Flaxman. 2017. European union regulations on algorithmic decision-making and a "right to explanation". *AI magazine*, 38(3):50–57.

Han Guo, Juan Cao, Yazi Zhang, Junbo Guo, and Jintao Li. 2018. Rumor detection with hierarchical social attention network. In *Proceedings of the 27th ACM International Conference on Information and Knowledge Management*, pages 943–951. ACM.

Eszter Hargittai and Gina Walejko. 2008. The participation divide: Content creation and sharing in the digital age. *Information, Community and Society*, 11(2):239–256.

Georgi Karadzhov, Pepa Gencheva, Preslav Nakov, and Ivan Koychev. 2018. We built a fake news & click-bait filter: what happened next will blow your mind! *arXiv preprint arXiv:1803.03786*.

Srijan Kumar, Justin Cheng, Jure Leskovec, and VS Subrahmanian. 2017. An army of me: Sockpuppets in online discussion communities. In *Proceedings of the 26th International Conference on World Wide Web*, pages 857–866.

Srijan Kumar, Bryan Hooi, Disha Makhija, Mohit Kumar, Christos Faloutsos, and VS Subrahmanian. 2018. Rev2: Fraudulent user prediction in rating platforms. In *Proceedings of the Eleventh ACM International Conference on Web Search and Data Mining*, pages 333–341. ACM.

Quanzhi Li, Qiong Zhang, and Luo Si. 2019. Rumor detection by exploiting user credibility information, attention and multi-task learning. In *Proceedings of the 57th Annual Meeting of the Association for Computational Linguistics*, pages 1173–1179.

Jing Ma, Wei Gao, Prasenjit Mitra, Sejeong Kwon, Bernard J Jansen, Kam-Fai Wong, and Meeyoung Cha. 2016. Detecting rumors from microblogs with recurrent neural networks. In *Ijcai*, pages 3818–3824.

Alexey N. Medvedev, Renaud Lambiotte, and Jean-Charles Delvenne. 2019. The anatomy of Reddit: An overview of academic research. *arXiv:1810.10881 [cs]*, pages 183–204. ArXiv: 1810.10881.

Tanushree Mitra, Graham P Wright, and Eric Gilbert. 2017. A parsimonious language model of social media credibility across disparate events. In *Proceedings of the ACM Conference on Computer Supported Cooperative Work and Social Computing (CSCW)*, pages 126–145. ACM.

Ji Ho Park, Jamin Shin, and Pascale Fung. 2018. Reducing gender bias in abusive language detection. In *Proceedings of the 2018 Conference on Empirical Methods in Natural Language Processing*, pages 2799–2804.

Hannah Rashkin, Eunsol Choi, Jin Yea Jang, Svitlana Volkova, and Yejin Choi. 2017. Truth of varying shades: Analyzing language in fake news and political fact-checking. In *Proceedings of the 2017 Conference on Empirical Methods in Natural Language Processing*, pages 2921–2927.

Bhavtosh Rath, Wei Gao, Jing Ma, and Jaideep Srivastava. 2017. From retweet to believability: Utilizing trust to identify rumor spreaders on twitter. In *Proceedings of the 2017 IEEE/ACM International Conference on Advances in Social Networks Analysis and Mining 2017*, pages 179–186. ACM.

Victoria L Rubin, Niall J Conroy, Yimin Chen, and Sarah Cornwell. 2016. Fake news or truth? Using satirical cues to detect potentially misleading news. In *Proceedings of NAACL-HLT*, pages 7–17.

Maarten Sap, Dallas Card, Saadia Gabriel, Yejin Choi, and Noah A Smith. 2019. The risk of racial bias in hate speech detection. In *Proceedings of the 57th Annual Meeting of the Association for Computational Linguistics*, pages 1668–1678.

Elisa Shearer and Elizabeth Grieco. 2019. Americans are wary of the role social media sites play in delivering the news. *Pew Research Center*.

Kai Shu, Deepak Mahudeswaran, Suhang Wang, and Huan Liu. 2020. Hierarchical propagation networks for fake news detection: Investigation and exploitation. In *Proceedings of the International AAAI Conference on Web and Social Media*, volume 14, pages 626–637.

Trevor van Mierlo. 2014. The 1% rule in four digital health social networks: An observational study. *Journal of medical Internet Research*, 16(2):e33.

Svitlana Volkova, Ellyn Ayton, Dustin L Arendt, Zhuanyi Huang, and Brian Hutchinson. 2019. Explaining multimodal deceptive news prediction models. In *Proceedings of the International AAAI Conference on Web and Social Media*, volume 13, pages 659–662.

Svitlana Volkova, Kyle Shaffer, Jin Yea Jang, and Nathan Hodas. 2017. Separating facts from fiction: Linguistic models to classify suspicious and trusted news posts on twitter. In *Proceedings of the 55th Annual Meeting of the Association for Computational Linguistics (Volume 2: Short Papers)*, pages 647–653, Vancouver, Canada. Association for Computational Linguistics.

William Yang Wang. 2017. "liar, liar pants on fire": A new benchmark dataset for fake news detection. In *Proceedings of the 55th Annual Meeting of the Association for Computational Linguistics (Volume 2: Short Papers)*, pages 422–426.

Galen Weld, Maria Glenski, and Tim Althoff. 2021. Political bias and factualness in news sharing across more than 100,000 online communities.

Qiang Zhang, Aldo Lipani, Shangsong Liang, and Emine Yilmaz. 2019. Reply-aided detection of misinformation via bayesian deep learning. In *WWW*, pages 2333–2343. ACM.

Arkaitz Zubiaga, Elena Kochkina, Maria Liakata, Rob Procter, Michal Lukasik, Kalina Bontcheva, Trevor Cohn, and Isabelle Augenstein. 2018. Discourse-aware rumour stance classification in social media using sequential classifiers. *Information Processing & Management*, 54(2):273–290.

Never guess what I heard... Rumor Detection in Finnish News: a Dataset and a Baseline

Mika Hämäläinen, Khalid Alnajjar, Niko Partanen and Jack Rueter
Department of Digital Humanities
University of Helsinki
firstname.lastname@helsinki.fi

Abstract

This study presents a new dataset on rumor detection in Finnish language news headlines. We have evaluated two different LSTM based models and two different BERT models, and have found very significant differences in the results. A fine-tuned FinBERT reaches the best overall accuracy of 94.3% and rumor label accuracy of 96.0% of the time. However, a model fine-tuned on Multilingual BERT reaches the best factual label accuracy of 97.2%. Our results suggest that the performance difference is due to a difference in the original training data. Furthermore, we find that a regular LSTM model works better than one trained with a pretrained word2vec model. These findings suggest that more work needs to be done for pretrained models in Finnish language as they have been trained on small and biased corpora.

1 Introduction

Contemporary online news media contains information from more and less reputable sources, and in many cases the reliability of individual news articles can be very questionable. This has far reaching impact on society and can even influence decision making, as everyone continuously encounters such material online. This is a real issue as identified by Paskin (2018). In their study, they found out that participating people could only, on the average, distinguish fake news from real news half of the time, and none of the participants was able to identify all samples of fake and real news correctly.

Ever since the 2016 US elections fake news and misinformation have become a hot topic in the English speaking world (Allcott and Gentzkow, 2017), however other countries are no less immune to the spread of such information. In this study we present for the first time a method for rumor detection in Finnish news headlines. Finnish language has not yet received any research interest in this topic, and for this reason we also propose a new dataset[1] for the task. We treat this task as a classification problem where each news headline is categorized as being either rumorous or factual.

Rumor detection is a very challenging task, and we believe that truly satisfactory results need to leverage other methods than only natural language processing. Whether a given text is a rumor or not is very strongly connected to real world knowledge and continuously changing world events that we don't believe that this can be solved within the analysis of individual strings without a larger context. However, if we can perform even a rough classification at this relatively simple level, this could be used as one step in more robust and complex implementations. Therefore, our initial approach should be seen as a baseline for future implementations, while it can be seen as an important advancement in this work, and in this case it is the starting point, as related work in matters of this topic for Finnish remains nonexistent.

2 Related Work

Rumor detection has in recent years become an active topic of investigation, especially due to the complex influence it has on modern societies through social media. There has been other work on rumor detection for languages other than English as well. Alzanin and Azmi (2019) studied rumor detection in Arabic tweets and Chernyaev et al. (2020) in Russian tweets. Recently, Ke et al. (2020) has also presented a method for rumor detection in Cantonese. A closely related topic, stance detection, has been studied in a comparable corpus of French Tweets (Evrard et al., 2020). In this section, we describe some of the related work in more detail.

Rubin et al. (2016) harnessed satire in the task of fake news detection, in their study, this figure of

[1] Our dataset is freely available for download on Zenodo https://zenodo.org/record/4697529

Proceedings of the 4th NLP4IF Workshop on NLP for Internet Freedom, pages 39–44
June 6, 2021. ©2021 Association for Computational Linguistics

language, that has also sparked research interest in detection (Li et al., 2020) and generation (Alnajjar and Hämäläinen, 2018) on its own, was useful in detecting fake news. They proposed an SVM (support vector machines) approach capturing five features: *Absurdity*, *Humor*, *Grammar*, *Negative Affect* and *Punctuation*. The idea of satire in fake news detection was also studied later on by Levi et al. (2019).

Tree LSTMs have been used recently in rumor detection (Kumar and Carley, 2019). They train the models on social media text which contains interactions as people reply to statements either providing supporting or contradicting statements. Their model is capable of taking these replies into account when doing predictions.

Sujana et al. (2020) detect rumors by using multiloss hierarchical BiLSTM models. The authors claim the hierarchical structure makes it possible to extract deep information form text. Their results show that their model outperforms a regular BiLSTM model.

Previous work on Finnish news materials include a study by (Ruokolainen et al., 2019), where the articles were annotated for named entities. In addition, other researchers have targeted Finnish news materials, especially historical newspapers that are openly available. Furthermore, (Mela et al., 2019) has studied NER (named entity recognition) in the context of historical Finnish newspapers, and (Marjanen et al., 2019; Hengchen et al., 2019) have tested methods for analyzing broader changes in a historical newspaper corpus. Our work departs from this, as we focus on modern newspaper headlines.

Additionally, to our knowledge there has not been any previous work on rumor detection for Finnish, which makes our work particularly novel and needed.

3 Data

We collect data from a Finnish news aggregation website[2], in particular, we crawl the news headlines in the rumor category to form samples of rumor data. In addition, we crawl the headlines in the category news from Finland to compile a list of headlines that do not contain rumors but actual fact-based news stories. This way we have gathered 2385 factual and 1511 rumorous headlines totaling to 3896 samples. As a preprocessing step, we tokenize the headlines with NLTK (Loper and Bird, 2002) word tokenizer.

	rumor	factual
train	1057	1669
test	227	358
validation	227	358

Table 1: The size of the data splits on a headline level

We shuffle the data and split it 70% for training, 15% for validation and 15% for testing. The actual sizes can be seen in Table 1. We use the same splits for all the models we train in this paper. An example of the data can be seen in Table 2. The dataset has been published with an open license on Zenodo with a permanent DOI[3]. The splits used in this paper can be found in the dataset_splits.zip file.

4 Detecting Rumors

In this section, we describe the different methods we tried out for rumor detection. We compare LSTM based models with transfer learning on two different BERT models.

We train our first model using a bi-directional long short-term memory (LSTM) based model (Hochreiter and Schmidhuber, 1997) using OpenNMT (Klein et al., 2017) with the default settings except for the encoder where we use a BRNN (bidirectional recurrent neural network) (Schuster and Paliwal, 1997) instead of the default RNN (recurrent neural network). We use the default of two layers for both the encoder and the decoder and the default attention model, which is the general global attention presented by Luong et al. (2015). The model is trained for the default 100,000 steps. The model is trained with tokenized headlines as its source and the rumor/factual label as its target.

We train an additional LSTM model with the same configuration and same random seed (3435) with the only difference being that we use pretrained word2vec embeddings for the encoder. We use the Finnish embeddings provided by (Kutuzov et al., 2017)[4]. The vector size is 100 and the model has been trained with a window size 10 using skipgrams on the Finnish CoNLL17 corpus.

In addition, we train two different BERT based sequence classification models based on the Finnish BERT model FinBERT (Virtanen et al.,

[2]https://www.ampparit.com/

[3]https://zenodo.org/record/4697529

[4]http://vectors.nlpl.eu/repository/20/42.zip

Headline	Rumor
Tutkimus: Silmälaseja käyttävillä ehkä pienempi riski koronatartuntaan *Study: People wearing eyeglasses may have a smaller risk of getting corona*	true
Koronaviruksella yllättävä sivuoire - aiheutti tuntikausien erektion *Coronavirus has a surprising symptom - caused an erection that lasted for hours*	true
Korona romahdutti alkoholin matkustajatuonnin *Corona caused a collapse in traveler import of alcohol*	false
Bussimatka aiheutti 64 koronatartuntaa *A bus trip caused 64 corona cases*	false

Table 2: Examples of rumorous and factual headlines related to COVID-19 from the corpus

	Overall	Factual	Rumor
LSTM	84.9%	93.2%	71.8%
LSTM + word2vec	71.6%	94.4%	35.6%
FinBERT	**94.3%**	93.2%	**96.0%**
Multilingual BERT	91.8%	**97.2%**	83.3%

Table 3: Overall and label level accuracies for each model

2019) and Multilingual BERT (Devlin et al., 2019), which has been trained on multiple languages, Finnish being one of them. We use the transformers package (Wolf et al., 2020) to conduct the fine tuning. As hyperparameters for the fine tuning, we use 3 epochs with 500 warm-up steps for the learning rate scheduler and 0.01 as the strength of the weight decay.

This setup takes into account the current state of the art at the field, and uses recently created resources such as Finnish BERT model, with our own custom made dataset. Everything is set up in an easily replicable manner, which ensures that our experiments and results can be used in further work on this important topic.

5 Results

In this section, we present the results of the models, in addition, we explain why these result were obtained by contrasting the task into the training data of each pretrained model. The accuracies of the models can be seen in Table 3.

The results vary greatly, with tens of percentages between different approaches. It is important to note that while FinBERT gets the best overall accuracy and the best accuracy in predicting rumorous headlines correctly, it does not get the best accuracy in predicting factual headlines correctly, as it is actually Multilingual BERT that gets the best accuracy for factual headlines. This makes us wonder why this might be so. When we look at the training data for these models, we can see that Multilingual BERT was trained on Wikipedia[5], whereas FinBERT was mainly trained on data from an internet forum, Suomi24[6], that is notorious for misinformation, (33% of the data) and Common Crawl[7] (60% of the data). Only 7% of the training data comes from a news corpus. When we put the results into perspective with the training data, it is not at all the case, as the authors of FinBERT claim in their paper: *"The results indicate that the multilingual models fail to deliver on the promises of deep transfer learning for lower-resourced languages"* (Virtanen et al., 2019). Instead, based on our results, it is only evident that Multilingual BERT outperforms FinBERT on factual headlines as its training data was based on an encyclopedia, and that FinBERT is better at detecting rumors as its training data had a large proportion of potentially rumorous text from Suomi24 forum.

In the same fashion, we can explain the results of the LSTM models. A great many papers (Qi et al., 2018; Panchendrarajan and Amaresan, 2018; Alnajjar, 2021) have found that pretrained embeddings improve prediction results when used with an LSTM model, however, in our case, we were better off without them. While the data description (Zeman et al., 2017) was not clear on what the data of the pretrained word2vec model consists of (apart from it being from Common Crawl), we can still inspect the overlap in the vocabulary of the training data and the pretrained model. Our training and validation datasets contain 17,729 unique tokens, out of which 5,937 were not present in the pretrained model. This means that approximately 33% of the

[5]https://github.com/google-research/bert/blob/master/multilingual.md

[6]https://keskustelu.suomi24.fi/

[7]https://commoncrawl.org/

tokens in our dataset were simply not present in the pretrained model.

This is partially due to the English driven tradition of not lemmatizing pretrained models, however, for a language such as Finnish this means that a simple overlap in vocabulary is not enough, instead one would even need to have overlap in the syntactic positions where the words have appeared in the data of a pretrained model and in the training data of the model that would utilize the pretrained embeddings. It is important to note that the pretrained word2vec model does not have a small vocabulary either (2,433,286 tokens).

In order to study whether the issue arises from the fact that the word2vec model is not lemmatized or from the fact that its training data was from a different domain, we conduct a small experiment. We lemmatize the words in our training and validation dataset and the words in the vocabulary of the word2vec model by using the Finnish morphological FST (finite-state transducer) Omorfi (Pirinen, 2015) through UralicNLP[8] (Hämäläinen, 2019). After lemmatization, our corpus contains 10,807 unique lemmas, 2,342 out of which are still not in the lemmatized vocabulary of the word2vec model. This means that even on the lemma level, 21.7% of the words are not covered by the word2vec model. The lemmatized vocabulary size of the pretrained model is 576,535 lemmas. It is clear that a model leveraging from sub-word units could not alleviate the situation either, as such models are mainly useful to cope with inflectional forms, but not with completely new words that merely look familiar on the surface.

6 Conclusions

Our study shows that with the tested settings it is possible to differentiate the rumor and non-rumor categories with a very high accuracy. As the experiment setup was relatively simple, yet elegant, we believe that similar results can also be repeated for other languages for which rumor detection systems have not yet been created. The experiments reported here are just one part in creating such a system for Finnish language. We believe that the path towards more thorough solutions lies in larger manually annotated datasets that contain even more variation than the materials we have now used. Although, some of these datasets could be automatically generated by using Finnish semantic databases (Hämäläinen, 2018) and syntax realization (Hämäläinen and Rueter, 2018) in conjunction with existing Finnish news headline generation methods (Alnajjar et al., 2019).

Possibly the most relevant finding of our study lies, however, in the results we detected with different BERT models and were able to connect into the differences in training data. These findings are important much beyond just rumor detection, which is only one domain where these models are being continuously used. As the question of training data seemed to be an important one also for the word2vec model in the LSTM experiment, we can only conclude that the level of the existing pretrained models for Finnish is not good enough for them to work in many different domains. This is not a question of Finnish being "low resourced" (see Hämäläinen 2021), as huge amounts of text exist in Finnish online, but more of a question of not enough academic interest in producing high-quality models. This is something we will look into in the future.

Further work is needed from a qualitative perspective to see what exactly leads to a certain classification, and which kind of error types can be detected. Since the classification was done solely based on linguistic features of the text, represented by the strings, we must assume there are lexical and stylistic differences that are very systematic. Not unlike in the case of the existing methods for rumor detection, our models did not have access to any real world knowledge about the rumors or factual and non-factual information at the time when the headlines were written. It is obvious that a very well functioning system can only be built in connection to this kind of sources, as the fact that something is a rumor is ultimately connected to the content and real world knowledge, and not just the words in the string. However, we argue that our system could already be useful in a rough classificatory tasks where rumor containing news could be automatically selected for manual verification, or for verification with a more specialized neural network. Naturally further work also has to take into account more non-rumor text types and genres, so that certain degree of robustness can be reached.

References

Hunt Allcott and Matthew Gentzkow. 2017. Social media and fake news in the 2016 election. *Journal of Economic Perspectives*, 31(2):211–36.

[8]We use the dictionary forms model

Khalid Alnajjar. 2021. When word embeddings become endangered. In Mika Hämäläinen, Niko Partanen, and Khalid Alnajjar, editors, *Multilingual Facilitation*. Rootroo Ltd.

Khalid Alnajjar and Mika Hämäläinen. 2018. A master-apprentice approach to automatic creation of culturally satirical movie titles. In *Proceedings of the 11th International Conference on Natural Language Generation*, pages 274–283.

Khalid Alnajjar, Leo Leppänen, and Hannu Toivonen. 2019. No time like the present: methods for generating colourful and factual multilingual news headlines. In *Proceedings of the 10th International Conference on Computational Creativity*. Association for Computational Creativity.

Samah M Alzanin and Aqil M Azmi. 2019. Rumor detection in Arabic tweets using semi-supervised and unsupervised expectation–maximization. *Knowledge-Based Systems*, 185:104945.

Aleksandr Chernyaev, Alexey Spryiskov, Alexander Ivashko, and Yuliya Bidulya. 2020. A rumor detection in Russian tweets. In *International Conference on Speech and Computer*, pages 108–118. Springer.

Jacob Devlin, Ming-Wei Chang, Kenton Lee, and Kristina Toutanova. 2019. Bert: Pre-training of deep bidirectional transformers for language understanding. In *Proceedings of the 2019 Conference of the North American Chapter of the Association for Computational Linguistics: Human Language Technologies, Volume 1 (Long and Short Papers)*, pages 4171–4186.

Marc Evrard, Rémi Uro, Nicolas Hervé, and Béatrice Mazoyer. 2020. French tweet corpus for automatic stance detection. In *Proceedings of The 12th Language Resources and Evaluation Conference*, pages 6317–6322.

Mika Hämäläinen. 2018. Extracting a semantic database with syntactic relations for finnish to boost resources for endangered uralic languages. *The Proceedings of Logic and Engineering of Natural Language Semantics 15 (LENLS15)*.

Mika Hämäläinen and Jack Rueter. 2018. Development of an open source natural language generation tool for finnish. In *Proceedings of the Fourth International Workshop on Computational Linguistics of Uralic Languages*, pages 51–58.

Simon Hengchen, Ruben Ros, and Jani Marjanen. 2019. A data-driven approach to the changing vocabulary of the 'nation'in english, dutch, swedish and finnish newspapers, 1750-1950. In *Digital Humanities 2019*.

Sepp Hochreiter and Jürgen Schmidhuber. 1997. Long short-term memory. *Neural computation*, 9(8):1735–1780.

Mika Hämäläinen. 2019. UralicNLP: An NLP library for Uralic languages. *Journal of Open Source Software*, 4(37):1345.

Mika Hämäläinen. 2021. Endangered languages are not low-resourced! In Mika Hämäläinen, Niko Partanen, and Khalid Alnajjar, editors, *Multilingual Facilitation*. Rootroo Ltd.

Liang Ke, Xinyu Chen, Zhipeng Lu, Hanjian Su, and Haizhou Wang. 2020. A novel approach for Cantonese rumor detection based on deep neural network. In *2020 IEEE International Conference on Systems, Man, and Cybernetics (SMC)*, pages 1610–1615. IEEE.

Guillaume Klein, Yoon Kim, Yuntian Deng, Jean Senellart, and Alexander M. Rush. 2017. OpenNMT: Open-Source Toolkit for Neural Machine Translation. In *Proc. ACL*.

Sumeet Kumar and Kathleen Carley. 2019. Tree LSTMs with convolution units to predict stance and rumor veracity in social media conversations. In *Proceedings of the 57th Annual Meeting of the Association for Computational Linguistics*, pages 5047–5058, Florence, Italy. Association for Computational Linguistics.

Andrei Kutuzov, Murhaf Fares, Stephan Oepen, and Erik Velldal. 2017. Word vectors, reuse, and replicability: Towards a community repository of large-text resources. In *Proceedings of the 58th Conference on Simulation and Modelling*, pages 271–276. Linköping University Electronic Press.

Or Levi, Pedram Hosseini, Mona Diab, and David Broniatowski. 2019. Identifying nuances in fake news vs. satire: Using semantic and linguistic cues. In *Proceedings of the Second Workshop on Natural Language Processing for Internet Freedom: Censorship, Disinformation, and Propaganda*, pages 31–35, Hong Kong, China. Association for Computational Linguistics.

Lily Li, Or Levi, Pedram Hosseini, and David Broniatowski. 2020. A multi-modal method for satire detection using textual and visual cues. In *Proceedings of the 3rd NLP4IF Workshop on NLP for Internet Freedom: Censorship, Disinformation, and Propaganda*, pages 33–38.

Edward Loper and Steven Bird. 2002. Nltk: The natural language toolkit. In *Proceedings of the ACL-02 Workshop on Effective Tools and Methodologies for Teaching Natural Language Processing and Computational Linguistics - Volume 1*, ETMTNLP '02, page 63–70, USA. Association for Computational Linguistics.

Minh-Thang Luong, Hieu Pham, and Christopher D Manning. 2015. Effective approaches to attention-based neural machine translation. *arXiv preprint arXiv:1508.04025*.

Jani Marjanen, Ville Vaara, Antti Kanner, Hege Roivainen, Eetu Mäkelä, Leo Lahti, and Mikko Tolonen. 2019. A national public sphere? analysing the language, location and form of newspapers in finland, 1771–1917. *Journal of European Periodical Studies*, 4(1):54–77.

Matti La Mela, Minna Tamper, and Kimmo Tapio Kettunen. 2019. Finding nineteenth-century berry spots: Recognizing and linking place names in a historical newspaper berry-picking corpus. In *Digital Humanities in the Nordic Countries Proceedings of the Digital Humanities in the Nordic Countries 4th Conference*. CEUR-WS. org.

Rrubaa Panchendrarajan and Aravindh Amaresan. 2018. Bidirectional LSTM-CRF for named entity recognition. In *Proceedings of the 32nd Pacific Asia Conference on Language, Information and Computation*, Hong Kong. Association for Computational Linguistics.

Danny Paskin. 2018. Real or fake news: who knows? *The Journal of Social Media in Society*, 7(2):252–273.

Tommi A Pirinen. 2015. Development and use of computational morphology of finnish in the open source and open science era: Notes on experiences with omorfi development. *SKY Journal of Linguistics*, 28:381–393.

Ye Qi, Devendra Sachan, Matthieu Felix, Sarguna Padmanabhan, and Graham Neubig. 2018. When and why are pre-trained word embeddings useful for neural machine translation? In *Proceedings of the 2018 Conference of the North American Chapter of the Association for Computational Linguistics: Human Language Technologies, Volume 2 (Short Papers)*, pages 529–535, New Orleans, Louisiana. Association for Computational Linguistics.

Victoria Rubin, Niall Conroy, Yimin Chen, and Sarah Cornwell. 2016. Fake news or truth? using satirical cues to detect potentially misleading news. In *Proceedings of the Second Workshop on Computational Approaches to Deception Detection*, pages 7–17, San Diego, California. Association for Computational Linguistics.

Teemu Ruokolainen, Pekka Kauppinen, Miikka Silfverberg, and Krister Lindén. 2019. A finnish news corpus for named entity recognition. *Language Resources and Evaluation*, pages 1–26.

Mike Schuster and Kuldip K Paliwal. 1997. Bidirectional recurrent neural networks. *IEEE transactions on Signal Processing*, 45(11):2673–2681.

Yudianto Sujana, Jiawen Li, and Hung-Yu Kao. 2020. Rumor detection on Twitter using multiloss hierarchical BiLSTM with an attenuation factor. In *Proceedings of the 1st Conference of the Asia-Pacific Chapter of the Association for Computational Linguistics and the 10th International Joint Conference on Natural Language Processing*, pages 18–26, Suzhou, China. Association for Computational Linguistics.

Antti Virtanen, Jenna Kanerva, Rami Ilo, Jouni Luoma, Juhani Luotolahti, Tapio Salakoski, Filip Ginter, and Sampo Pyysalo. 2019. Multilingual is not enough: Bert for finnish. *arXiv preprint arXiv:1912.07076*.

Thomas Wolf, Lysandre Debut, Victor Sanh, Julien Chaumond, Clement Delangue, Anthony Moi, Pierric Cistac, Tim Rault, Rémi Louf, Morgan Funtowicz, Joe Davison, Sam Shleifer, Patrick von Platen, Clara Ma, Yacine Jernite, Julien Plu, Canwen Xu, Teven Le Scao, Sylvain Gugger, Mariama Drame, Quentin Lhoest, and Alexander M. Rush. 2020. Transformers: State-of-the-art natural language processing. In *Proceedings of the 2020 Conference on Empirical Methods in Natural Language Processing: System Demonstrations*, pages 38–45, Online. Association for Computational Linguistics.

Daniel Zeman, Martin Popel, Milan Straka, Jan Hajic, Joakim Nivre, Filip Ginter, Juhani Luotolahti, Sampo Pyysalo, Slav Petrov, Martin Potthast, Francis Tyers, Elena Badmaeva, Memduh Gokirmak, Anna Nedoluzhko, Silvie Cinkova, Jan Hajic jr., Jaroslava Hlavacova, Václava Kettnerová, Zdenka Uresova, Jenna Kanerva, Stina Ojala, Anna Missilä, Christopher D. Manning, Sebastian Schuster, Siva Reddy, Dima Taji, Nizar Habash, Herman Leung, Marie-Catherine de Marneffe, Manuela Sanguinetti, Maria Simi, Hiroshi Kanayama, Valeria dePaiva, Kira Droganova, Héctor Martínez Alonso, Çağrı Çöltekin, Umut Sulubacak, Hans Uszkoreit, Vivien Macketanz, Aljoscha Burchardt, Kim Harris, Katrin Marheinecke, Georg Rehm, Tolga Kayadelen, Mohammed Attia, Ali Elkahky, Zhuoran Yu, Emily Pitler, Saran Lertpradit, Michael Mandl, Jesse Kirchner, Hector Fernandez Alcalde, Jana Strnadová, Esha Banerjee, Ruli Manurung, Antonio Stella, Atsuko Shimada, Sookyoung Kwak, Gustavo Mendonca, Tatiana Lando, Rattima Nitisaroj, and Josie Li. 2017. Conll 2017 shared task: Multilingual parsing from raw text to universal dependencies. In *Proceedings of the CoNLL 2017 Shared Task: Multilingual Parsing from Raw Text to Universal Dependencies*, pages 1–19, Vancouver, Canada. Association for Computational Linguistics.

Extractive and Abstractive Explanations for Fact-Checking and Evaluation of News

Ashkan Kazemi, Zehua Li, Verónica Peréz-Rosas and Rada Mihalcea
{ashkank, simonli, vrncapr, mihalcea}@umich.edu
University of Michigan, Ann Arbor

Abstract

In this paper, we explore the construction of natural language explanations for news claims, with the goal of assisting fact-checking and news evaluation applications. We experiment with two methods: (1) an extractive method based on Biased TextRank – a resource-effective unsupervised graph-based algorithm for content extraction; and (2) an abstractive method based on the GPT-2 language model. We perform comparative evaluations on two misinformation datasets in the political and health news domains, and find that the extractive method shows the most promise.

1 Introduction

Navigating the media landscape is becoming increasingly challenging given the abundance of misinformation, which reinforces the importance of keeping our news consumption focused and informed. While fake news and misinformation have been a recent focus of research studies (Pérez-Rosas et al., 2018; Thorne and Vlachos, 2018; Lu and Li, 2020), the majority of this work aims to categorize claims, rather than generate explanations that support or deny them. This is a challenging problem that has been mainly tackled by expert journalists who manually verify the information surrounding a given claim and provide a detailed verdict based on supporting or refuting evidence. More recently, there has been a growing interest in creating computational tools able to assist during this process by providing supporting explanations for a given claim based on the news content and context (Atanasova et al., 2020; Fan et al., 2020). While a true or false veracity label does not provide enough information and a detailed fact-checking report or news article might take long to read, bite-sized explanations can bridge this gap and improve the transparency of automated news evaluation systems.

To contribute to this line of work, our paper explores two approaches to generate supporting explanations to assist with the evaluation of news. First, we investigate how an extractive method based on Biased TextRank (Kazemi et al., 2020) can be used to generate explanations. Second, we explore an abstractive method based on GPT-2, a large generative language model (Radford et al., 2019).

Our methods take as input a news article and a claim and generate a claim-focused explanation by extracting or generating relevant information to the original article in relation to the claim. We evaluate our proposed methods on the health care and political domains, where misinformation is abundant. As current news on the COVID-19 pandemic and the elections are overloading social media outlets, we find these domains to be of timely importance. Through comparative experiments, we find that both methods are effective at generating explanations for news claims, with the extractive approach showing the most promise for this task.

2 Related Work

While explainability in AI has been a central subject of research in recent years (Poursabzi-Sangdeh et al., 2018; Lundberg and Lee, 2017; Core et al., 2006), the generation of natural language explanations is still relatively understudied. Camburu et al. (2018) propose e-SNLI, a natural language (NL) inference dataset augmented with human-annotated NL explanations. In their paper, Camburu et al. generated NL explanations for premise and hypothesis pairs for an inference task using the InferSent (Conneau et al., 2017) architecture. Kumar and Talukdar (2020) propose the task of generating "faithful" (i.e., aligned with the model's internal decision making) NL explanations and propose NILE, a method that jointly produces NLI labels and faithful NL explanations.

Generating explanations in the context of news and fact-checking is a timely and novel topic in the

Proceedings of the 4th NLP4IF Workshop on NLP for Internet Freedom, pages 45–50
June 6, 2021.

Claim: nearly half of Oregon's children are poor.
Fact-Check Report: ...Jim Francesconi...said..."Nearly half of Oregon's children are poor." He said the information came from a 2012 report...According to that report, "nearly 50% of children are either poor or low-income." Francesconi almost immediately realized his mistake. "In retrospect, I wish I would have said poor or low income."...there is a distinction between poor and low income as far as the U.S. government is concerned." ... If you check the...Census information, you'll find that...23 percent of children in Oregon live in...below...poverty level while another 21 percent live in low-income families. As far as the U.S. government is concerned, about a quarter of the state's children are poor, not half... (redacted)
Supporting Explanation (Ground Truth): So where does this leave us? Francesconi said in an opinion piece that "nearly half of Oregon's children are poor." In fact, if you use federal definitions for poverty, about a quarter are poor and another quarter are low-income. But experts tell us that families that are described as low-income still struggle to meet their basic needs and, for all intents and purposes, qualify as poor. Be that as it may, Francesconi was referencing a report that used the federal definitions.
Biased TextRank (Extractive): "Nearly half of Oregon's children are poor." According to that report, "nearly 50% of children are either poor or low-income." Low income refers to families between 100 and 200 percent of the federal poverty level. As far as the U.S. government is concerned, about a quarter of the state's children are poor, not half.
GPT-2 Based (Abstractive):" That's still below the federal poverty level. But that's not half. About 47 percent of Oregon's children are not poor, according to the Census data. So the percentage of children in the state who are poor is not half yet. It's actually closer to half.

Table 1: An example data point from the LIAR-PLUS dataset, with ground truth explanations, and explanations generated by our methods.

NLP community (Atanasova et al., 2020; Fan et al., 2020; Kotonya and Toni, 2020). In (Atanasova et al., 2020) the authors proposed a supervised BERT (Devlin et al., 2019) based model for jointly predicting the veracity of a claim by extracting supporting explanations from fact-checked claims in the LIAR-PLUS (Alhindi et al., 2018) dataset. Kotonya and Toni (2020) constructed a dataset for a similar task in the public health domain and provided baseline models for explainable fact verification using this dataset. Fan et al. (2020) used explanations about a claim to assist fact-checkers and showed that explanations improved both the efficiency and the accuracy of the fact-checking process.

3 Methods

We explore two methods for producing natural language explanations: an extractive unsupervised method based on Biased TextRank, and an abstractive method based on GPT-2.

3.1 Extractive: Biased TextRank

Introduced by Kazemi et al. (2020) and based on the TextRank algorithm (Mihalcea and Tarau, 2004), Biased TextRank is a targeted content extraction algorithm with a range of applications in keyword and sentence extraction. The TextRank algorithm ranks text segments for their importance by running a random walk algorithm on a graph built by including a node for each text segment (e.g., sentence), and drawing weighted edges by linking the text segment using a measure of similarity.

The Biased TextRank algorithm takes an extra "bias" input and ranks the input text segments considering both their own importance and their relevance to the bias term. The bias query is embedded into Biased TextRank using a similar idea introduced by Haveliwala (2002) for topic-sensitive PageRank. The similarity between the text segments that form the graph and the "bias" is used to set the restart probabilities of the random walker in a run of PageRank over the text graph. That means the more similar each text segment is to the bias query, the more likely it is for that node to be visited in each restart and therefore, it has a better chance of ranking higher than the less similar nodes to the bias query. During our experiments, we use SBERT (Reimers and Gurevych, 2019) contextual embeddings to transform text into sentence vectors and cosine similarity as similarity measure.

3.2 Abstractive: GPT-2 Based

We implement an abstractive explanation generation method based on GPT-2, a transformer-based language model introduced in Radford et al. (2019) and trained on 8 million web pages containing 40 GBs of text.

Aside from success in language generation tasks (Budzianowski and Vulić, 2019; Ham et al., 2020), the pretrained GPT-2 model enables us to generate abstractive explanations for a relatively small dataset through transfer learning.

In order to generate explanations that are closer in domain and style to the reference explanation, we conduct an initial fine-tuning step. While fine tuning, we provide the news article, the claim, and its corresponding explanation as an input to the model and explicitly mark the beginning and the end of each input argument with bespoke tokens. At test time, we provide the article and query inputs in similar format but leave the explanation field to be completed by the model. We use top-k sampling to generate explanations. We stop the generation after the model outputs the explicit end of the text token introduced in the fine-tuning process.

Overall, this fine-tuning strategy is able to generate explanations that follow a style similar to the reference explanation. However, we identify cases where the model generates gibberish and/or repetitive text, which are problems previously reported in the literature while using GPT-2 (Holtzman et al., 2019; Welleck et al., 2020). To address these issues, we devise a strategy to remove unimportant sentences that could introduce noise to the generation process. We first use Biased TextRank to rank the importance of the article sentences towards the question/claim. Then, we repeatedly remove the least important sentence (up to 5 times) and input the modified text into the GPT-2 generator. This approach keeps the text generation time complexity in the same order of magnitude as before and reduces the generation noise rate to close to zero.

4 Evaluation

4.1 Experimental Setup

We use a medium (355M hyper parameters) GPT-2 model (Radford et al., 2019) as implemented in the Huggingface transformers (Wolf et al., 2019) library. We use ROUGE (Lin, 2004), a common measure for language generation assessment as our main evaluation metric for the generated explanations and report the F score on three variations of ROUGE: ROUGE-1, ROUGE-2 and ROUGE-L.

We compare our methods against two baselines. The first is an explanation obtained by applying TextRank on the input text. The second, called "embedding similarity", ranks the input sentences by their embedding cosine similarity to the question and takes the top five sentences as an explanation.

4.2 Datasets

LIAR-PLUS. The LIAR-PLUS (Alhindi et al., 2018) dataset contains 10,146 train, 1,278 validation and 1,255 test data points collected from PolitiFact.com, a political fact-checking website in the U.S. A datapoint in this dataset contains a claim, its verdict, a news-length fact-check report justifying the verdict and a short explanation called "Our ruling" that summarizes the fact-check report and the verdict on the claim. General statistics on this dataset are presented in Table 2.

Health News Reviews (HNR). We collect health news reviews along with ratings and explanations from healthnewsreview.org, a website dedicated to evaluating healthcare journalism in the US. [1] The news articles are rated with a 1 to 5 star scale and the explanations, which justify the news' rating, consist of short answers for 10 evaluative questions on the quality of information reported in the article. The questions cover informative aspects that should be included in the news such as intervention costs, treatment benefits, discussion of harms and benefits, clinical evidence, and availability of treatment among others. Answers to these questions are further evaluated as either satisfactory, non-satisfactory or non-applicable to the given news item. For our experiments, we select 1,650 reviews that include both the original article and the accompanying metadata as well as explanations. Explanations' statistics are presented in Table 2.

Dataset	Total count	Av. Words	Av. Sent.
LIAR-PLUS	12,679	98.89	5.20
HNR	16,500	87.82	4.63

Table 2: Dataset statistics for explanations; total count, average words and sentences per explanation.

Model	ROUGE-1	ROUGE-2	ROUGE-L
TextRank	27.74	7.42	23.24
GPT-2 Based	24.01	5.78	21.15
Biased TextRank	**30.90**	**10.39**	**26.22**

Table 3: ROUGE-N scores of generated explanations on the LIAR-PLUS dataset.

To further study explanations in this dataset, we randomly select 50 articles along with their corresponding questions and explanations. We then manually label sentences in the original article that are relevant to the quality aspect being measured.[2] During this process we only include explanations that are deemed as "satisfactory," which means that relevant information is included in the original article.

4.3 Producing Explanations

We use the Biased TextRank and the GPT-2 based models to automatically generate explanations for each dataset. With LIAR-PLUS, we seek to generate the explanation provided in the "Our ruling" section. For HNR we aim to generate the explanation provided for the different evaluative questions described in section 4.2. We use the provided train-

[1] We followed the restrictions in the site's *robots.txt* file.

[2] The annotation was conducted by two annotators, with a Pearson's correlation score of 0.62 and a Jaccard similarity of 0.75.

Model	Explanations			Relevant Sentences		
	ROUGE-1	ROUGE-2	ROUGE-L	ROUGE-1	ROUGE-2	ROUGE-L
Embedding Similarity	18.32	2.96	15.25	22.02	8.79	20.21
GPT-2 Based	**20.02**	**4.32**	**17.67**	15.74	2.58	13.32
Biased TextRank	19.41	3.41	15.87	**23.54**	**10.15**	**21.88**

Table 4: ROUGE evaluation on the HNR dataset. Left columns under "Explanations" have the actual explanations as reference and the columns on the right provide results for comparison against question-relevant sentences.

Model	Acc.	F1 (+)	F1 (-)
GPT-2 Based	64.40%	49.04%	54.67%
Biased TextRank	**65.70%**	**56.69%**	**57.96%**

Table 5: Downstream evaluation results on the HNR dataset, averaged over 10 runs and 9 questions.

ing, validation and test splits for the LIAR-PLUS dataset. For HNR, we use 20% of the data as the test set and we study the first nine questions for each article only and exclude question #10 as answering it requires information beyond the news article. We use explanations and question-related article sentences as our references in ROUGE evaluations over the HNR dataset, and the section labeled "Our ruling" as ground truth for LIAR-PLUS.

Extractive Explanations. To generate extractive explanations for the LIAR dataset, we apply Biased TextRank on the original article and its corresponding claim and pick the top 5 ranked sentences as the explanation (based on the average length of explanations in the dataset). To generate explanations on the HNR dataset, we apply Biased TextRank on each news article and question pair for 9 of the evaluative questions and select the top 5 ranked sentences as the extracted explanation (matching the dataset average explanation length).

Abstractive Explanations. We apply the GPT-2 based model to generate abstractive explanations for each dataset using the original article and the corresponding claim or question as an input. We apply this method directly on the LIAR-PLUS dataset. On the HNT dataset, since we have several questions, we train separate GPT-2 based models per question. In addition, each model is trained using the articles corresponding to questions labeled as "satisfactory" only as the "unsatisfactory" or "not applicable" questions do not contain information within the scope of the original article.

4.4 Downstream Evaluation

We also conduct a set of experiments to evaluate to what extent we can answer the evaluation questions in the HNR dataset with the generated explanations. For each question, we assign binary labels to the articles (1 for satisfactory answers, 0 for not satisfactory and NA answers) and train individual classifiers aiming to discriminate between these two labels. During these experiments each classifier is trained and evaluated ten times on the test set and the results are averaged over the ten runs.

5 Experimental Results

As results in Table 3 suggest, while our abstractive GPT-2 based model fails to surpass extractive baselines on the LIAR-PLUS dataset, Biased TextRank outperforms the unsupervised TextRank baseline. Biased TextRank's improvements over TextRank suggest that a claim-focused summary of the article is better at generating supporting explanations than a regular summary produced by TextRank. Note that the current state-of-the-art results for this dataset, presented in (Atanasova et al., 2020) achieve 35.70, 13.51 and 31.58 in ROUGE-1, 2 and L scores respectively. However, a direct comparison with their method would not be accurate as it is a method that is *supervised* (versus the unsupervised Biased TextRank) and *extractive* (versus the abstractive GPT-2 based model).

Table 4 presents results on automatic evaluation of generated explanations for the HNR dataset, showing that the GPT-2 based model outperforms Biased TextRank when evaluated against actual explanations and Biased TextRank beats GPT-2 against the extractive baseline. This indicates the GPT-2 based method is more effective in this dataset and performs comparably with Biased TextRank. Results for the downstream task using both methods are shown in Table 5. As observed, results are significantly different and demonstrate that Biased TextRank significantly outperforms (t-test $p = 0.05$) the GPT-2-based abstractive method, thus suggesting that Biased TextRank generates good quality explanations for the HNR dataset.

6 Discussion

Our evaluations indicate that Biased TextRank shows the most promise, while the GPT-2 based model mostly follows in performance. Keeping in mind that the GPT-2 based model is solving the harder problem of *generating* language, it is worth noting the little supervision it receives on both datasets, especially on the HNR dataset where the average size of the training data is 849.

In terms of resource efficiency and speed, Biased TextRank is faster and lighter than the GPT-2 based model. Excluding the time needed to fine-tune the GPT-2 model, it takes approximately 60 seconds on a GPU to generate a coherent abstractive explanation on average on the LIAR-PLUS dataset, while Biased TextRank extracts explanations in the order of milliseconds and can even do it without a GPU in a few seconds. We find Biased TextRank's efficiency as another advantage of the unsupervised algorithm over the GPT-2 based model.

7 Conclusion

In this paper, we presented extractive and abstractive methods for generating supporting explanations for more convenient and transparent human consumption of news. We evaluated our methods on two domains and found promising results for producing explanations. In particular, Biased TextRank (an extractive method) outperformed the unsupervised baselines on the LIAR-PLUS dataset and performed reasonably close to the extractive ground-truth on the HNR dataset.

For future work, we believe generating abstractive explanations should be a priority, since intuitively an increase in the readability and coherence of the supporting explanations will result in improvements in the delivery and perception of news.

Acknowledgments

We are grateful to Dr. Stacy Loeb, Professor of Urology and Population Health at New York University, for her expert feedback, which was instrumental for this work. This material is based in part upon work supported by the Precision Health initiative at the University of Michigan, by the National Science Foundation (grant #1815291), and by the John Templeton Foundation (grant #61156). Any opinions, findings, and conclusions or recommendations expressed in this material are those of the author and do not necessarily reflect the views of the Precision Health initiative, the National Science Foundation, or John Templeton Foundation.

References

Tariq Alhindi, Savvas Petridis, and Smaranda Muresan. 2018. Where is your evidence: Improving fact-checking by justification modeling. In *Proceedings of the First Workshop on Fact Extraction and VERification (FEVER)*, pages 85–90, Brussels, Belgium. Association for Computational Linguistics.

Pepa Atanasova, Jakob Grue Simonsen, Christina Lioma, and Isabelle Augenstein. 2020. Generating fact checking explanations. In *Proceedings of the 58th Annual Meeting of the Association for Computational Linguistics*, pages 7352–7364, Online. Association for Computational Linguistics.

Paweł Budzianowski and Ivan Vulić. 2019. Hello, it's GPT-2 - how can I help you? towards the use of pretrained language models for task-oriented dialogue systems. In *Proceedings of the 3rd Workshop on Neural Generation and Translation*, pages 15–22, Hong Kong. Association for Computational Linguistics.

Oana-Maria Camburu, Tim Rocktäschel, Thomas Lukasiewicz, and Phil Blunsom. 2018. e-snli: Natural language inference with natural language explanations. In S. Bengio, H. Wallach, H. Larochelle, K. Grauman, N. Cesa-Bianchi, and R. Garnett, editors, *Advances in Neural Information Processing Systems 31*, pages 9539–9549. Curran Associates, Inc.

Alexis Conneau, Douwe Kiela, Holger Schwenk, Loïc Barrault, and Antoine Bordes. 2017. Supervised learning of universal sentence representations from natural language inference data. In *Proceedings of the 2017 Conference on Empirical Methods in Natural Language Processing*, pages 670–680, Copenhagen, Denmark. Association for Computational Linguistics.

Mark G Core, H Chad Lane, Michael Van Lent, Dave Gomboc, Steve Solomon, and Milton Rosenberg. 2006. Building explainable artificial intelligence systems. In *AAAI*, pages 1766–1773.

Jacob Devlin, Ming-Wei Chang, Kenton Lee, and Kristina Toutanova. 2019. BERT: Pre-training of deep bidirectional transformers for language understanding. In *Proceedings of the 2019 Conference of the North American Chapter of the Association for Computational Linguistics: Human Language Technologies, Volume 1 (Long and Short Papers)*, pages 4171–4186, Minneapolis, Minnesota. Association for Computational Linguistics.

Angela Fan, Aleksandra Piktus, Fabio Petroni, Guillaume Wenzek, Marzieh Saeidi, Andreas Vlachos, Antoine Bordes, and Sebastian Riedel. 2020. Generating fact checking briefs. In *Proceedings of the*

2020 Conference on Empirical Methods in Natural Language Processing (EMNLP)*, pages 7147–7161, Online. Association for Computational Linguistics.

Donghoon Ham, Jeong-Gwan Lee, Youngsoo Jang, and Kee-Eung Kim. 2020. End-to-end neural pipeline for goal-oriented dialogue systems using GPT-2. In *Proceedings of the 58th Annual Meeting of the Association for Computational Linguistics*, pages 583–592, Online. Association for Computational Linguistics.

Taher H Haveliwala. 2002. Topic-sensitive pagerank. In *Proceedings of the 11th international conference on World Wide Web*, pages 517–526. ACM.

Ari Holtzman, Jan Buys, Li Du, Maxwell Forbes, and Yejin Choi. 2019. The curious case of neural text degeneration. In *International Conference on Learning Representations*.

Ashkan Kazemi, Verónica Pérez-Rosas, and Rada Mihalcea. 2020. Biased TextRank: Unsupervised graph-based content extraction. In *Proceedings of the 28th International Conference on Computational Linguistics*, pages 1642–1652, Barcelona, Spain (Online). International Committee on Computational Linguistics.

Neema Kotonya and Francesca Toni. 2020. Explainable automated fact-checking for public health claims. In *Proceedings of the 2020 Conference on Empirical Methods in Natural Language Processing (EMNLP)*, pages 7740–7754, Online. Association for Computational Linguistics.

Sawan Kumar and Partha Talukdar. 2020. NILE : Natural language inference with faithful natural language explanations. In *Proceedings of the 58th Annual Meeting of the Association for Computational Linguistics*, pages 8730–8742, Online. Association for Computational Linguistics.

Chin-Yew Lin. 2004. ROUGE: A package for automatic evaluation of summaries. In *Text Summarization Branches Out*, pages 74–81, Barcelona, Spain. Association for Computational Linguistics.

Yi-Ju Lu and Cheng-Te Li. 2020. GCAN: Graph-aware co-attention networks for explainable fake news detection on social media. In *Proceedings of the 58th Annual Meeting of the Association for Computational Linguistics*, pages 505–514, Online. Association for Computational Linguistics.

Scott M Lundberg and Su-In Lee. 2017. A unified approach to interpreting model predictions. In *Advances in Neural Information Processing Systems*, pages 4765–4774.

Rada Mihalcea and Paul Tarau. 2004. Textrank: Bringing order into text. In *Proceedings of the 2004 conference on empirical methods in natural language processing*, pages 404–411.

Verónica Pérez-Rosas, Bennett Kleinberg, Alexandra Lefevre, and Rada Mihalcea. 2018. Automatic detection of fake news. In *Proceedings of the 27th International Conference on Computational Linguistics*, pages 3391–3401, Santa Fe, New Mexico, USA. Association for Computational Linguistics.

Forough Poursabzi-Sangdeh, Daniel G Goldstein, Jake M Hofman, Jennifer Wortman Vaughan, and Hanna Wallach. 2018. Manipulating and measuring model interpretability. *arXiv preprint arXiv:1802.07810*.

Alec Radford, Jeffrey Wu, Rewon Child, David Luan, Dario Amodei, and Ilya Sutskever. 2019. Language models are unsupervised multitask learners. *OpenAI Blog*, 1(8):9.

Nils Reimers and Iryna Gurevych. 2019. Sentence-BERT: Sentence embeddings using Siamese BERT-networks. In *Proceedings of the 2019 Conference on Empirical Methods in Natural Language Processing and the 9th International Joint Conference on Natural Language Processing (EMNLP-IJCNLP)*, pages 3982–3992, Hong Kong, China. Association for Computational Linguistics.

James Thorne and Andreas Vlachos. 2018. Automated fact checking: Task formulations, methods and future directions. In *Proceedings of the 27th International Conference on Computational Linguistics*, pages 3346–3359, Santa Fe, New Mexico, USA. Association for Computational Linguistics.

Sean Welleck, Ilia Kulikov, Jaedeok Kim, Richard Yuanzhe Pang, and Kyunghyun Cho. 2020. Consistency of a recurrent language model with respect to incomplete decoding. *arXiv preprint arXiv:2002.02492*.

Thomas Wolf, Lysandre Debut, Victor Sanh, Julien Chaumond, Clement Delangue, Anthony Moi, Pierric Cistac, Tim Rault, R'emi Louf, Morgan Funtowicz, and Jamie Brew. 2019. Huggingface's transformers: State-of-the-art natural language processing. *ArXiv*, abs/1910.03771.

Generalisability of Topic Models in Cross-corpora Abusive Language Detection

Tulika Bose, Irina Illina, Dominique Fohr
Université de Lorraine, CNRS, Inria, LORIA, F-54000 Nancy, France
tulika.bose, illina, dominique.fohr@loria.fr

Abstract

Rapidly changing social media content calls for robust and generalisable abuse detection models. However, the state-of-the-art supervised models display degraded performance when they are evaluated on abusive comments that differ from the training corpus. We investigate if the performance of supervised models for cross-corpora abuse detection can be improved by incorporating additional information from topic models, as the latter can infer the latent topic mixtures from unseen samples. In particular, we combine topical information with representations from a model tuned for classifying abusive comments. Our performance analysis reveals that topic models are able to capture abuse-related topics that can transfer across corpora, and result in improved generalisability.

1 Introduction

With the exponentially increased use of social networking platforms, concerns on *abusive* language has increased at an alarming rate. Such language is described as hurtful, toxic, or obscene, and targets individuals or a larger group based on common societal characteristics such as race, religion, ethnicity, gender, etc. The increased spread of such content hampers free speech as it can potentially discourage users from expressing themselves without fear, and intimidate them into leaving the conversation. Considering variations of online abuse, toxicity, hate speech, and offensive language as abusive language, this work addresses the detection of abusive versus non-abusive comments.

Automatic detection of abuse is challenging as there are problems of changing linguistic traits, subtle forms of abuse, amongst others (Vidgen et al., 2019). Moreover, the performance of models trained for abuse detection are found to degrade considerably, when they encounter abusive comments that differ from the training corpus (Wiegand et al., 2019; Arango et al., 2019; Swamy et al., 2019; Karan and Šnajder, 2018). This is due to the varied sampling strategies used to build training corpus, topical and temporal shifts (Florio et al., 2020), and varied targets of abuse across corpora. Since social media content changes rapidly, abusive language detection models with better generalisation can be more effective (Yin and Zubiaga, 2021). To this end, a cross-corpora analysis and evaluation is important.

Topic models have been explored for generic cross-domain text classification (Jing et al., 2018; Zhuang et al., 2013; Li et al., 2012), demonstrating better generalisability. Moreover, they can be learnt in an unsupervised manner and can infer topic mixtures from unseen samples. This inspires us to exploit topic model representations for cross-corpora abuse detection.

Recently, Caselli et al. (2021) have "retrained" BERT (Devlin et al., 2019) over large-scale abusive Reddit comments to provide the *HateBERT* model which has displayed better generalisability in cross-corpora experiments. Furthermore, Peinelt et al. (2020) show that combination of topic model and BERT representations leads to better performance at semantic similarity task. Taking these studies into account, we investigate if combining topic representation with contextualised HateBERT representations can result in better generalisability in cross-corpora abuse detection. Cross corpora evaluation on three common abusive language corpora supports and demonstrates the effectiveness of this approach. Besides, we bring some insights into how the association of unseen comments to abusive topics obtained from original training data can help in cross-corpora abusive language detection.

The rest of the paper is organised as follows: Section 2 describes the architecture of the combination of topic model and HateBERT. Section 3 presents our experimental settings. An analysis of the results obtained is present in Section 4, and Section 5 concludes the paper.

Proceedings of the 4th NLP4IF Workshop on NLP for Internet Freedom, pages 51–56
June 6, 2021.

2 Combining Topic Model and HateBERT

In this work, we leverage the Topically Driven Neural Language Model (TDLM) (Lau et al., 2017) to obtain topic representations, as it can employ *pre-trained* embeddings which are found to be more suitable for short Twitter comments (Yi et al., 2020). The original model of TDLM applies a Convolutional Neural Network (CNN) over word-embeddings to generate a comment embedding. This comment embedding is used to learn and extract topic distributions. Cer et al. (2018) show that transfer learning via sentence embeddings performs better than word-embeddings on a variety of tasks. Hence, we modify TDLM to accept the transformer based Universal Sentence Encoder (USE) (Cer et al., 2018) embeddings extracted from input comments, instead of the comment embeddings from CNN. The modified model is denoted as U-TDLM hereon. Refer to Appendix A.1 for the architecture of U-TDLM and also to Lau et al. (2017).

U-TDLM is trained on the train set from the source corpus and is used to infer on the test set from a different target corpus. The topic distribution per comment c is given by $T_c = [p(t_i|c)]_{i=1:k}$, where k is the number of topics. T_c is passed through a Fully Connected (FC) layer to obtain transformed representation $T_c^{'}$. Besides, we first perform supervised fine-tuning of HateBERT[1] on the train set of the source corpus. The vector corresponding to the [CLS] token in the final layer of this fine-tuned HateBERT model is chosen as the HateBERT representation for a comment. It is transformed through an FC layer to obtain the C vector. Finally, in the *combined model* (HateBERT+U-TDLM), the concatenated vector $[T_c^{'}; C]$ is passed through a final FC and a softmax classification layer. The readers are referred to Appendix A.2 for the architecture of the individual, and the combined models.

3 Evaluation Set-up

3.1 Experimental Settings

We perform experiments on three different publicly available abusive tweet corpora, namely, *HatEval* (Basile et al., 2019), *Waseem* (Waseem and Hovy, 2016), and *Davidson* (Davidson et al., 2017). We target a binary classification task with classes: *abusive* and *non abusive*, following the precedent of previous work on cross corpora analysis (Wiegand et al., 2019; Swamy et al., 2019; Karan and Šnajder, 2018). For *HatEval*, we use the standard partition of the shared task, whereas the other two datasets are randomly split into train (80%),development (10%), and test (10%). The statistics of the train-test splits of these datasets are listed in Table 1.

Datasets	**Number of comments**		**Average comment length**	**Abuse %**
	Train	**Test**		
HatEval	9000	3000	21.3	42.1
Waseem	8720	1090	14.7	26.8
Davidson	19817	2477	14.1	83.2

.

Table 1: Statistics of the datasets used (average comment length is calculated in terms of word numbers).

We choose a topic number of 15 for our experiments based on the results for in-corpus performance and to maintain a fair comparison. Besides, the best model checkpoints are selected by performing early-stopping of the training using the respective development sets. The FC layers are followed by Rectified Linear Units (ReLU) in the individual as well as the combined models. In the individual models, the FC layers for transforming T_c and the HateBERT representation have 10 and 600 hidden units, respectively. The final FC layer in the combined model has 400 hidden units. Classification performance is reported in terms of mean F1 score and standard deviation over five runs, with random initialisations.

3.2 Data Pre-processing

We remove the URLs from the Twitter comments, but retain Twitter handles as they can contribute to topic representations.[2] Hashtags are split into constituent words using the tool CrazyTokenizer[3], and words are converted into lower-case. U-TDLM involves prediction of words from the comments based on topic representations. In this part, our implementation uses stemmed words and skips stop-words.

4 Results and Analysis

Table 2 presents the in-corpus and cross-corpora evaluation of the HateBERT and U-TDLM models.

[1]Pre-trained model from `https://osf.io/tbd58/`

[2]Eg., the topic associated with @realDonaldTrump.

[3]`https://redditscore.readthedocs.io/en/master/tokenizing.html`

Train set	In-corpus performance		Cross-corpus test set	Cross-corpora performance		
	HateBERT	U-TDLM		HateBERT	U-TDLM	HateBERT + U-TDLM
HatEval	53.9±1.7	41.5±0.6	Waseem	66.5±2.2	55.5±2.6	**67.8**±2.4
			Davidson	59.2±2.5	**64.4**±2.3	60.4±1.4
Waseem	86.1±0.4	73.7±1.4	HatEval	**55.8**±1.4	36.7±0.0	55.4±0.7
			Davidson	59.8±3.6	28.2±2.4	**64.8**±1.8
Davidson	93.7±0.2	75.6±0.8	HatEval	**51.8**±0.2	50.5±1.3	**51.8**±0.3
			Waseem	66.6±3.0	48.7±3.3	**68.5**±2.1
Average	77.9	63.6		60.0	47.3	**61.5**

Table 2: Macro average F1 scores (mean±std-dev) for in-corpus and cross-corpora abuse detection. The best in each row for the cross-corpora performance is marked in bold.

All models are trained on the train set of the source corpus. The in-corpus performance of the models is obtained on the source corpora test sets, while the cross-corpora performance is obtained on target corpora test sets. It is shown in Table 2 that the cross-corpora performance degrades substantially as compared to the in-corpus performance, except for *HatEval* which indeed has a low in-corpus performance. *HatEval* test set is part of a shared task, and similar in-corpus performance have been reported in prior work (Caselli et al., 2021). Overall, comparing the cross-corpora performances of all models, we can observe that the combined model (HateBERT + U-TDLM) either outperforms HateBERT or retains its performance. This hints that incorporating topic representations can be useful in cross-corpora abusive language detection. As an ablation study, we replaced U-TDLM features with random vectors to evaluate the combined model. Such a concatenation decreased the performance in the cross-corpora setting, yielding an average macro-F1 score of 59.4. This indicates that the topic representations improve generalisation along with HateBERT.

4.1 Case-studies to Analyse Improvements from U-TDLM

We investigate the cases in Table 2 which report relatively large improvements, as compared to HateBERT, either with HateBERT+U-TDLM (train on *Waseem*, test on *Davidson*) or only with U-TDLM (train on *HateEval*, test on *Davidson*). Some of the prominent topics from *Waseem* and *HateEval* associated with abuse, and the top words corresponding to these topics are provided in Table 3 and Table 5, respectively. For better interpretation, topic names are manually assigned based on the top words and the knowledge of the individual corpora. We consider the abusive class as positive, and the non-abusive class as negative in the subsequent discussion.

Topic id	Names	Top words
4	Sexism in sports	football, sex, sport, feminist, drive, woman, call, sexist
9	Feminism	feminist, article, ebook, equality, patriarchy, abuse, freebsd, harass
12	Cooking show	katie, score, mkr, cook, c*nt, blond, less, strategic

Table 3: U-TDLM trained on Waseem's train set (topic names are assigned manually for interpretation).

Train on *Waseem* →Test on *Davidson*: In this case, U-TDLM shows poor performance due to the large number of *False Negatives* (#FN for U-TDLM: 1824), and less *True Positives* (#TP for U-TDLM: 266). The combined model, on the other hand, has higher *True Positives* compared to those obtained from HateBERT (#TP for HateBERT+U-TDLM: 1556, #TP for HateBERT: 1267). The count of *True Negatives* with the combined model remains similar to that in HateBERT (#TN for HateBERT + U-TDLM: 314, #TN for HateBERT: 340). This indicates that U-TDLM introduces some complementary information in the combined model.

We analyse a few abusive comments in the test set of *Davidson* (target) in Table 4, which are wrongly classified by HateBERT, but correctly detected as abusive by the combined model. The topical membership of these abusive comments from *Davidson* indicates that U-TDLM associates high

Source →Target	Abusive Comments in Target	Source topics
Waseem →Davidson	When women are so proud that they don't like to cook; clean b*tch stop being lazy..It's not cute.	4, 12
	ya girl is a slimy ass h*e. get her under control and tell her to stop spraying bullshit out her mouth all day.	4, 9, 12
HatEval →Davidson	No. Its wrong to try to change f*ggots; There is no "therapy"....sympathize like they are retards.	3, 7
	Naturally, when a shitty leftist rag talks trash about another shitty leftist rag, you better fall in line...	10

Table 4: Abusive comments in the target corpus, correctly classified by HateBERT+U-TDLM (Waseem →Davidson) and U-TDLM (HatEval →Davidson). "Source topics" : topics that are assigned high weights by U-TDLM trained on Source.

Topic id	Names	Top words
3	Explicit abuse 1	men, c*ck, d*ck, woman, picture, sl*t, s*ck, guy
7	Explicit abuse 2	b*tch, ho*, n*gger, girlfriend, f*ck, shit, s*ck, dumb
10	Politics related	therickwilson, anncoulter, c*nt, commies, tr*nny, judgejeanine, keitholbermann, donaldjtrumpjr

Table 5: U-TDLM trained on HatEval's train set (topic names are assigned manually for interpretation).

weights to the relevant abuse-related topics from *Waseem*. As indicated in the first example, an abusive comment against women that discusses cooking, in *Davidson*, is mapped to the topics 4 (sexism) and 12 (cooking show) from *Waseem*. Similarly, the second comment gets high weight in the three topics 4, 9 and 12 due to its sexist content and use of a profane word. Other pairs of corpora that yield improved performance with the combined model also follow similar trends as above.

Train on *HatEval* →Test on *Davidson*: In this case, while U-TDLM performs considerably well, the combined model only provides a slight improvement over HateBERT, as per Table 2. U-TDLM has a higher TP when compared to both HateBERT and the combined model (#TP for U-TDLM: 1924, #TP for HateBERT+U-TDLM: 1106, #TP for HateBERT: 1076), with lower TN (#TN for U-TDLM: 130, #TN for HateBERT+U-TDLM: 373, #TN for HateBERT: 374).

Few abusive comments from *Davidson* that are correctly classified by U-TDLM alone are presented in Table 4. The first comment for this case have high weights for the abuse-related topics 3 and 7 from *HatEval* due to the presence of the profane word "f*ggot". The second comment only gets a high weight for topic 10, which deals with politics. This is due to the word "leftist", which is associated with a political ideology. As per our analysis, we found that all of these source topics are highly correlated with the abusive labels in the source corpus of *HatEval*. As such, these comments from the target corpus of *Davidson* are correctly classified as abusive by U-TDLM.

5 Discussion and Conclusion

An in-corpus and cross-corpora evaluation of HateBERT and U-TDLM has helped us confirm our perspective on generalisation in the abusive language detection task. A contextualised representation model like HateBERT can achieve great levels of performance on the abusive language detection task, only when the evaluation dataset does not differ from the training set. The performance of this model degrades drastically on abusive language comments from unseen contexts. Topic models like U-TDLM, which express comments as a mixture of topics learnt from a corpus, allow unseen comments to trigger abusive language topics. While topic space representations tend to lose the exact context of a comment, combining them with HateBERT representations can give modest improvements over HateBERT or at the least, retain the performance of HateBERT. These results should fuel interest and motivate further developments in the generalisation of abusive language detection models.

Acknowledgements

This work was supported partly by the french PIA project "Lorraine Université d'Excellence", reference ANR-15-IDEX-04-LUE.

References

Aymé Arango, Jorge Pérez, and Barbara Poblete. 2019. Hate speech detection is not as easy as you may think: A closer look at model validation. In *Proceedings of the 42nd International ACM SIGIR Conference on Research and Development in Information Retrieval*, SIGIR'19, page 45–54, New York, NY, USA. Association for Computing Machinery.

Valerio Basile, Cristina Bosco, Elisabetta Fersini, Debora Nozza, Viviana Patti, Francisco Manuel Rangel Pardo, Paolo Rosso, and Manuela Sanguinetti. 2019. SemEval-2019 task 5: Multilingual detection of hate speech against immigrants and women in twitter. In *Proceedings of the 13th International Workshop on Semantic Evaluation*, pages 54–63, Minneapolis, Minnesota, USA. Association for Computational Linguistics.

Tommaso Caselli, Valerio Basile, Jelena Mitrović, and Michael Granitzer. 2021. Hatebert: Retraining bert for abusive language detection in english. *arXiv preprint arXiv:2010.12472*.

Daniel Cer, Yinfei Yang, Sheng yi Kong, Nan Hua, Nicole Lyn Untalan Limtiaco, Rhomni St. John, Noah Constant, Mario Guajardo-Céspedes, Steve Yuan, Chris Tar, Yun hsuan Sung, Brian Strope, and Ray Kurzweil. 2018. Universal sentence encoder. In *EMNLP demonstration*, Brussels, Belgium.

Thomas Davidson, Dana Warmsley, Michael Macy, and Ingmar Weber. 2017. Automated hate speech detection and the problem of offensive language. In *Proceedings of the 11th International AAAI Conference on Web and Social Media*, ICWSM '17, pages 512–515.

Jacob Devlin, Ming-Wei Chang, Kenton Lee, and Kristina Toutanova. 2019. BERT: Pre-training of deep bidirectional transformers for language understanding. In *Proceedings of the 2019 Conference of the North American Chapter of the Association for Computational Linguistics: Human Language Technologies, Volume 1 (Long and Short Papers)*, pages 4171–4186, Minneapolis, Minnesota. Association for Computational Linguistics.

Komal Florio, Valerio Basile, Marco Polignano, Pierpaolo Basile, and Viviana Patti. 2020. Time of your hate: The challenge of time in hate speech detection on social media. *Applied Sciences*, 10(12).

Baoyu Jing, Chenwei Lu, Deqing Wang, Fuzhen Zhuang, and Cheng Niu. 2018. Cross-domain labeled LDA for cross-domain text classification. In *IEEE International Conference on Data Mining, ICDM 2018, Singapore, November 17-20, 2018*, pages 187–196. IEEE Computer Society.

Mladen Karan and Jan Šnajder. 2018. Cross-domain detection of abusive language online. In *Proceedings of the 2nd Workshop on Abusive Language Online (ALW2)*, pages 132–137, Brussels, Belgium. Association for Computational Linguistics.

Jey Han Lau, Timothy Baldwin, and Trevor Cohn. 2017. Topically driven neural language model. In *Proceedings of the 55th Annual Meeting of the Association for Computational Linguistics (Volume 1: Long Papers)*, pages 355–365, Vancouver, Canada. Association for Computational Linguistics.

Lianghao Li, Xiaoming Jin, and Mingsheng Long. 2012. Topic correlation analysis for cross-domain text classification. In *Proceedings of the Twenty-Sixth AAAI Conference on Artificial Intelligence*, AAAI'12, page 998–1004. AAAI Press.

Nicole Peinelt, Dong Nguyen, and Maria Liakata. 2020. tBERT: Topic models and BERT joining forces for semantic similarity detection. In *Proceedings of the 58th Annual Meeting of the Association for Computational Linguistics*, pages 7047–7055, Online. Association for Computational Linguistics.

Steve Durairaj Swamy, Anupam Jamatia, and Björn Gambäck. 2019. Studying generalisability across abusive language detection datasets. In *Proceedings of the 23rd Conference on Computational Natural Language Learning (CoNLL)*, pages 940–950, Hong Kong, China. Association for Computational Linguistics.

Bertie Vidgen, Alex Harris, Dong Nguyen, Rebekah Tromble, Scott Hale, and Helen Margetts. 2019. Challenges and frontiers in abusive content detection. In *Proceedings of the Third Workshop on Abusive Language Online*, pages 80–93, Florence, Italy. Association for Computational Linguistics.

Zeerak Waseem and Dirk Hovy. 2016. Hateful symbols or hateful people? predictive features for hate speech detection on Twitter. In *Proceedings of the NAACL Student Research Workshop*, pages 88–93, San Diego, California. Association for Computational Linguistics.

Michael Wiegand, Josef Ruppenhofer, and Thomas Kleinbauer. 2019. Detection of Abusive Language: the Problem of Biased Datasets. In *Proceedings of the 2019 Conference of the North American Chapter of the Association for Computational Linguistics: Human Language Technologies, Volume 1 (Long and Short Papers)*, pages 602–608, Minneapolis, Minnesota. Association for Computational Linguistics.

F. Yi, B. Jiang, and J. Wu. 2020. Topic modeling for short texts via word embedding and document correlation. *IEEE Access*, 8:30692–30705.

Wenjie Yin and Arkaitz Zubiaga. 2021. Towards generalisable hate speech detection: a review on obstacles and solutions. *arXiv preprint arXiv:2102.08886*.

Fuzhen Zhuang, Ping Luo, Peifeng Yin, Qing He, and Zhongzhi Shi. 2013. Concept learning for cross-domain text classification: A general probabilistic framework. In *IJCAI International Joint Conference on Artificial Intelligence*, pages 1960–1966.

A Appendices

A.1 Topic Model U-TDLM

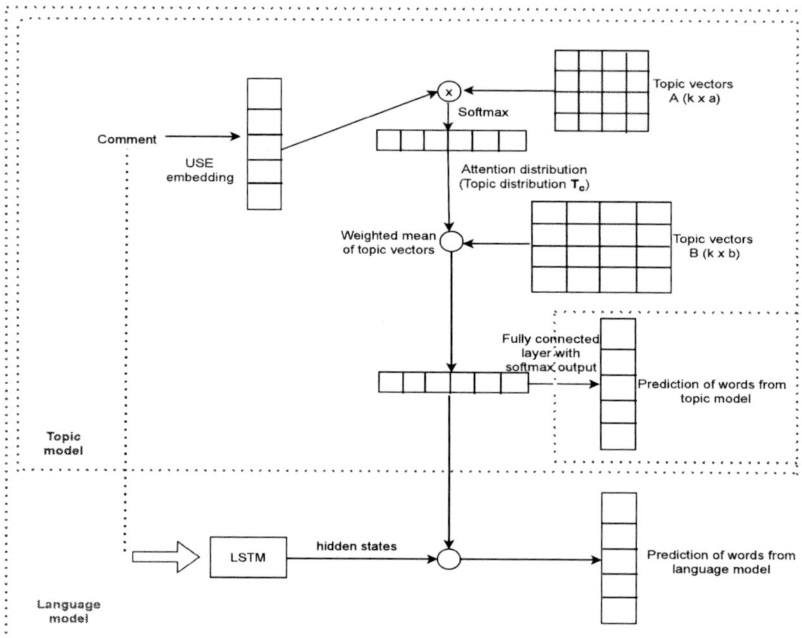

Figure 1: Architecture of U-TDLM. As compared to TDLM (Lau et al., 2017), CNN on comment is replaced by USE (Universal Sentence Embedding). k = number of topics.

A.2 Architecture of Combined Model

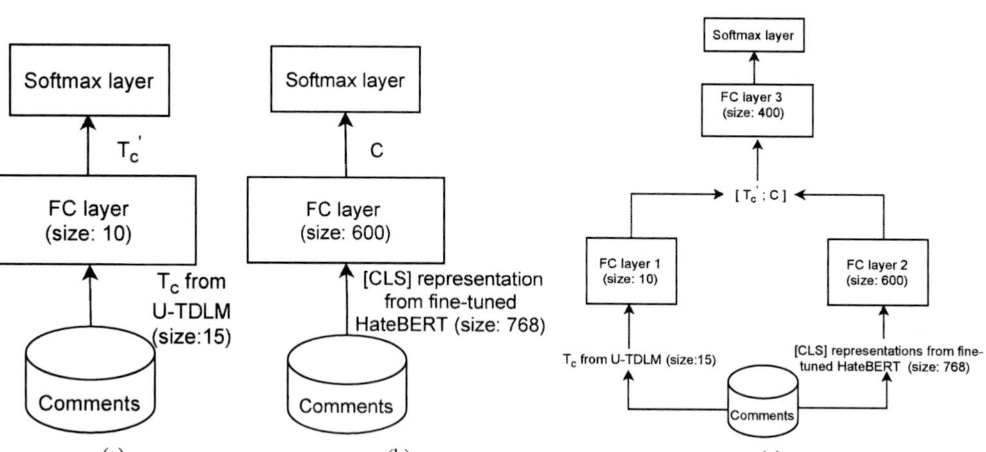

Figure 2: Architecture of classifier for individual models: (a) U-TDLM, (b) HateBERT, and the combined model (c) HateBERT + U-TDLM; FC: Fully Connected.

AraStance: A Multi-Country and Multi-Domain Dataset of Arabic Stance Detection for Fact Checking

Tariq Alhindi,[1] **Amal Alabdulkarim,**[2] **Ali Alshehri,**[3]
Muhammad Abdul-Mageed,[4] **and Preslav Nakov**[5]
[1]Department of Computer Science, Columbia University
[2]Georgia Institute of Technology, [3]The State University of New York at Buffalo
[4]The University of British Columbia, [5]Qatar Computing Research Institute, HBKU
tariq@cs.columbia.edu, amal@gatech.edu, alimoham@buffalo.edu
muhammad.mageed@ubc.ca, pnakov@hbku.edu.qa

Abstract

With the continuing spread of misinformation and disinformation online, it is of increasing importance to develop combating mechanisms at scale in the form of automated systems that support multiple languages. One task of interest is claim veracity prediction, which can be addressed using stance detection with respect to relevant documents retrieved online. To this end, we present our new Arabic Stance Detection dataset (AraStance) of 4,063 claim–article pairs from a diverse set of sources comprising three fact-checking websites and one news website. AraStance covers false and true claims from multiple domains (e.g., politics, sports, health) and several Arab countries, and it is well-balanced between related and unrelated documents with respect to the claims. We benchmark AraStance, along with two other stance detection datasets, using a number of BERT-based models. Our best model achieves an accuracy of 85% and a macro F1 score of 78%, which leaves room for improvement and reflects the challenging nature of AraStance and the task of stance detection in general.

1 Introduction

The proliferation of social media has made it possible for individuals and groups to share information quickly. While this is useful in many situations such as emergencies, where disaster management efforts can make use of shared information to allocate resources, this evolution can also be dangerous, e.g., when the news shared is not precise or is even intentionally misleading. Polarization in different communities further aggravates the problem, causing individuals and groups to believe and to disseminate information without necessarily verifying its veracity (misinformation) or even making up stories that support their world views (disinformation). These circumstances motivate a need to develop tools for detecting fake news online, including for a region with opposing forces and ongoing conflicts such as the Arab world.

Our work here contributes to these efforts a new dataset and baseline results on it. In particular, we create a new dataset for stance detection of claims collected from a number of websites covering different domains such as politics, health, and economics. The websites cover several Arab countries, which enables wider applicability of our dataset. This compares favorably to previous work for Arabic stance detection such as the work of Baly et al. (2018), who focused on a single country. We use the websites as our source to collect true and false claims, and we carefully crawl web articles related to these claims. Using the claim–article pairs, we then manually assign *stance* labels to the articles. By stance we mean whether an article *agrees, disagrees, discusses* a claim or it is just *unrelated.* This allows us to exploit the resulting dataset to build models that automatically identify the stance with respect to a given claim, which is an important component of fact-checking and fake news detection systems. To develop these models, we resort to transfer learning by fine-tuning language models on our labeled dataset. We also benchmark our models on two existing datasets for Arabic stance detection. Finally, we make our dataset publicly available.[1]

Our contributions can be summarized as follows:

1. We release a new multi-domain, multi-country dataset labeled for both stance and veracity.
2. We introduce a multi-query related document retrieval approach for claims from diverse topics in Arabic, resulting in a dataset with balanced label distributions across classes.
3. We compare our dataset to two other Arabic stance detection datasets using four BERT-based (Devlin et al., 2019) models.

[1]The data can be found at http://github.com/Tariq60/arastance.

Proceedings of the 4th NLP4IF Workshop on NLP for Internet Freedom, pages 57–65
June 6, 2021. ©2021 Association for Computational Linguistics

2 Related Work

Stance detection started as a standalone task, unrelated to fact-checking (Küçük and Can, 2020). One type of stance models the relation (e.g., *for, against, neutral*) of a text segment towards a *topic*, usually a controversial one such as abortion or gun control (Mohammad et al., 2016; Abbott et al., 2016). Another one models the relation (e.g., *agree, disagree, discuss, unrelated*) between two pieces of text (Hardalov et al., 2021b; Ferreira and Vlachos, 2016). The latter definition is used in automatic fact-checking, fake news detection, and rumour verification (Vlachos and Riedel, 2014).

There are several English datasets that model fact-checking as a stance detection task on text from multiple genres such as Wikipedia (Thorne et al., 2018), news articles (Pomerleau and Rao, 2017; Ferreira and Vlachos, 2016), and social media (Gorrell et al., 2019; Derczynski et al., 2017). Most related to our work here is the Fake News Challenge, or FNC, (Pomerleau and Rao, 2017), which is built by randomly matching claim–article pairs from the Emergent dataset (Ferreira and Vlachos, 2016), which itself pairs 300 claims to 2,500 articles. In FNC, this pairing is done at random, and it yielded a large number of unrelated claim–article pairs. There are several approaches attempting to predict the stance on the FNC dataset using LSTMs, memory networks, and transformers (Hanselowski et al., 2018; Conforti et al., 2018; Mohtarami et al., 2018; Zhang et al., 2019; Schiller et al., 2021; Schütz et al., 2021).

There are two datasets for Arabic stance detection with respect to claims. The first one collected their false claims from a single political source (Baly et al., 2018), while we cover three sources from multiple countries and topics. They retrieved relevant documents and annotated the claim–article pairs using the four labels listed earlier (i.e., *agree, disagree, discuss, unrelated*). They also annotated "rationales," which are segments in the articles where the stance is most strongly expressed. The other Arabic dataset by Khouja (2020) uses headlines from news sources and generated true and false claims by modifying the headlines. They used a three-class labeling scheme of stance by merging the *discuss* and the *unrelated* classes in one class called *other*.

Our work is also related to detecting machine-generated and manipulated text (Jawahar et al., 2020; Nagoudi et al., 2020).

3 AraStance Construction

We constructed our AraStance dataset similarly to the way this was done for the English Fake News Challenge (FNC) dataset (Pomerleau and Rao, 2017) and for the Arabic dataset of Baly et al. (2018). Our dataset contains true and false claims, where each claim is paired with one or more documents. Each claim–article pair has a stance label: *agree*, *disagree*, *discuss*, or *unrelated*. Below, we decribe the three steps of building AraStance: (*i*) claim collection and pre-processing, (*ii*) relevant document retrieval, and (*iii*) stance annotations.

3.1 Claim Collection and Preprocessing

We collected false claims from three fact-checking websites: ARAANEWS[2], DABEGAD[3], and NORUMORS[4], based in the UAE, Egypt, and Saudi Arabia, respectively. The claims were from 2012 to 2018 and covered multiple domains such as politics, sports, and health. As the three fact-checking websites only debunk false claims, we looked for another source for true claims: following Baly et al. (2018), we collected true claims from the Arabic website of REUTERS[5], assuming that their content was trustworthy. We added topic and date restrictions when collecting the true claims in order to make sure they were similar to the false claims. Moreover, in order to ensure the true claims were from the same topics as the false ones, we used a subset of the false claims as seeds to retrieve true claims that were within three months of the seed false claims, and we ranked them by TF.IDF, similarity to the seeds. We kept a maximum of ten true claims per seed false claim. For all claims, we removed the ones that contained no-text and/or were multimedia-centric. Moreover, we manually modified the false claims by removing phrases like "*It is not true that*", "*A debunked rumor about*", or "*The reality of*", which are often used by fact-checking websites. This sometimes required us to add a noun at the beginning of the claim based on the text of the target articles, or to make some grammatical edits. We show examples of two false claims before and after preprocessing in Table 1. Note that the headlines we retrieved from REUTERS were already phrased as claims, and thus we did not have to edit them in any way.

[2]http://araanews.ae
[3]http://dabegad.com
[4]http://norumors.net
[5]http://ara.reuters.com

Original Claim	Preprocessed Claim
لا صحة لما يتم تداوله حول تسجيل مكالمات ورسائل المقيمين *What is being circulated about recording residents' calls and messages is not true*	الحكومة تسجل مكالمات ورسائل المقيمين *The government is recording calls and messages of residents*
اشعة الكوزمو القادمة من كوكب المريخ اشاعة كاذبة من٢٠٠٨ *Cosmo rays coming from Mars is a false rumor from 2008*	ناسا تحذر من اشعة الكوزمو الخطيرة القادمة من كوكب المريخ هذه الليلة من الساعة ١٢.٣٠-٣.٣٠ *NASA warns of dangerous cosmic rays coming from Mars tonight from 12.30-3.30*

Table 1: Examples of false claims before and after preprocessing.

3.2 Document Retrieval

For each claim, we retrieved relevant documents using multiple queries and the Google Search API. It was harder to find relevant documents for the false claims by passing their preprocessed version as queries because of their nature, locality, and diversity. For some false claims, there were extra clauses and modifiers that restricted the search results significantly as shown in the examples below:

1. طفلة تظهر بنصف جسم بشري، النصف الاخر ثعبان
   A female child with half a human body, and the other half is a snake
2. يتم تنظيف الرئتين عند المدخنين من خلال شم بخار اللبن و الماء لمدة عشرة أيام
   Lungs of smokers are cleaned by smelling the steam of milk and water for ten days

To remedy this, we boosted the quality of the retrieved documents by restricting the date range to two months before and after the date of the claim, prepending named entities and removing extra clauses using parse trees. In order to emphasize the presence of the main entity(s) in the claim, we extracted named entities using the Arabic NER corpus by Benajiba et al. (2007) and Stanford's CoreNLP Arabic NER tagger (Manning et al., 2014). We further used Stanford's CoreNLP Arabic parser to extract the first verb phrase (VP) and all its preceeding tokens in the claim, as this has been shown to improve document retrieval results for claim verification, especially for lengthy claims (Chakrabarty et al., 2018). For the two examples shown above, we would keep the claims until the comma for the first example and the word *and* for the second one, and we would consider those as the queries.

For each false claim, we searched for relevant documents using the following five queries: (*i*) the manually preprocessed claim as is, (*ii*) the preprocessed claim with date restriction, (*iii*) the preprocessed claim with named entities and date restriction, (*iv*) the first VP and all preceding tokens with date restriction, and lastly (*v*) the first VP and all preceding tokens with named entities and date restriction. For the true claims, due to wider coverage that led to easier retrieval, we only ran two queries, using the claim with and without date restriction.

We combined the results from all queries, and we kept a maximum of ten documents per claim. If the retrieved documents exceeded this limit, we only kept documents from news sources[6], or from sources used in previous work on Arabic stance detection (Baly et al., 2018; Khouja, 2020). If we still had more than ten documents after filtering by source, we ranked the documents by their TF.IDF similarity with the claim, and we kept the top ten documents. We limited the number of documents to ten per claim in order to avoid having claims with very high numbers of documents and others with only one or two documents. Ultimately, this helped us keep the dataset balaced in terms of both sources and topics.

3.3 Stance Annotation

We set up the annotation task as follows: given a claim–article pair, what is the stance of the document towards the claim? The stance was to be annotated using one of the following labels: *agree, disagree, discuss*, or *unrelated*, which were also used in previous work (Pomerleau and Rao, 2017; Baly et al., 2018).

[6]We used Google News as a reference of news sources for the three countries of the fact-checking websites: `https://news.google.com/?hl=ar&gl=X&ceid=X%3Aar`, where **X** is **AE, EG,** or **SA**, standing for UAE, Egypt and Saudi Arabia, respectively.

Claim	Document Title	A1	A2	A3
اللحوم والدواجن المستوردة من البرازيل فاسدة *Meat and poultry imported from Brazil are rotten*	فضيحة البرازيل: اللحوم الفاسدة تهدد الانتعاش الاقتصادي *Brazil scandal: Rotten meat threatens economic recovery*	D	A	D
تشارك مصر في عملية انقاذ أطفال الكهف في تايلاند *Egypt participates in the rescue operation of cave children in Thailand*	الإنقاذ يبدأون عملية لإخراج صبية من داخل كهف في تايلاند *Rescuers begin operation to remove the teenage boys from the cave in Thailand*	D	U	U

Table 2: Disagreement between the annotators on the *discuss (D)* label with the *agree (A)* (first example) and the *unrelated (U)* labels (second example).

We explained the labels to annotators as follows:

- *agree:* the document agrees with the main claim in the statement clearly and explicitly;
- *disagree:* the document disagrees with main claim in the statement clearly and explicitly;
- *discuss:* the document discusses the same event without taking a position towards its validity;
- *unrelated:* the document talks about a different event, regardless of how similar the two events might be.

Our annotators were three graduate students in computer science and linguistics, all native speakers of Arabic. We adopted guidelines similar to the ones introduced by Baly et al. (2018). First, we conducted a pilot annotation round on 315 claim–article pairs, where each pair was annotated by all annotators. The annotators agreed on the same label for 220 out of the 315 pairs (70% of the pairs), while for 89 pairs (28%) there were two annotators agreeing on the label, and for the remaining 6 pairs (2% of the pairs) there was a three-way disagreement. The main disagreements between the annotators were related to the *discuss* label, which was confused with either *agree* or *unrelated.*

We show two examples in Table 2 where the annotators labeled the example on the top of the table as *discuss* and *agree*. The two annotators that labeled this example as *discuss* justified their choice by arguing that the document only mentioned the claims without agreeing or disagreeing and mainly analyzed the impact of rotten meat on Brazil's economy in great detail. The example in the bottom of the table was labeled by one annotator as *discuss* and by two annotators as *unrelated*. The annotators who labeled it as *unrelated* argued that there was no mention of Egypt's involvement in the rescue efforts, while the annotator who labeled the pair as *discuss* maintained that the document discussed the same event of children trapped in the cave.

These disagreements were resolved through discussions between the annotators, which involved refining the guidelines to label a pair as *discuss* if it only talks about the exact same event of the claim without taking any clear position. The annotators were also asked not to take into consideration any other factors, e.g., the date of article, its publisher, or its veracity.

For the rest of the data, each claim–article pair was annotated by two annotators, where the differences were resolved by the third annotator. This is very similar to labeling all pairs by three annotators with majority voting, but with less labor requirements. We measured the inter-annotator agreement (IAA) using Fleiss kappa, which accounts for multiple annotators (Fleiss and Cohen, 1973), obtaining an IAA of 0.67, which corresponds to substantial agreement.

3.4 Statistics About the Final Dataset

Table 3 shows the number of claims and articles for each website with their veracity label (by-publisher) and final stance annotations. The distribution of the four stance classes in training, development, and test is shown in Table 4. After selecting the gold annotations, we discarded all claims that had all of their retrieved documents labeled as *unrelated*, aiming to reduce the imbalance with respect to the *unrelated* class, and we only focused on claims with related documents, which can be seen as a proxy for check-worthiness. We ended up with a total of 4,063 claim–articles pairs based on 910 claims: 606 false and 304 true. The dataset is imbalanced towards the false claims, but as our main task is stance detection rather than claim veracity, we aimed at having a balanced distribution for the four stance labels. As shown in Table 4, around half of the labels are from the *unrelated* class, but it is common for stance detection datasets to have higher proportion of this class (Pomerleau and Rao, 2017; Baly et al., 2018).

Source	Veracity	Claims	Articles	Stance			
				Agree	Disagree	Discuss	Unrelated
ARANEWS	False	170	518	80	82	51	305
DABEGAED	False	278	1,413	225	249	143	796
NORUMERS	False	158	490	26	103	32	329
REUTERS	True	304	1,642	691	15	161	775
Total	–	910	4,063	1,022	449	387	2,205

Table 3: Statistics about the number of claims, articles and claim–article pairs and the distribution of their stances for each source.

Label	Train	Dev	Test
Agree	739	129	154
Disagree	309	76	64
Discuss	247	70	70
Unrelated	1,553	294	358
Total	2,848	569	646

Table 4: Statistics about the claim–article pairs with stances in the training, development and test sets.

There are various approaches that can mitigate the impact of the class imbalance caused by the *unrelated* class. These are related to (*i*) task setup, (*ii*) modeling, and (*iii*) evaluation.

First, the task can be approached differently by only doing stance detection on the three related classes (Conforti et al., 2018), or by merging the *discuss* and the *unrelated* classes into one class, e.g., called *neutral* or *other* (Khouja, 2020).

Second, it is possible to keep all classes, but to train a two-step model: first to predict related vs. unrelated, and then, if the example is judged to be related, to predict the stance for the three related classes only (Zhang et al., 2019).

Third, one could adopt an evaluation measure that rewards models that make correct predictions for the related classes more than for the *unrelated* class. Such a measure was adopted by the Fake News Challenge (Pomerleau and Rao, 2017). However, such measures have to be used very carefully, as they might be exploited. For example, it was shown that the FNC measure can be exploited by random prediction from the related classes and never from the *unrelated* class, which has a lower reward under the FNC evaluation measure (Hanselowski et al., 2018). We leave such considerations about the impact of class imbalance to future work.

4 Experimental Setup

4.1 External Datasets

We experimented with a number of BERT-based models, pre-trained on Arabic or on multilingual data, which we fine-tuned and applied to our dataset, as well as to the following two Arabic stance detection datasets for comparison purposes:

- **Baly et al. (2018) Dataset.** This dataset has 1,842 claim–article pairs for training (278 *agree*, 37 *disagree*, 266 *discuss*, and 1,261 *unrelated*), 587 for development (86 *agree*, 25 *disagree*, 73 *discuss*, and 403 *unrelated*), and 613 for testing (110 *agree*, 25 *disagree*, 70 *discuss*, and 408 *unrelated*).
- **Khouja (2020) Dataset.** This dataset has 2,652 claim–article pairs for training (903 *agree*, 1,686 *disagree*, and 63 *other*), 755 for development (268 *agree*, 471 *disagree*, and 16 *other*) and 379 for testing (130 *agree*, 242 *disagree*, and 7 *other*).

The dataset by Baly et al. (2018) has 203 true claims from REUTERS and 219 false claims from the Syrian fact-checking website VERIFY-SY,[7] which focuses on debunking claims about the Syrian civil war. Thus, the dataset contains claims that focus primarily on war and politics. They retrieved the articles and performed manual annotation of claim–article pairs for stance, following a procedure that is very close to the one we used for AraStance. Moreover, their dataset has annotations of rationales, which give the reason for selecting an *agree* or a *disagree* label. The dataset has a total of about 3,000 claim–article pairs, 2,000 of which are from the *unrelated* class. The dataset comes with a split into five folds of roughly equal sizes. We use folds 1-3 for training, fold 4 for development, and fold 5 for testing.

[7] http://www.verify-sy.com/

The dataset by Khouja (2020) is based on sampling a subset of news titles from the Arabic News Text (ANT) corpus (Chouigui et al., 2017), and then making true and false alterations of these titles using crowd-sourcing. The stance detection task is then defined between pairs of original news titles and their respective true/false alterations. This essentially maps to detecting paraphrases for true alterations (stance labeled as *agree*) and contradictions for false ones (stance labeled as *disagree*). They further have a third stance label, *other*, which is introduced by pairing the alterations with other news titles that have high TF.IDF similarity with the news title originally paired with the alteration. Overall, Khouja (2020)'s dataset is based on *synthetic statements* that are paired with *news titles*. This is quite different from AraStance and the dataset of Baly et al. (2018), which have *naturally occurring claims* that are paired with *full news articles*. Moreover, as both AraStance and Baly et al. (2018)'s datasets have naturally occurring data from the web, they both exhibit certain level of noise and irregularities, e.g., some very long documents, words/characters in other languages such as English, etc. Such a noise is minimal in Khouja (2020)'s dataset, which is a third differentiating factor compared to the other two datasets. Nevertheless, we include Khouja (2020)'s dataset in our experiments in order to empirically test the impact of these differences.

4.2 Models

We fine-tuned the following four models for each of the three Arabic datasets:

1. Multilingual BERT (mBERT), base size, which is trained on the Wikipedias of 100 different languages, including Arabic (Devlin et al., 2019).
2. ArabicBERT, base size, which is trained on 8.2 billion tokens from the OSCAR corpus[8] as well as on the Arabic Wikipedia (Safaya et al., 2020).
3. ARBERT, which is trained on 6.2 billion tokens of mostly Modern Standard Arabic text (Abdul-Mageed et al., 2020).
4. MARBERT, which is trained on one billion Arabic tweets, which in turn use both Modern Standard Arabic and Dialectal Arabic (Abdul-Mageed et al., 2020).

The four models are comparable in size, all having a *base* architecture, but with varying vocabulary sizes. More information about the different models can be found in the original publications about them. We fine-tuned each of them for a maximum of 25 epochs with an early stopping patience value of 5, a maximum sequence length of 512, a batch size of 16, and a learning rate of 2e-5.

5 Results

The evaluation results are shown in Tables 5 and 6 for the development and for the test sets, respectively. We use accuracy and macro-F1 to account for the different class distributions; we also report per-class F1 scores. Note that Khouja (2020) uses three labels rather than four, merging *discuss* and *unrelated* into *other*. Their label distribution has a majority of *disagree*, followed by *agree*, and very few instances of *other*, which is different from our dataset and from Baly et al. (2018)'s.

We can see that ARBERT yields the best overall and per-class performance on dev for the Khouja (2020) dataset and AraStance. It also generalizes very well to the test sets, where it even achieved a higher macro-F1 score for the Khouja (2020) dataset. The performance of the other three models (mBERT, ArabicBERT, and MARBERT) drops slightly on the test set compared to dev for both AraStance and the Khouja (2020) dataset. This might be due to ARBERT being pre-trained on more suitable data, which includes Books, Gigaword and Common Crawl data primarily from MSA, but also a small amount of Egyptian Arabic. Since half of our data comes from an Egyptian website (DABEGAD), this could be helpful. Indeed, while ArabicBERT is pretrained on slightly more data than ARBERT, it was almost exclusively pretrained on MSA, without dialectal data, and AraStance it performs worse.

About the other models: The datasets on which ArabicBERT was trained have duplicates, which could explain the model being outperformed. For MARBERT, it is pretrained on tweets that have both MSA and dialectal Arabic. MARBERT's data come from social media, which is different from the news articles or titles from which all the experimental downstream three datasets are derived. Also, it seems that ARBERT and MARBERT are better than the other two models at predicting the stance between a pair of sentences, as it is the case with the Khouja (2020) dataset.

[8] http://oscar-corpus.com

Model	Baly et al. (2018) Dataset						Khouja (2020) Dataset					AraStance					
	A	D	Ds	U	Acc	F1	A	D	O	Acc	F1	A	D	Ds	U	Acc	F1
mBERT	**.63**	0	.11	**.84**	**.73**	.40	.74	.84	.76	.81	.78	.81	.68	.58	.92	.82	.75
ArabicBERT	.58	**.14**	.24	.82	.69	.45	.74	.86	.84	.82	.81	**.85**	.75	.56	.92	.84	.77
ARBERT	.56	**.14**	**.30**	.83	.70	**.46**	**.81**	**.89**	**.87**	**.86**	**.86**	**.85**	**.82**	**.60**	**.93**	**.86**	**.80**
MARBERT	.44	**.14**	.23	.78	.62	.40	.80	.88	.79	.85	.82	**.85**	.80	.53	.89	.84	.77

Table 5: Results on the development set for the three Arabic Stance Detection datasets. Shown are the F1-scores for each class (**A**: Agree, **D**: Disagree, **Ds**: Discuss, **U**: Unrelated, **O**: Other), as well as the overall Accuracy (**Acc**), and the Macro-Average F1 score (Macro-F1).

Model	Baly et al. (2018) Dataset						Khouja (2020) Dataset					AraStance					
	A	D	Ds	U	Acc	F1	A	D	O	Acc	F1	A	D	Ds	U	Acc	F1
mBERT	.64	0	.12	**.85**	**.73**	.40	.67	.81	.86	.76	.78	.83	.77	.51	.93	**.85**	.76
ArabicBERT	**.66**	**.35**	**.27**	.80	.67	**.52**	.72	.85	.71	.81	.76	.84	.74	.52	**.94**	**.85**	.76
ARBERT	.65	.29	**.27**	.81	.68	.51	**.80**	**.89**	**1.0**	**.86**	**.90**	.85	**.78**	**.55**	.92	**.85**	**.78**
MARBERT	.51	0	.25	.77	.60	.38	.78	.88	.92	.84	.86	**.86**	.72	.41	.90	.84	.72

Table 6: Results on the test set for the three Arabic Stance Detection datasets. Shown are the F1-scores for each class (**A**: Agree, **D**: Disagree, **Ds**: Discuss, **U**: Unrelated, **O**: Other), as well as the overall Accuracy (**Acc**), and the Macro-Average F1 score (Macro-F1).

This could be due to the diversity of their pretraining data, which improves the model's ability to capture inter-sentence relations such as paraphrases and contradictions. Another factor that could explain ARBERT's better performace compared to MARBERT is that the latter is trained with a masking objective only, while ARBERT is trained with both a masking objective *and* a next sentence prediction objective. The use of the latter objective by ARBERT could explain its ability to capture information in our claim–stance pairs, although these pairs are different from other types of pairs such as in the question and answer task, where the pair occurs in an extended piece of text.

On the other hand, there is no consistently best model for the Baly et al. (2018) dataset. This could be due to a number of reasons. First, that dataset has a severe class imbalance, as we have explained in Section 4. Second, the dataset (especially the false claims) is derived from one particular domain, i.e., the Syrian war, which might not be well represented in the pretraining data. Therefore, additional modeling considerations such as adaptive pretraining on a relevant unlabelled corpus before fine-tuning on the target labeled data could help.

Surprisingly, ArabicBERT and ARBERT perform much better on the test set than on the development set of the Baly et al. (2018) dataset for the *disagree* class, which has the lowest frequency: from 0.14 F1 to 0.29–0.35 F1.

Since the number of *disagree* instances is very low (25 documents for 10–12 unique claims), it is possible that the claims in the test set happen to be more similar to the ones in the training data than it is for development. This is plausible because we did our train-dev-test split based on the five-folds prepared by the authors as explained in Section 4. It is worth noting that the multilingual model (mBERT) has the highest overall accuracy and F1 score for the *unrelated* class of the Baly et al. (2018) dataset. Multilingual text representations such as mBERT might over-predict from the majority class, and thus would perform poorly on the two low-frequency classes; indeed, mBERT has an F1-score of 0 for *disagree*, and no more than 0.12 for *discuss* on development and testing.

Finally, we observe very high performance for all models for the *unrelated* class of AraStance. This could be an indication of strong signals that differentiate the *related* and the *unrelated* classes, whereas the *discuss* class is the most challenging one in AraStance, due to its strong resemblance to *agree* in some examples such as the one shown in Table 2. This indicates that all models offer an area for improvement, where a single classifier can excel for both frequent and infrequent classes for the stance detection within and across datasets. We leave further experimentation, including with models developed for FNC and the Baly et al. (2018) dataset, for future work.

6 Conclusion and Future Work

We presented AraStance, a new multi-topic Arabic stance detection dataset with claims extracted from multiple fact-checking sources across three countries and one news source. We discussed the process of data collection and approaches to overcome challenges in related document retrieval for claims with low online presence, e.g., due to topic or country specificity. We further experimented with four BERT-based models and two additional Arabic stance detection datasets.

In future work, we want to further investigate the differences between the three Arabic stance detection datasets and to make attempts to mitigate the impact of class imbalance, e.g., by training with weighted loss, by upsampling or downsampling the classes, etc. We further want to examine the *discuss* class across datasets and to compare the choice of annotation scheme —three-way vs. four-way— on this task. Moreover, we plan to enrich AraStance by collecting more true claims from other websites, thus creating a dataset that would be more evenly distributed across the claim veracity labels. Furthermore, we would like to investigate approaches for improving stance detection by extracting the parts of the documents that contain the main stance rather than truncating the documents after the first 512 tokens. Finally, we plan to experiment with cross-domain (Hardalov et al., 2021a) and cross-language approaches (Mohtarami et al., 2019).

Acknowledgements

Tariq Alhindi is supported by the KACST Graduate Studies Scholarship. Muhammad Abdul-Mageed gratefully acknowledges support from the Social Sciences and Humanities Research Council of Canada through an Insight Grant on contextual misinformation detection for Arabic social media, the Natural Sciences and Engineering Research Council of Canada, Canadian Foundation for Innovation, Compute Canada, and UBC ARC-Sockeye.[9] Preslav Nakov is supported by the Tanbih mega-project, which is developed at the Qatar Computing Research Institute, HBKU, and aims to limit the impact of "fake news," propaganda, and media bias by making users aware of what they are reading. We would also like to thank Firas Sabbah for his help in collecting the false and true claims, and the anonymous reviewers for their helpful feedback.

[9] https://doi.org/10.14288/SOCKEYE.

References

Rob Abbott, Brian Ecker, Pranav Anand, and Marilyn Walker. 2016. Internet argument corpus 2.0: An SQL schema for dialogic social media and the corpora to go with it. In *Proceedings of the Tenth International Conference on Language Resources and Evaluation*, LREC '16, pages 4445–4452, Portorož, Slovenia.

Muhammad Abdul-Mageed, AbdelRahim Elmadany, and El Moatez Billah Nagoudi. 2020. ARBERT & MARBERT: Deep Bidirectional Transformers for Arabic. *arXiv preprint arXiv:2101.01785.*

Ramy Baly, Mitra Mohtarami, James Glass, Lluís Màrquez, Alessandro Moschitti, and Preslav Nakov. 2018. Integrating stance detection and fact checking in a unified corpus. In *Proceedings of the 2018 Conference of the North American Chapter of the Association for Computational Linguistics: Human Language Technologies*, NAACL-HLT '18, pages 21–27, New Orleans, Louisiana, USA.

Yassine Benajiba, Paolo Rosso, and José Miguel Benedíruiz. 2007. ANERsys: An Arabic named entity recognition system based on maximum entropy. In *International Conference on Intelligent Text Processing and Computational Linguistics*, CICLING '07, pages 143–153.

Tuhin Chakrabarty, Tariq Alhindi, and Smaranda Muresan. 2018. Robust document retrieval and individual evidence modeling for fact extraction and verification. In *Proceedings of the First Workshop on Fact Extraction and VERification*, FEVER '18, pages 127–131, Brussels, Belgium.

Amina Chouigui, Oussama Ben Khiroun, and Bilel Elayeb. 2017. ANT corpus: an Arabic news text collection for textual classification. In *Proceedings of the 14th International IEEE/ACS Conference on Computer Systems and Applications*, AICCSA '17, pages 135–142, Hammamet, Tunisia.

Costanza Conforti, Mohammad Taher Pilehvar, and Nigel Collier. 2018. Towards automatic fake news detection: cross-level stance detection in news articles. In *Proceedings of the First Workshop on Fact Extraction and VERification*, FEVER '18, pages 40–49, Brussels, Belgium.

Leon Derczynski, Kalina Bontcheva, Maria Liakata, Rob Procter, Geraldine Wong Sak Hoi, and Arkaitz Zubiaga. 2017. SemEval-2017 task 8: RumourEval: Determining rumour veracity and support for rumours. In *Proceedings of the 11th International Workshop on Semantic Evaluation*, SemEval '17, pages 69–76, Vancouver, Canada.

Jacob Devlin, Ming-Wei Chang, Kenton Lee, and Kristina Toutanova. 2019. BERT: Pre-training of deep bidirectional transformers for language understanding. In *Proceedings of the 2019 Conference of the North American Chapter of the Association for Computational Linguistics: Human Language Technologies*, NAACL-HLT '19, pages 4171–4186, Minneapolis, Minnesota, USA.

William Ferreira and Andreas Vlachos. 2016. Emergent: a novel data-set for stance classification. In *Proceedings of the 2016 Conference of the North American Chapter of the Association for Computational Linguistics: Human Language Technologies*, NAACL-HLT '16, pages 1163–1168, San Diego, California, USA.

Joseph L Fleiss and Jacob Cohen. 1973. The equivalence of weighted kappa and the intraclass correlation coefficient as measures of reliability. *Educational and psychological measurement*, 33(3):613–619.

Genevieve Gorrell, Elena Kochkina, Maria Liakata, Ahmet Aker, Arkaitz Zubiaga, Kalina Bontcheva, and Leon Derczynski. 2019. SemEval-2019 task 7: RumourEval, determining rumour veracity and support for rumours. In *Proceedings of the 13th International Workshop on Semantic Evaluation*, SemEval '19, pages 845–854, Minneapolis, Minnesota, USA.

Andreas Hanselowski, PVS Avinesh, Benjamin Schiller, Felix Caspelherr, Debanjan Chaudhuri, Christian M Meyer, and Iryna Gurevych. 2018. A retrospective analysis of the fake news challenge stance-detection task. In *Proceedings of the 27th International Conference on Computational Linguistics*, COLING '18, pages 1859–1874, Santa Fe, New Mexico, USA.

Momchil Hardalov, Arnav Arora, Preslav Nakov, and Isabelle Augenstein. 2021a. Cross-domain label-adaptive stance detection. *arXiv preprint arXiv:2104.07467*.

Momchil Hardalov, Arnav Arora, Preslav Nakov, and Isabelle Augenstein. 2021b. A survey on stance detection for mis- and disinformation identification. *arXiv preprint arXiv:2103.00242*.

Ganesh Jawahar, Muhammad Abdul-Mageed, and VS Laks Lakshmanan. 2020. Automatic detection of machine generated text: A critical survey. In *Proceedings of the 28th International Conference on Computational Linguistics*, COLING '20, pages 2296–2309, Barcelona, Spain (Online).

Jude Khouja. 2020. Stance prediction and claim verification: An Arabic perspective. In *Proceedings of the Third Workshop on Fact Extraction and VERification*, FEVER '20, pages 8–17, Online.

Dilek Küçük and Fazli Can. 2020. Stance detection: A survey. *ACM Computing Surveys (CSUR)*, 53(1):1–37.

Christopher Manning, Mihai Surdeanu, John Bauer, Jenny Finkel, Steven Bethard, and David McClosky. 2014. The Stanford CoreNLP natural language processing toolkit. In *Proceedings of 52nd Annual Meeting of the Association for Computational Linguistics: System Demonstrations*, ACL '14, pages 55–60, Baltimore, Maryland, USA.

Saif Mohammad, Svetlana Kiritchenko, Parinaz Sobhani, Xiaodan Zhu, and Colin Cherry. 2016. SemEval-2016 task 6: Detecting stance in tweets. In *Proceedings of the 10th International Workshop on Semantic Evaluation*, SemEval '16, pages 31–41, San Diego, California, USA.

Mitra Mohtarami, Ramy Baly, James Glass, Preslav Nakov, Lluís Màrquez, and Alessandro Moschitti. 2018. Automatic stance detection using end-to-end memory networks. In *Proceedings of the 2018 Conference of the North American Chapter of the Association for Computational Linguistics: Human Language Technologies*, NAACL-HLT '18, pages 767–776, New Orleans, Louisiana, USA.

Mitra Mohtarami, James Glass, and Preslav Nakov. 2019. Contrastive language adaptation for cross-lingual stance detection. In *Proceedings of the 2019 Conference on Empirical Methods in Natural Language Processing and the 9th International Joint Conference on Natural Language Processing*, EMNLP-IJCNLP '19, pages 4442–4452, Hong Kong, China.

El Moatez Billah Nagoudi, AbdelRahim Elmadany, Muhammad Abdul-Mageed, Tariq Alhindi, and Hasan Cavusoglu. 2020. Machine generation and detection of Arabic manipulated and fake news. In *Proceedings of the Fifth Arabic Natural Language Processing Workshop*, ANLP '20, pages 69–84, Barcelona, Spain (Online).

Dean Pomerleau and Delip Rao. 2017. The fake news challenge: Exploring how artificial intelligence technologies could be leveraged to combat fake news. *Fake News Challenge*.

Ali Safaya, Moutasem Abdullatif, and Deniz Yuret. 2020. KUISAIL at SemEval-2020 task 12: BERT-CNN for offensive speech identification in social media. In *Proceedings of the Fourteenth Workshop on Semantic Evaluation*, SemEval '20, pages 2054–2059, Barcelona (online).

Benjamin Schiller, Johannes Daxenberger, and Iryna Gurevych. 2021. Stance detection benchmark: How robust is your stance detection? *KI - Künstliche Intelligenz*.

Mina Schütz, Alexander Schindler, Melanie Siegel, and Kawa Nazemi. 2021. Automatic fake news detection with pre-trained transformer models. In *Proceedings of the ICPR International Workshops and Challenges*, pages 627–641.

James Thorne, Andreas Vlachos, Oana Cocarascu, Christos Christodoulopoulos, and Arpit Mittal. 2018. The fact extraction and VERification (FEVER) shared task. In *Proceedings of the First Workshop on Fact Extraction and VERification*, FEVER '18, pages 1–9, Brussels, Belgium.

Andreas Vlachos and Sebastian Riedel. 2014. Fact checking: Task definition and dataset construction. In *Proceedings of the ACL 2014 Workshop on Language Technologies and Computational Social Science*, pages 18–22, Baltimore, Maryland, USA.

Qiang Zhang, Shangsong Liang, Aldo Lipani, Zhaochun Ren, and Emine Yilmaz. 2019. From stances' imbalance to their hierarchical representation and detection. In *Proceedings of the World Wide Web Conference*, WWW '19, pages 2323–2332, Lyon, France.

MEAN: Multi-head Entity Aware Attention Network for Political Perspective Detection in News Media

Chang Li
Department of Computer Science
Purdue University, West Lafayette, IN
li1873@purdue.edu

Dan Goldwasser
Department of Computer Science
Purdue University, West Lafayette, IN
dgoldwas@purdue.edu

Abstract

The way information is generated and disseminated has changed dramatically over the last decade. Identifying the political perspective shaping the way events are discussed in the media becomes more important due to the sharp increase in the number of news outlets and articles. Previous approaches usually only leverage linguistic information. However, news articles attempt to maintain credibility and seem impartial. Therefore, bias is introduced in subtle ways, usually by emphasizing different aspects of the story. In this paper, we propose a novel framework that considers entities mentioned in news articles and external knowledge about them, capturing the bias with respect to those entities. We explore different ways to inject entity information into the text model. Experiments show that our proposed framework achieves significant improvements over the standard text models, and is capable of identifying the difference in news narratives with different perspectives.

1 Introduction

The perspectives underlying the way information is conveyed to readers can prime them to take similar stances and shape their world view (Gentzkow and Shapiro, 2010, 2011). Given the highly polarized coverage of news events, recognizing these perspectives can help ensure that all point of view are represented by news aggregation services, and help avoid "information echo-chambers" in which only a single view point is represented.

Past work studying expression of bias in text has focused on lexical and syntactic representations of bias (Greene and Resnik, 2009; Recasens et al., 2013; Elfardy et al., 2015). Expressions of bias can include the use of the passive voice (e.g., *"mistakes were made"*), or references to known ideological talking points and framing decisions (Baumer et al., 2015; Budak et al., 2016; Card et al., 2016; Field et al., 2018; Morstatter et al., 2018) (e.g., *"pro-life"* vs. *"pro-choice"*). However, bias in news media is often more nuanced, expressed through informational choices (Fan et al., 2019), which highlight different aspects of the news story, depending on the *entity* or *relation* being discussed. For example, consider the following articles, discussing the same news story from different perspectives.

***Adapted from* Huffington Post** *(Left)*

Rep. **Adam Schiff** (D-Calif.), one of the managers, pressed the case for additional witnesses, noting that **Trump** last month — in a video clip Schiff played senators — said he would "love" to have former administration officials testify in his Senate trial. "The Senate has an opportunity to take the president up on his offer to make his senior aides available",Schiff said. "But now the president is changing his tune."

***Adapted from* Fox News** *(Right)*

House Intelligence Committee Chairman **Adam Schiff** of California, the leading House impeachment manager for Democrats, hurled the usual inflammatory accusations from his grab-bag of anti-**Trump** invectives ("corruption... cover-ups... misdeeds... lawlessness... guilt!") He tried to enliven his monotonous delivery with graphics, but the excessive words only added tedium to his largely laborious argument

Both stories describe the same set of events regarding the 2020 U.S Senate impeachment trial. In the top article, with a left leaning perspective, Rep. Schiff, leading the Democrats in the case, is quoted directly, while the bottom article, with a right leaning perspective, describes a negative reaction to his speech. Mapping the attitudes expressed in the text, to the appropriate right or left leaning perspective, requires extensive world knowledge about the identity of the people mentioned and their relationship, as well as the ability to associate relevant text with them. In the example above, recognizing that the negative sentiment words are associated with Rep. Schiff (rather than President Trump who is also mentioned in the article), and that he is associated with the left side of the political map, is the key to identifying the right leaning perspective of the article.

Proceedings of the 4th NLP4IF Workshop on NLP for Internet Freedom, pages 66–75
June 6, 2021.

In this paper, we tackle this challenge and suggest an entity-centric approach to bias detection in news media. We follow the observation that expressions of bias often revolve around the main characters described in news stories, by associating them with different properties, highlighting their contribution to some events, while diminishing it, in others. To help account for the world knowledge needed to contextualize the actions and motives of entities mentioned in the news we train **entity** and **relation** (defined as a pair of entities in this paper) representations, incorporating information from external knowledge source and the news article dataset itself. We use the generalized term **aspect** to refer to either entity-specific or relation-specific view of the biased content in the article. We apply these representations in a **M**ulti-head **E**ntity **A**ware Attention **N**etwork (MEAN), which creates an entity-aware representation of the text.

We conducted our experiments over two datasets, Allsides (Li and Goldwasser, 2019) and SemEval Hyperpartisan news detection (Kiesel et al., 2019). We compared our approach to several competitive text classification models, and conducted a careful ablation study designed to evaluate the individual contribution of representing world knowledge using entity embedding, and creating the entity-aware text representation using multi-head attention. Our results demonstrate the importance of both aspects, each contributing to the model's performance.

2 Related Work

The problem of perspective identification is originally studied as a text classification task (Lin et al., 2006; Greene and Resnik, 2009; Iyyer et al., 2014), in which a classifier is trained to differentiate between specific perspectives. Other works use linguistic indicators of bias and expressions of implicit sentiment (Recasens et al., 2013; Baumer et al., 2015; Field et al., 2018).

Recent work by Fan et al., 2019 aims to characterize content relevant for bias detection. Unlike their work which relies on annotated spans of text, we aim to characterize this content without explicit supervision.

In the recent SemEval-2019, a hyperpartisan news article detection task was suggested[1]. Many works attempt to solve this problem with deep learning models (Jiang et al., 2019; Hanawa et al., 2019). We build on these works to help shape our text representation approach.

Several recent works also started to make use of concepts or entities appearing in text to get a better representation. Wang et al., 2017 treats the extracted concepts as pseudo words and appending them to the original word sequence which is then fed to a CNN. The KCNN (Wang et al., 2018) model, used for news recommendation, concatenates entity embeddings with the respective word embeddings at each word position to enhance the input. We take a different approach, and instead learn a document representation with respect to each entity in the article.

Using auxiliary information to improve text model was studied recently. Tang et al. proposes user-word composition vector model that modifies word embeddings given author representations in order to capture user-specific modification to word meanings. Other works incorporate user and product information to compute attentions over different semantic levels in the context of sentiment classification of online review (Chen et al., 2016; Wu et al., 2018). In this work, we learn the entity embedding based on external knowledge source (i.e. Wikipedia) or text, instead of including them in the training of bias prediction task. Therefore, we are able to capture rich knowledge about entities from various sources.

Another series of work that is closely related to ours is aspect based sentiment analysis. It aims at determining the sentiment polarity of a text span in a specific aspect or toward a target in the text. Many neural network based approaches have been proposed (Wang et al., 2016; Chen et al., 2017; Fan et al., 2018) to incorporate the aspect term into the text model. Recently, several works (Zeng et al., 2019; Song et al., 2019) designed their model based on BERT (Devlin et al., 2019). Unlike these works, we are not trying to determine the sentiment toward each entity mentioned in text. Instead, we are interested in identifying the underlying political perspective through the angles of these entities.

3 Model

The problem of political perspective detection in news media can be formalised as follows. Given a news article d, where d consists of sentences s_i, $i \in [1, L]$, and each sentence s_i consists of words w_{it}, $t \in [1, T]$. L and T are the number of sentences in d and number of words in s_i respectively. The goal of this task is to predict the political perspective

[1] https://pan.webis.de/semeval19/semeval19-web/

y of the document. Given different datasets, this can either be a binary classification task, where $y \in \{0, 1\}$ (hyperpartisan or not), or a multi-class classification problem, where $y \in \{0, 1, 2\}$ (left, center, right).

To inject knowledge about entities and relations, which would help solve the above classification problem, we first extract entities from the data corpus, and then learn knowledge representations for them using both external knowledge and the text corpus itself. In the second part, we describe how the learned aspect representations can be used in our Multi-head Entity Aware Attention Network. The overall architecture of our model is shown in Figure 1. It includes two sequence encoders, one for word level and another for sentence level. Our model learns a document representation with respect to each entity or relation in the document. The hidden states from an encoder are combined through a multi head entity-aware attention mechanism such that the generated sentence and document vectors will consider not only the context within the text but also the knowledge about the target entity (e.g. their political affiliation, or stance on controversial issues) or relation. We explain the acquisition of entity and relation knowledge representation and the structure of MEAN in details below.

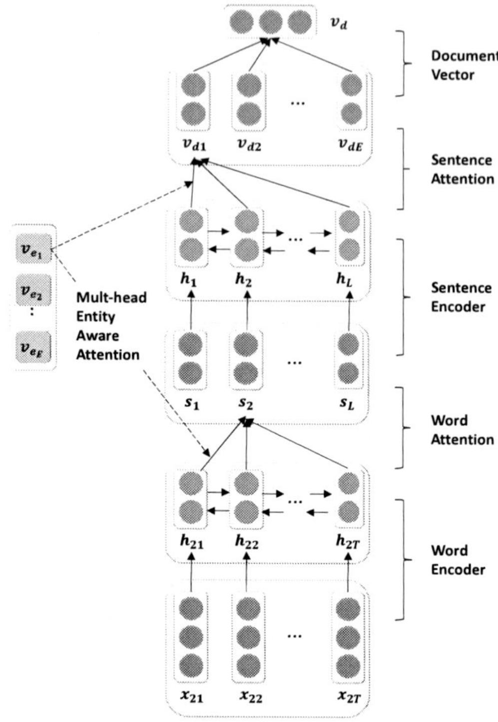

Figure 1: Overall Architecture of MEAN Model

3.1 Entity and Relation Knowledge Representation

We utilize the entity linking system DBpedia Spotlight (Daiber et al., 2013) to recognize and disambiguate the entities in news articles. We use the default configuration of DBpedia Spotlight, including the confidence threshold of 0.35, which helps to exclude uncertain or wrong entity annotations. We keep only entities with Person or Organization types that appear in the corpus. For each news article, we extract the top 5 entities (relations) based on number of mentions in the article as anchor aspects and learn a document representation with respect to each of them. The intuition is that the anchor aspects are the major figures and interactions discussed in a news article. By examining how each anchor aspect is discussed, our model can make better overall bias prediction. In this section, we introduce our pre-training models for learning entity and relation representations.

3.1.1 Wikipedia Based Entity Representation

Wikipedia2Vec (Yamada et al., 2018) is a model that learns entity embeddings from Wikipedia. It learns embeddings of words and entities by iterating over the entire Wikipedia pages and maps similar words and entities close to one another in a continuous vector space. It jointly optimizes the representations by modeling entity-entity, word-word and entity-word relationships. We use entity representation from Wikipedia2Vec to initialize our entity embedding model in 3.1.2 which enables us to use the background knowledge of entities without training on a very large corpus.

3.1.2 Text Based Entity Representation

Inspired by the masked language modeling objective used in BERT (Devlin et al., 2019), we propose an entity-level masking task for learning meaningful representations of entities based on the news articles in which they are mentioned. The objective is to predict the masked entity based on the context provided by the other words in a sentence. Specifically, the entity mentions (regardless of number of tokens in text) are replaced with a special token "[MASK]" during preprocessing. We use a bidirectional LSTM to encode the sentence, and the hidden state of the mask token will be used for prediction. It has the same structure as the sentence level encoder we describe in 3.2.2. We use negative sampling to randomly generate negative entity candidates from all possible entities uniformly. The learned entity representations can directly capture the context in the news articles they appear in.

3.1.3 Text Based Relation Representation

Similarly, we learn representation for an entity pair to encode the relationship between them. Given a sentence with two entity mentions masked, our model tries to predict the pair of entities. Again, a bidirectional LSTM with self attention is adopted to encode the sentence and the sentence representation are then used for prediction. We generate negative relation candidates from all possible relations uniformly.

3.2 Multi-Head Entity-Aware Attention Network

The basic component of our model is the Hierarchical LSTM model (Yang et al., 2016). The goal of our model is to learn document representation d_e with respect to an aspect e mentioned in it for bias prediction. In order to incorporate knowledge of aspects to better capture the nuance between news articles with different bias, we use aspect embeddings obtained in Section 3.1 to adjust the attention weight given to each sentence and word. It consists of several parts: a word sequence encoder, a word-level attention layer, a sentence sequence encoder and a sentence-level attention layer. The following sections describe the details of these components.

3.2.1 LSTM Networks

Long Short Term Memory networks (LSTMs) (Hochreiter and Schmidhuber, 1997) are a special kind of RNN, capable of learning long-term dependencies. Many recent works have demonstrated their ability to generate meaningful text representations. To capture the context in both directions, we use bidirectional LSTM in this work. For each element in the input sequence, the hidden state h is a concatenation of the forward hidden state $\overrightarrow{h}$ and backward hidden state $\overleftarrow{h}$ computed by the respective LSTM cells.

3.2.2 Hierarchical Aspect Attention

Word Sequence Encoder Given a sentence with words $w_{it}, t \in [1, T]$, each word is first converted to its embedding vector x_{it}. We can adopt pre-trained Glove (Pennington et al., 2014) word embeddings or deep contextualized word representation ELMo (Gardner et al., 2017) for this step. The word vectors are then fed into a word level bidirectional LSTM network to incorporate contextual information within the sentence. The hidden states h_{it} from the bidirectional LSTM network, are passed to the next layer.

Word Level Attention In (Yang et al., 2016), a self attention mechanism is introduced to identify words that are important to the meaning of the sentence, and therefore higher weights are given to them when forming the aggregated sentence vector. Actually the same words can also convey different meanings on distinct entities or relations. Following this intuition, we extend the idea by taking the aspect knowledge into account.

$$p_{itw} = tanh(W_w h_{it} + U_w v_e + b_w) \quad (1)$$

$$\alpha_{itw} = \frac{exp(p_{itw}^T p_w)}{\sum_t exp(p_{itw}^T p_w)} \quad (2)$$

$$s_{iw} = \sum_t \alpha_{itw} h_{it} \quad (3)$$

In addition to using the hidden states h_{it} alone to compute attention weight, we add the vector v_e for the anchor aspect e as another source of information. As a result, p_{itw} encode the importance of a specific word not only according to its context, but also the aspect of interest. p_{itw} is compared with the word level preference vector p_w to compute a similarity score, which is then normalized to get the attention weight α_{itw} through a softmax function. A weighted sum of the word hidden states are computed based on the attention weight as the sentence vector s_{iw}

Inspired by the multi-head attention scheme in (Vaswani et al., 2017), we propose a multi-head attention in our model to extend its ability to jointly attend to information at different positions. The sentence vector s_i is computed as an average of s_{iw} obtained from different attention heads. Note that we learn a separate copy of the parameters W_w, U_w, b_w and p_w for each attention head.

$$s_i = \frac{\sum_w s_{iw}}{NH_W} \quad (4)$$

NH_W is the number of word-level attention head.

Sentence Sequence Encoder and Sentence Level Attention Given the sentence vectors s_i, $i \in [1, L]$, we can generate the document vector in a similar way. Hidden states h_i together with the aspect embedding v_e are used to compute the attention weight for each sentence. After that, the document vector v_{des} is obtained as a weighted average of hidden states h_i. v_{des} obtained from different attention heads are averaged to generate aspect oriented document representation v_{de}.

$$v_{de} = \frac{\sum_s v_{des}}{NH_S} \tag{5}$$

where NH_S is the number of attention heads at sentence level.

Document Classification The document representations v_{de} with respect to aspect e captures the bias related information in news article d from the angle of aspect e. They can be used as features for predicting the document bias label.

$$p_{de} = \text{softmax}(W_c v_{de} + b_c) \tag{6}$$

We use the negative log likelihood of the correct labels as classification training loss:

$$L = -\sum_{d} \sum_{e \in E_d} \log p_{dej} \tag{7}$$

where E_d is the set of aspects mentioned in news article d, and j is the bias label of d.

Note that we use the bias label for the entire news article d as label for each aspect oriented document representation v_{de} during training. This is not ideal as the narratives about some aspects in the article may not be consistent with the overall political perspective. But it is a reasonable approximation given the labels for aspect oriented document representations are expensive to obtain. At test time, we use average pooling to get the aggregated document representation v_d which combine the political perspective targeting each aspect of interest.

$$v_d = \frac{\sum_e v_{de}}{|E_d|} \tag{8}$$

Given the entity and relation representations are not in the same space, we use them to train separate models. We regard the MEAN model using entity embedding and relation embedding for attention as **MEAN_ENT** and **MEAN_REL** respectively. We also explore a simple ensemble **MEAN_Ensemble**, which makes prediction based on the sum of probability scores p_{de} from the above two models at test time. Note that this does not require retraining.

4 Experiments

4.1 Datasets and Evaluation

We run experiments on two news article datasets: Allsides and SemEval. The statistics of both datasets is shown in Table 1.

Allsides This dataset (Li and Goldwasser, 2019) is collected from two news aggregation websites[2] on 2020 different events discussing 94 event types. The websites provide news coverage from multiple perspectives, indicating the bias of each article using crowdsourced and editorial reviewed approaches. Each article has a bias label left, center or right. We used the same randomly separated splits for evaluation in this paper so that our results are directly comparable with previous ones.

SemEval This is the official training dataset from SemEval 2019 Task 4: Hyperpartisan News Detection (Kiesel et al., 2019). The task is to decide whether a given news article follows a hyperpartisan argumentation. There are 645 articles in this dataset and each is labelled manually with a binary label to indicate whether it is hyperpartisan or not. Since the test set is not available at this time, we conducted 10-fold cross validation on the training set with exactly the same splits as in (Jiang et al., 2019) so that we can compare with the system that ranked in the first place.

Dataset	Center	Left	Right	Avg # Sent.	Avg # Words
Allsides	4164	3931	2290	49.96	1040.05
		Hyperpartisan			
SemEval	407	238		27.11	494.29

Table 1: Datasets Statistics

4.2 Baselines

We compare our model with several baseline methods, including traditional approaches that utilize textual information alone, and other strategies to utilize knowledge of entities.

[2] Allsides.com and Memeorandum.com

4.2.1 Methods using only textual information

SkipThought regard each document as a long sentence, and map it to a 4800-dimension vector with the sentence level encoder Skip-Thought (Kiros et al., 2015).

HLSTM first tokenize a document into sentences, then each sentence was tokenized into words. A word-level and a sentence-level bidirectional LSTM are used to construct a vector representation for each sentence and then the document. Self attention is used to aggregate hidden states at both word and sentence levels.

BERT is a language representation model based on deep bidirectional Transformer architectures (Vaswani et al., 2017). It was pre-trained with masked language model and next sentence prediction tasks on huge corpus. As a result, it can achieve state-of-the-art results on a wide range of tasks by fine-tuning with just one additional output layer.

CNN_Glove (CNN_ELMo) is the model from the team that ranked first in hyperpartisan news detection task in SemEval 2019 (Jiang et al., 2019). It uses the pre-trained Glove (ELMo) word vectors, which is then averaged as sentence vectors. The sentences vectors are fed into 5 convolutional layers of different kernal sizes. The outputs for all convolution layers are concatenated for prediction.

4.2.2 Methods using entity information

Models listed below have the same architecture with MEAN, including multi-head self attention. The only difference is how and where entity information is used.

HLSTM_Embed concatenate the entity embedding with word embedding at each position such that the new input to word level LSTM $x'_{it} = [x_{it}; v_e]$ where ; is the concatenation operator. This model has the potential to bias the political preference of a word. This is because a word can be associated with bias when describing one entity while neutral when describing others.

HLSTM_Output concatenate the entity embedding with the document vector v_d generated by HLSTM such that $v'_d = [v_d; v_e]$. This means that we bias the probability distribution of political bias based on the final document encoding. If an entity is usually associated with one bias in certain topics, then this model would be able to capture that.

4.3 Implementation Details

We use the spaCy toolkit for preprocessing the documents. All models are implemented with PyTorch (Paszke et al., 2017)[3]. The 300d Glove word vectors (Pennington et al., 2014) trained on 6 billion tokens are used to convert words to word embeddings. They are not updated during training. The sizes of LSTM hidden states for both word level and sentence level are 300 for both Allsides and SemEval dataset. The number of attention head at both word and sentence levels are set to 4 for Allsides, while only one head is used for SemEval due to the limited data size. For the training of the neural network, we used the Adam optimizer (Kingma and Ba, 2014) to update the parameters. On Allsides dataset, 5% of the training data is used as the validation set. We perform early stopping using the validation set. However, same as (Jiang et al., 2019), we use the evaluation part of each fold for early stopping and model selection. The learning rate lr is set to 0.001 for all models except BERT for which $2e-5$ is used. The mini-batch size is $b = 10$ for all models except for relation attention models which can only set $b = 8$ due to the size of GPU memory.

4.4 Results

4.4.1 Results on Allsides

We report the micro F1 and macro F1 scores on test set for Allsides dataset in Table 4. The results are divided into two groups based on whether contextualized word representations are used. In the first group, we have the results of models using only textual information, which are reported in (Li and Goldwasser, 2019). Although baseline models using entity information significantly outperform the HLSTM baseline, they are no better than our MEAN model, indicating these two strategies of using entity embedding is not optimal. Our MEAN model achieves the best result in terms of both micro and macro F1 scores no matter whether contextualized word embeddings are used or not. This demonstrates our model can use knowledge encoded in entity embedding as additional context to identify bias expressed in more subtle ways. Therefore it generates high-quality document representation for political perspective prediction. The gaps between our model and baselines decrease when contextualized word representations are used

[3]Please refer to https://github.com/BillMcGrady/MEAN for data and source code

since local context is better captured in this setting. We also observe our MEAN_REL models is not as good as MEAN_ENT models. This is expected since we do not have good initialization for the relation representations. However, it is worth noting that performance of our framework further improves by using ensemble of our MEAN_ENT and MEAN_REL models for prediction. This demonstrates that the relation embedding learned does encode some additional signal for the task.

Model	Micro F1	Macro F1
SkipThought †	68.67	-
HLSTM †	74.59	-
HLSTM_Embed	76.45	74.95
HLSTM_Output	76.66	75.39
MEAN_Glove_ENT	78.22	77.19
MEAN_Glove_REL	77.85	76.70
MEAN_Glove_Ensemble	**80.56**	**79.62**
HLSTM_ELMo	80.11	79.02
BERT	79.58	77.91
MEAN_ELMo_ENT	80.87	80.00
MEAN_ELMo_REL	79.25	77.93
MEAN_ELMo_Ensemble	**82.32**	**81.30**

Table 2: Test Results on Allsides Dataset. † indicates results reported in (Li and Goldwasser, 2019).

4.4.2 Results on SemEval

The performance of various models on SemEval dataset can be found in Table 3. Again the results are grouped based on word representation used. CNN_Glove and CNN_ELMo are results reported by the winning team in the SemEval competition. They proposed an ensemble of multiple CNN models. Still, our model outperforms the winning team, showing the advantages of representing text with respect to different aspects. The other trends hold as well in SemEval dataset although the margin is smaller comparing to Allsides. This is partially due to the limited size of this dataset. Again, although MEAN_REL does not outperform baselines themselves, it helps to achieve the best accuracy score when combined with MEAN_ENT.

4.4.3 Ablation Study

We show the results for ablations of our MEAN_Glove_ENT model. The performance drops slightly when removing entity embedding at attention computation or not using multi-head attention. If both entity embedding and multi-head attention are removed, there is a dramatic decrease in performance, signaling these two modules complement each other in this task. Note that when both entity embedding and multi-head attention are not used, our model is equivalent

Model	Accuracy
CNN_Glove ‡	79.63
HLSTM	81.58
HLSTM_Embed	81.71
HLSTM_Output	81.25
MEAN_Glove_ENT	82.65
MEAN_Glove_REL	80.78
MEAN_Glove_Ensemble	**83.12**
CNN_ELMo ‡	84.04
HLSTM_ELMo	83.28
BERT	83.41
MEAN_ELMo_ENT	84.51
MEAN_ELMo_REL	83.09
MEAN_ELMo_Ensemble	**85.22**

Table 3: Test Results on SemEval Dataset. ‡ indicates results reported in (Jiang et al., 2019). Our full model outperforms the system ranked first in SemEval-2019 Hyperpartisan News Detection Task.

to HLSTM. We attribute the difference in performance between our result and that reported in (Li and Goldwasser, 2019) to random initialization and hyper-parameters setting.

Model	Micro F1	Macro F1
MEAN_Glove_ENT	78.22	77.19
w/o Entity Embedding	76.69	75.03
w/o Multi-head attention	77.82	76.42
w/o Both	73.99	72.47

Table 4: Ablation Study on Allsides Dataset.

4.4.4 Qualitative Results

Sentiment Lemmas for Entities and Relations To better understand the effectiveness and meaning of the learnt attention scores, we find the most attended to sentiment lemmas in Allsides dataset with respect to a certain entity or relation. We calculate the attention given to a token x_{it} by an article as the sentence attention multiplied by word attention in the sentence $\alpha_{x_{it}} = \alpha_i * \alpha_{it}$. We average the attention given by multiple heads in this evaluation. To aggregate information better, we lemmatized all tokens.

Given the lemma attention definition above, we can compute the attention scores of a lemma across the dataset with respect to an aspect by averaging the attention score of each occurrence of that lemma. We extract lemmas with most attention and filter out neutral ones using the VADER sentiment lexicon (Hutto and Gilbert, 2014). We present top five lemmas for some prominent entities and relations between them from Democratic Party and Republican Party in Table 5. The phrases are selected from articles with left or right bias. There are several interesting findings from the table:

1. The top lemmas from left and right articles

Entities/Relations	Left Articles	Right Articles
Barack Obama	admire, motivate, blame, murder, amaze	blame, terrorist, admire, like, love
Hillary Clinton	brutal, admire, disgusting, promote, disturbing	super, lie, hack, destroy, defeat
Bernie Sanders	rig, destroy, kill, accuse, dedicated	rig, fire, help, win, clear
Donald Trump	ugly, fascinate, mislead, damn, scary	special, bizarre, suspect, loyal, super
Mitch McConnell	special, accuse, argue, regret, criticize	like, illegal, best, promised, clear
Mitt Romney	illegal, support, entitle, create, interest	accuse, illegal, great, support, argue
Donald Trump - Hillary Clinton	insult, dam, honest, horrible, amaze	hack, positive, warn, great, kill
Donald Trump - Mitch McConnell	condemn, respect, scream, tick, love	respect, wish, bright, like, happy
Hillary Clinton - Barack Obama	relax, respect, benefit, enjoy, compliment	innocent, hope, hate, great, super
Hillary Clinton - Bernie Sanders	complain, insult, promote, mourn, enjoy	destroy, merry, excite, cheat, wrong

Table 5: Top Sentiment Lemmas with Most Attention Scores

Sentence with Attention	Human Annotation	Entity
President Donald Trump announced Friday a short - term plan that will reopen the government for three weeks so that border security negotiations may continue without the devastating effects of the partial government shutdown .	devastating	Donald Trump
Netanyahu , who has a famously frosty relationship with President Obama , mentions neither Obama nor Republican challenger Mitt Romney , with whom Netanyahu worked in the mid-1970s at Boston Consulting Group .	famously frosty	Barack Obama
In the last few weeks , the fight turned particularly nasty – with Trump canceling a Democratic congressional trip to Afghanistan after House Speaker Nancy Pelosi called on Trump to delay his State of the Union address or submit it in writing .	Whole Sentence	Nancy Pelosi
However , Democrats rejected the plan even before Trump announced it , and a Senate version of the plan failed to get the 60 votes needed on Thursday .	However, ... announced it	Democratic Party

Table 6: Comparison between Model Attention and Human Annotation

show different sentiment sometimes but not always. One cause of this is we do not know how a sentiment word is used with only unigrams. The bias would be totally different when someone is blamed or blame others for an event.

2. Different entities may pay attention to the same lemma since attention in our setting encodes "relatedness to bias prediction" instead of "association to a specific bias". For example, the lemma "illegal", which may refer to the illegal immigrants issue, receives high attention score with respect to both Mitch McConnell and Mitt Romney, indicating the opinion expressed toward this topic can reflect the bias of an article.

3. For relations, the sentiment lemmas reflect bias. For rivals from different party (e.g. Donald Trump and Hillary Clinton), the negative sentiment dominates in both sides. However, the depiction of relationship differs for both sides for allies. (e.g. Donald Trump and Mitch McConnell).

Human Annotation Comparison The BASIL dataset (Fan et al., 2019) has human annotation of bias spans. It contains 300 articles on 100 events with 1727 bias spans annotated. On the sentence level, spans of lexical and informational bias are identified by annotators by analyzing whether the text tends to affect a reader's feeling towards one of the main entities. We show example sentences with attention assigned by our model and human annotated bias span in Table 6.

5 Conclusion

In this work, we propose an entity-centric framework for political perspective detection. Entity and relation representations learnt from external knowledge source and text corpus are utilized to compute attention at both word and sentence levels. A document representation with respect to each aspect in the article is then generated for prediction. Empirical experiments on two recent news article datasets show that our model achieve significantly better performance in bias detection comparing to traditional text models and other strategies of incorporating entity information.

In fact, relations are highly dependent on individual entities. We intend to extend this work to learn better relation representations given entity embeddings based on description of entity interactions in text. Moreover, we would like to weigh the importance of each aspect toward the overall perspective of an article instead of having all of them contribute equally to the final prediction.

References

E. Baumer, E. Elovic, Y. Qin, F. Polletta, and G. Gay. 2015. Testing and comparing computational approaches for identifying the language of framing in political news. In *NAACL*, pages 1472–1482, Denver, Colorado. Association for Computational Linguistics.

C. Budak, S. Goel, and J. M. Rao. 2016. Fair and balanced? quantifying media bias through crowdsourced content analysis. *Public Opinion Quarterly*, 80(S1):250–271.

Dallas Card, Justin Gross, Amber Boydstun, and Noah A. Smith. 2016. Analyzing framing through the casts of characters in the news. In *EMNLP*, pages 1410–1420, Austin, Texas. Association for Computational Linguistics.

Huimin Chen, Maosong Sun, Cunchao Tu, Yankai Lin, and Zhiyuan Liu. 2016. Neural sentiment classification with user and product attention. In *EMNLP*, pages 1650–1659, Austin, Texas. Association for Computational Linguistics.

Peng Chen, Zhongqian Sun, Lidong Bing, and Wei Yang. 2017. Recurrent attention network on memory for aspect sentiment analysis. In *Proceedings of the 2017 Conference on Empirical Methods in Natural Language Processing*, pages 452–461, Copenhagen, Denmark. Association for Computational Linguistics.

J. Daiber, M. Jakob, C. Hokamp, and P. N. Mendes. 2013. Improving efficiency and accuracy in multilingual entity extraction. In *I-SEMANTICS*, I-SEMANTICS '13, pages 121–124, New York, NY, USA. ACM.

Jacob Devlin, Ming-Wei Chang, Kenton Lee, and Kristina Toutanova. 2019. BERT: Pre-training of deep bidirectional transformers for language understanding. In *Proceedings of the 2019 Conference of the North American Chapter of the Association for Computational Linguistics: Human Language Technologies, Volume 1 (Long and Short Papers)*, pages 4171–4186, Minneapolis, Minnesota. Association for Computational Linguistics.

Heba Elfardy, Mona Diab, and Chris Callison-Burch. 2015. Ideological perspective detection using semantic features. In *STARSEM*, pages 137–146, Denver, Colorado. Association for Computational Linguistics.

Feifan Fan, Yansong Feng, and Dongyan Zhao. 2018. Multi-grained attention network for aspect-level sentiment classification. In *Proceedings of the 2018 Conference on Empirical Methods in Natural Language Processing*, pages 3433–3442, Brussels, Belgium. Association for Computational Linguistics.

L. Fan, M. White, E. Sharma, R. Su, P. K. Choubey, R. Huang, and L. Wang. 2019. Media bias through the lens of factual reporting. In *EMNLP*.

A. Field, D. Kliger, S. Wintner, J. Pan, D. Jurafsky, and Y. Tsvetkov. 2018. Framing and agenda-setting in Russian news: a computational analysis of intricate political strategies. In *EMNLP*, pages 3570–3580, Brussels, Belgium. Association for Computational Linguistics.

M. Gardner, J. Grus, M. Neuman, O. Tafjord, P. Dasigi, N. F. Liu, M. Peters, M. Schmitz, and L.S. Zettlemoyer. 2017. Allennlp: A deep semantic natural language processing platform.

Matthew Gentzkow and Jesse M Shapiro. 2010. What drives media slant? evidence from us daily newspapers. *Econometrica*, 78(1):35–71.

Matthew Gentzkow and Jesse M Shapiro. 2011. Ideological segregation online and offline. *The Quarterly Journal of Economics*, 126(4):1799–1839.

Stephan Greene and Philip Resnik. 2009. More than words: Syntactic packaging and implicit sentiment. In *NAACL-HLT*, pages 503–511, Boulder, Colorado. Association for Computational Linguistics.

K. Hanawa, S. Sasaki, H. Ouchi, J. Suzuki, and K. Inui. 2019. The sally smedley hyperpartisan news detector at SemEval-2019 task 4. In *SemEval*, pages 1057–1061, Minneapolis, Minnesota, USA. Association for Computational Linguistics.

S. Hochreiter and J. Schmidhuber. 1997. Long short-term memory. *Neural Comp.*, 9(8):1735–1780.

C. Hutto and E. Gilbert. 2014. Vader: A parsimonious rule-based model for sentiment analysis of social media text. In *ICWSM*.

Mohit Iyyer, Peter Enns, Jordan Boyd-Graber, and Philip Resnik. 2014. Political ideology detection using recursive neural networks. In *ACL*, pages 1113–1122, Baltimore, Maryland. Association for Computational Linguistics.

Ye Jiang, Johann Petrak, Xingyi Song, Kalina Bontcheva, and Diana Maynard. 2019. Hyperpartisan news detection using ELMo sentence representation convolutional network. In *SemEval*, pages 840–844, Minneapolis, Minnesota, USA. Association for Computational Linguistics.

J. Kiesel, M. Mestre, R. Shukla, E. Vincent, P. Adineh, D. Corney, B. Stein, and M. Potthast. 2019. SemEval-2019 task 4:hyperpartisan news detection. pages 829–839, Minneapolis, Minnesota, USA. Association for Computational Linguistics.

Diederik P. Kingma and Jimmy Ba. 2014. Adam: A method for stochastic optimization. *CoRR*, abs/1412.6980.

R. Kiros, Y. Zhu, R R Salakhutdinov, R. Zemel, R. Urtasun, A. Torralba, and S. Fidler. 2015. Skip-thought vectors. In C. Cortes, N. D. Lawrence, D. D. Lee, M. Sugiyama, and R. Garnett, editors, *NIPS*, pages 3294–3302. Curran Associates, Inc.

C. Li and D. Goldwasser. 2019. Encoding social information with gcn for political perspective detection in news media. In *ACL*, pages 2594–2604, Florence, Italy. Association for Computational Linguistics.

W-H Lin, T. Wilson, J. Wiebe, and A. Hauptmann. 2006. Identifying perspectives at the document and sentence levels. In *CoNLL*, CoNLL-X '06, pages 109–116, Stroudsburg, PA, USA. Association for Computational Linguistics.

F. Morstatter, L. Wu, U. Yavanoglu, S. R. Corman, and H. Liu. 2018. Identifying framing bias in online news. *Trans. Soc. Comput.*, 1(2):5:1–5:18.

A. Paszke, S. Gross, S. Chintala, G. Chanan, E. Yang, Z. DeVito, Z. Lin, A. Desmaison, L. Antiga, and A. Lerer. 2017. Automatic differentiation in PyTorch. In *NIPS Autodiff Workshop*.

J. Pennington, R. Socher, and C. Manning. 2014. Glove: Global vectors for word representation. In *EMNLP*, pages 1532–1543, Doha, Qatar. Association for Computational Linguistics.

M. Recasens, C. Danescu-Niculescu-Mizil, and D. Jurafsky. 2013. Linguistic models for analyzing and detecting biased language. In *ACL*, pages 1650–1659, Sofia, Bulgaria. Association for Computational Linguistics.

Youwei Song, Jiahai Wang, Tao Jiang, Zhiyue Liu, and Yanghui Rao. 2019. Attentional encoder network for targeted sentiment classification. *arXiv preprint arXiv:1902.09314*.

Duyu Tang, Bing Qin, Ting Liu, and Yuekui Yang. 2015. User modeling with neural network for review rating prediction. In *IJCAI*.

Ashish Vaswani, Noam Shazeer, Niki Parmar, Jakob Uszkoreit, Llion Jones, Aidan N Gomez, Ł ukasz Kaiser, and Illia Polosukhin. 2017. Attention is all you need. In I. Guyon, U. V. Luxburg, S. Bengio, H. Wallach, R. Fergus, S. Vishwanathan, and R. Garnett, editors, *Advances in Neural Information Processing Systems 30*, pages 5998–6008. Curran Associates, Inc.

Hongwei Wang, Fuzheng Zhang, Xing Xie, and Minyi Guo. 2018. Dkn: Deep knowledge-aware network for news recommendation. In *WWW*, WWW' 18, pages 1835–1844, Republic and Canton of Geneva, Switzerland. International World Wide Web Conferences Steering Committee.

J. Wang, Z. Wang, D. Zhang, and J. Yan. 2017. Combining knowledge with deep convolutional neural networks for short text classification. In *IJCAI*, IJCAI, pages 2915–2921. AAAI Press.

Yequan Wang, Minlie Huang, Xiaoyan Zhu, and Li Zhao. 2016. Attention-based LSTM for aspect-level sentiment classification. In *Proceedings of the 2016 Conference on Empirical Methods in Natural Language Processing*, pages 606–615, Austin, Texas. Association for Computational Linguistics.

Z. Wu, X.Y Dai, C. Yin, S. Huang, and J. Chen. 2018. Improving review representations with user attention and product attention for sentiment classification. In *AAAI*.

I. Yamada, A. Asai, H. Shindo, H. Takeda, and Y. Takefuji. 2018. Wikipedia2vec: An optimized tool for learning embeddings of words and entities from wikipedia. *arXiv*.

Zichao Yang, Diyi Yang, Chris Dyer, Xiaodong He, Alex Smola, and Eduard Hovy. 2016. Hierarchical attention networks for document classification. In *Proceedings of the 2016 Conference of the North American Chapter of the Association for Computational Linguistics: Human Language Technologies*, pages 1480–1489, San Diego, California. Association for Computational Linguistics.

Biqing Zeng, Heng Yang, Ruyang Xu, Wu Zhou, and Xuli Han. 2019. Lcf: A local context focus mechanism for aspect-based sentiment classification. *Applied Sciences*, 9:3389.

An Empirical Assessment of the Qualitative Aspects of Misinformation in Health News

Chaoyuan Zuo, Qi Zhang, and **Ritwik Banerjee**
Computer Science, Stony Brook University
{chzuo, qizhang5, rbanerjee}@cs.stonybrook.edu

Abstract

The explosion of online health news articles runs the risk of the proliferation of low-quality information. Within the existing work on fact-checking, however, relatively little attention has been paid to medical news. We present a health news classification task to determine whether medical news articles satisfy a set of review criteria deemed important by medical experts and health care journalists. We present a dataset of 1,119 health news paired with systematic reviews. The review criteria consist of six elements that are essential to the accuracy of medical news. We then present experiments comparing the classical token-based approach with the more recent transformer-based models. Our results show that detecting qualitative lapses is a challenging task with direct ramifications in misinformation, but is an important direction to pursue beyond assigning *True* or *False* labels to short claims.

1 Introduction

In recent years, health information-seeking behavior (HISB) – which refers to the ways in which individuals seek information about their health, risks, illnesses, and health-protective behaviors (Lambert and Loiselle, 2007; Mills and Todorova, 2016) – has become increasingly reliant on Online news articles (Fox and Duggan, 2013; Medlock et al., 2015; Basch et al., 2018). Some studies also posit that with increasing involvement of the news media in health-related discussions, and direct-to-consumer campaigns by pharmaceutical companies, people are turning to the Internet as their first source of health information, instead of healthcare practitioners (Jacobs et al., 2017). This behavior is primarily driven by the users' need to gain knowledge (Griffin et al., 1999) about some form of intervention (e.g., drugs, nutrition, diagnostic and screening tests, dietary recommendations, psychotherapy). Furthermore, and perhaps counter-intuitively, information seekers seldom spend a lot of time on health websites. Instead, they repeatedly jump between search engine results and reading health-related articles (Pang et al., 2014, 2015).

News headline: Experts warn coronavirus is 'as dangerous as Ebola' in shocking new study.
Source: www.express.co.uk/life-style/health/1275700/ebola-elderly-patients-coronavirus-experts-study-research-death-figures
Published: Apr 30, 2020 *Accessed*: March 21, 2021

Cause of misinformation
Comparing numbers from two different contexts: (1) the hospital fatality rate of COVID-19, and (2) the overall case fatality rate of Ebola.

Table 1: Medical misinformation due to a lack of understanding of domain-specific terminology.

In stark contrast to HISB, there is also growing lack of trust in the accuracy of health information provided on the Internet (Massey, 2016). This is perhaps to be expected, given how widespread health-related misinformation has become. For instance, in surveys where expert panels have judged the accuracy of health news articles, nearly half were found to be inaccurate (Moynihan et al., 2000; Yavchitz et al., 2012). Health-related misinformation, however, is rarely a binary distinction between *true* and *fake* news. In medical news, multiple aspects of an intervention are typically presented, and a loss of nuance or incomplete understanding of the process of medical research can lead to various types of qualitative failures, exacerbating misinformation in this domain.

Recently, news articles citing leading medical journals have suffered because of this. Table 1 shows an example that was disseminated widely in the United Kingdom, where technically correct facts were juxtaposed with misleading contexts – the *case* fatality rate of Ebola was incorrectly compared with the *hospital* fatality rate of COVID-19 (Winters et al., 2020). Indeed, medical misinformation is often a correct fact presented in an incorrect context (Southwell et al., 2019). Moreover, health-related articles are also known to present

Proceedings of the 4th NLP4IF Workshop on NLP for Internet Freedom, pages 76–81
June 6, 2021.

(1)	Does the story/news release adequately discuss the costs of the intervention?
(2)	Does the story/news release adequately quantify the benefits of the intervention?
(3)	Does the story/news release adequately explain/quantify the harms of the intervention?
(4)	Does the story/news release seem to grasp the quality of the evidence?
(5)	Does the story/news release commit disease-mongering?
(6a)	Does the story use independent sources and identify conflicts of interest?
(6b)	Does the news release identify funding sources & disclose conflicts of interest?
(7)	Does the story/news release compare the new approach with existing alternatives?
(8)	Does the story/news release establish the availability of the treatment/test/product/procedure?
(9)	Does the story/news release establish the true novelty of the approach?
(10a)	Does the story appear to rely solely or largely on a news release?
(10b)	Does the news release include unjustifiable, sensational language, including in the quotes of researchers?

Table 2: **Review criteria.** The ten criteria for public relations news releases are almost identical to the ones for news stories (except for 6 and 10).

"disease-mongering", where a normal state is exaggerated and presented as a condition or a disease (Wolinsky, 2005).

Given how these issues are specific to medical misinformation, and how intricately the accuracy of medical facts is intertwined with the quality of health care journalism, the imperative to move beyond a binary classification of *true* and *fake* becomes clear. To this end, a set of specific principles and criteria have been proposed by scientists and journalists, based largely on the acclaimed work by Moynihan et al. (2000) and the Statement of Principles by the Association of Health Care Journalists (Association of Health Care Journalists, 2007).

We present a dataset (Sec. 2) specifically tailored for health news, and labeled according to a set of domain-specific criteria by a multi-disciplinary team of journalists and health care professionals. The detailed data annotation was carried out from 2006 to 2018 (Schwitzer, 2006). For each criterion, we present a classification task to determine whether or not a given news article satisfies it (Sec. 3), and discuss the results. Finally, we present relevant prior work (Sec. 4) before concluding.

2 Dataset

Our data is collected from Health News Review (Schwitzer, 2006)[1], which contains systematic reviews of 2,616 news stories and 606 public relations (PR) news releases from a period of 13 years, from 2006 to 2018. Ten specific and standardized criteria were used for the reviews. These were chosen to align with the needs of readers seeking health information, and are shown in Table 2. The dataset consists only of articles that discuss a specific medical intervention, since the review criteria were deemed by journalists as being generally not applicable to discussions of multiple interventions or conditions. Each article is reviewed by two or three experts from journalism or medicine, and the results for each criterion include *Satisfactory*, *Not Satisfactory* and *Not Applicable*. The last label is reserved for cases where it is impossible or unreasonable for an article to address that criterion. Table 3 illustrates the utility of this label with one example from the dataset.

News headline: Virtual reality to help detect early risk of Alzheimer's
Source: www.theguardian.com/society/2018/dec/16/alzheimers-dementia-cure-virtual-reality-navigation-skills
Published: Dec 16, 2018 *Accessed*: April 26, 2021

Criterion labeled "not applicable": (2) Does the story adequately quantify the benefits of the treatment/test/product/procedure?

Table 3: **Review criteria not applicable.** In this example, the study being reported has not yet taken place, so criterion (2) in Table 2 is not germane.

Going beyond the reviews themselves, we then collect the news articles being reviewed from the original news sites. However, nearly 30% of those pages have ceased to exist. Further, some articles could not be retrieved due to paywalls. Multiple prominent news organizations are featured in this data, with Fig. 1 showing the distribution over these organizations (for brevity, we show the top ten entities, with the tenth being "others").

Our final dataset comprises 1,119 articles (740 news stories and 379 PR news releases) along with their criteria-driven reviews. These are maintained as $(n, \{c_i\})$ tuples, where n is the news article, and c_i are the review results for each criteria. Since criteria 6 and 10 are slightly different for news stories and PR releases, we remove these from our empirical experiments. Further, we also remove criteria 5 and 9, since these require highly topic-specific medical knowledge. We do this in order to have our approach reflect the extent of medical knowledge available to the lay reader, who is unlikely to fully comprehend the specialized language of medical research publications (McCray, 2005).

[1]www.healthnewsreview.org/

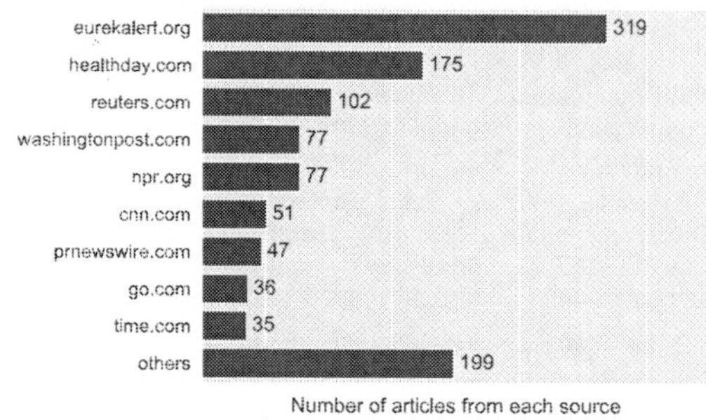

Figure 1: Distribution over news organizations.

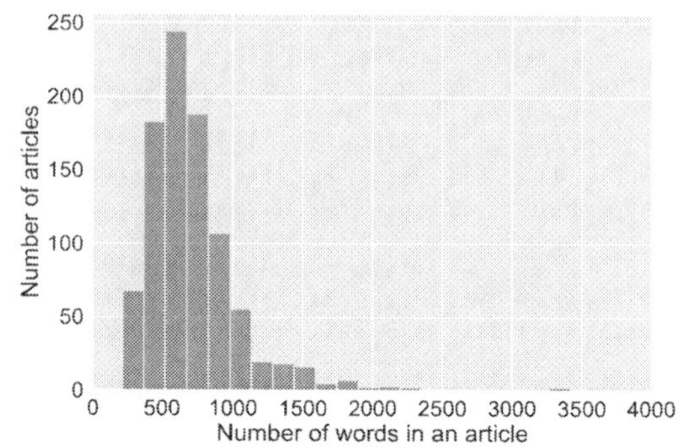

Figure 2: The distribution of the size of news articles.

3 Experiments

We approach the problem as a series of supervised classification tasks, where the performance is evaluated separately for each review criterion. Moreover, since the reviewers use the *Not Applicable* label based on additional topic-specific medical knowledge, we discard the $(n, \{c_i\})$ tuples where c_i carries this label. This eliminates approximately 2.35% of the total number of tuples in our dataset, and paves the way for a binary classification task where each article is deemed satisfactory or not for the criterion c_i. The numbers of remaining news for each criterion are as shown in below Table 4.

In all experiments, we use 70% of the data for training. The rest is used as the test set. As a simple baseline, we use the Zero Rule (also called ZeroR or 0-R), which uses the base rate and classifies according to the prior, always predicting the majority class. We then experiment with the classical representation using TF-IDF feature encoding, as well as the state-of-the-art transformer-based models. In both approaches, we use 5-fold cross-validation during training to select the best hyperparameters for each model. These are described next.

	Number of news			
Criteria	**Training**	**Test**	**Total**	**% of Positive samples**
1	651	273	924	20.5
2	774	331	1105	30.9
3	733	309	1042	32.4
4	781	336	1117	34.3
7	745	316	1061	47.8
8	684	288	972	70.3

Table 4: **Data distribution across review criteria.** The percentage of positive samples for each criterion is shown in the last column. Note that the classes are quite imbalanced for every criteria except 7.

3.1 Models

For the feature-based models, we perform some preprocessing, which consists of removing punctuation, converting the tokens into lowercase, removing function words, and lemmatization. We use two supervised learning algorithms: support vector machines (SVM) and gradient boosting (GB). As noted in Table 4, our dataset suffers from class imbalance for every criteria except for one. Thus, for the remaining five criteria, we use adaptive synthetic sampling, viz., ADASYN (He et al., 2008). Further, to reduce the high dimensions of the feature space, we apply the recursive feature elimination algorithm from Scikit-learn (Buitinck et al., 2013) with SVM. In this process, the estimator is trained on the initial set of features, and the importance of each feature is determined by the weight coefficient. The least important features are then pruned. We recursively apply this process by selecting progressively smaller feature sets, until the 300 best features remain.

Next, we use several transformer-based models. Namely, BERT (Devlin et al., 2019), XLNet (Yang et al., 2019), RoBERTa (Liu et al., 2019), ALBERT (Lan et al., 2020), DistilBERT (Sanh et al., 2019) and Longformer (Beltagy et al., 2020). The maximum sequence length is set to 512 for every model, except for Longformer, for which the value is 4,096. We use random undersampling to mitigate the class imbalance, since the model's performance would otherwise be similar to the Zero Rule baseline.

3.2 Results and discussion

The results of our experiments are shown in Table 5. As the dataset is imbalanced for all but one criterion, our simple baseline is the Zero Rule instead of a random baseline. We measure the classifier

Criteria	*0R* F1	*0R* P	*0R* R	*SVM* F1	*SVM* P	*SVM* R	*SVM*†* F1	*SVM*†* P	*SVM*†* R	*GB* F1	*GB* P	*GB* R	*GB** F1	*GB** P	*GB** R	*GB*†* F1	*GB*†* P	*GB*†* R
1	44.4	39.9	50.0	57.7	73.3	57.0	60.2	70.0	58.8	**66.3**	**76.3**	**63.6**	63.8	70.6	61.8	63.4	71.9	61.3
2	41.2	35.0	50.0	**64.4**	65.4	**63.8**	64.2	64.2	64.2	56.7	**65.9**	57.3	58.5	59.3	58.2	60.9	60.9	60.8
3	40.1	33.5	50.0	57.2	57.4	57.0	57.9	58.0	57.8	61.0	63.3	60.7	65.4	68.9	64.5	**67.4**	**67.9**	**67.0**
4	39.8	33.2	50.0	60.1	61.0	59.8	60.7	61.2	60.4	53.8	55.8	54.3	61.1	63.5	60.7	**68.1**	**69.1**	**67.5**
7	34.0	25.8	50.0	55.0	55.0	55.2	55.7	55.7	55.7	58.4	59.3	58.8	-	-	-	53.4	53.6	53.6
8	42.4	36.8	50.0	52.1	56.3	53.2	54.3	55.8	54.2	50.8	51.5	51.1	51.9	52.1	51.9	56.1	56.0	56.8
	BERT			*ALBERT*			*XLNet*			*RoBERTa*			*DistilBERT*			*Longformer*		
Criteria	**F1**	**P**	**R**	**F1**	**P**	**R**	**F1**	**P**	**R**	**F1**	**P**	**R**	**F1**	**P**	**R**	**F1**	**P**	**R**
1	55.6	55.4	56.4	57.2	59.1	63.9	63.6	62.8	65.8	62.6	62.7	68.4	62.8	63.0	69.1	62.8	62.2	66.4
2	48.5	55.7	56.1	52.0	52.4	52.7	60.9	60.7	62.0	60.8	61.0	62.7	54.6	56.4	57.6	62.2	62.3	64.2
3	58.2	58.1	58.3	55.4	55.5	55.5	55.9	56.1	56.6	59.4	59.3	60.0	53.1	57.9	54.4	63.8	63.8	65.4
4	40.7	58.2	50.2	49.8	54.0	54.0	47.6	57.0	56.1	56.1	58.2	59.2	55.6	57.0	57.9	50.2	52.4	52.7
7	61.2	62.8	62.1	40.2	58.1	52.0	48.4	55.9	53.4	**62.3**	**62.7**	**62.6**	57.4	57.5	57.4	56.8	60.0	58.8
8	54.7	57.6	59.7	55.8	56.1	55.6	54.6	54.7	55.3	**58.8**	**61.1**	**64.3**	55.5	57.6	59.9	53.5	58.7	54.3

Table 5: **Experiment results.** Models trained with oversampled data are marked with *. Models for which feature selection was performed are marked with †. For criterion 7 (see Tables 2 and 4), oversampling was not performed.

performances using macro-average of precision, recall, and F_1-score.

Gradient boosting achieves better performance on criteria 1, 3, 4, and 8. Also, the introduction of oversampling and feature selection increases the model performance for some criteria but not uniformly across the board.

The feature-based models outperform the transformer-based models in the first four criteria. We suspect this is mainly due to the size of the dataset after undersampling. We also check the number of words for the news collected (Fig 2), and more than half of which have more than 512 words. However, the Longformer model with maximum sequence length 4,096 does not achieve significantly better performance than other transformer-based models. The reason might be the "inverted pyramid" structure of news articles, which places essential information in the lead paragraph (Pöttker, 2003). We also notice that the first four criteria are more specific than the rest. For example, the first criterion is about the cost of the intervention, which could be answered by token-level searching. It is still a challenging task, however, given that even human readers find it difficult to follow the review criteria without expert training.

4 Related Work

For many years now, concerns have been raised about medical misinformation in the coverage by news media (Moynihan et al., 2000; Ioannidis, 2005). Moynihan et al. studied 207 news stories about the benefits and risks of three medications to prevent major diseases, and found that 40% of the news did not report benefits quantitatively while only 47% mentioned potential harms.

Various tasks and approaches have been formulated (Thorne and Vlachos, 2018) for fact-checking information. Multiple datasets have also been put forth. Ferreira and Vlachos (Ferreira and Vlachos, 2016) released a collection of 300 claims with corresponding news. This dataset was later significantly enlarged in the fake news challenge (Pomerleau and Rao, 2017). At a similarly large scale, Wang introduced a dataset comprising 12.8K manually labeled statements from `POLITIFACT.COM` and treated it as a text classification task. A large body of work, however, has dealt with fact-checking of short claims, both for fact-checking (Hassan et al., 2017) as well as for identifying what to check (Nakov et al., 2018).

Furthermore, a vast majority of prior work was on political news, while medical misinformation remained relatively neglected until its impact was underscored by the COVID-19 pandemic (e.g., Hossain et al. (2020); Serrano et al. (2020), among others). This body of work, however, continues to assign true/false labels or binary stance labels to short claims. In contrast, our work analyzes long articles and identifies whether or not they satisfy various qualitative criteria specifically important to medical news, as determined by journalists and health care professionals.

5 Conclusion

We present a first empirical analysis of qualitative reviews of medical news, since the traditional true/fake dichotomy does not adequately capture the nuanced world of medical misinformation. To this end, we collect a dataset of medical news along with their detailed reviews based on multiple criteria. The novelty of this work lies in highlighting the importance of a deeper review and analysis of medical news to understand misinformation in this domain. For example, misinformation may easily be caused by the use of sensational language, or disease-mongering, or not disclosing a conflict of interest (all of which are criteria used in this work).

Our results show that this is a challenging task. The data reveals that for most of the criteria, less than half of the news articles are satisfactory. The commonly perceived notion of reputation notwithstanding, several articles from well-known sources (such as the ones shown in Fig. 1) also fall short of these qualitative benchmarks set by domain experts. This presents a clear data-driven picture of how the qualitative aspects of misinformation defy our expectations. We have presented a first step in this direction, and our hope is that this work leads to collaborative creation of similar datasets at larger scale by computer scientists and journalists, and in multiple domains even outside of health care.

Acknowledgment

This work was supported in part by the Division of Social and Economic Sciences of the U.S. National Science Foundation (NSF) under the award SES-1834597.

References

Corey H. Basch, Sarah A. MacLean, Rachelle-Ann Romero, and Danna Ethan. 2018. Health Information Seeking Behavior Among College Students. Journal of Community Health, 43:1094–1099.

Iz Beltagy, Matthew E. Peters, and Arman Cohan. 2020. Longformer: The Long-Document Transformer. arXiv:2004.05150.

Lars Buitinck, Gilles Louppe, Mathieu Blondel, Fabian Pedregosa, Andreas Mueller, Olivier Grisel, Vlad Niculae, Peter Prettenhofer, Alexandre Gramfort, Jaques Grobler, Robert Layton, Jake VanderPlas, Arnaud Joly, Brian Holt, and Gaël Varoquaux. 2013. API design for machine learning software: experiences from the scikit-learn project. In ECML PKDD Workshop: Languages for Data Mining and Machine Learning, pages 108–122.

Jacob Devlin, Ming-Wei Chang, Kenton Lee, and Kristina Toutanova. 2019. BERT: Pre-training of Deep Bidirectional Transformers for Language Understanding. In Proc. 2019 Conference of the North American Chapter of the Association for Computational Linguistics: Human Language Technologies, Volume 1 (Long and Short Papers), pages 4171–4186, Minneapolis, Minnesota. ACL.

William Ferreira and Andreas Vlachos. 2016. Emergent: a novel data-set for stance classification. In Proc. of the 2016 Conference of the North American chapter of the Association for Computational Linguistics: Human Language Technologies, pages 1163–1168.

Susannah Fox and Maeve Duggan. 2013. Health Online 2013. Internet & Technology, Pew Research Center. Last accessed: May 31, 2020.

Robert J. Griffin, Sharon Dunwoody, and Kurt Neuwirth. 1999. Proposed Model of the Relationship of Risk Information Seeking and Processing to the Development of Preventive Behaviours. Environmental Research, 80(2):S230–S245.

Naeemul Hassan, Gensheng Zhang, Fatma Arslan, Josue Caraballo, Damian Jimenez, Siddhant Gawsane, Shohedul Hasan, Minumol Joseph, Aaditya Kulkarni, Anil Kumar Nayak, et al. 2017. Claimbuster: The first-ever end-to-end fact-checking system. Proc. of the VLDB Endowment, 10(12):1945–1948.

Haibo He, Yang Bai, Edwardo A Garcia, and Shutao Li. 2008. ADASYN: Adaptive Synthetic Sampling Approach for Imbalanced Learning. In Proc. of the IEEE Joint Conference on Neural Networks (IJCNN), 2008., pages 1322–1328. IEEE.

Tamanna Hossain, Robert L. Logan IV, Arjuna Ugarte, Yoshitomo Matsubara, Sean Young, and Sameer Singh. 2020. COVIDLies: Detecting COVID-19 misinformation on social media. In Proc. of the 1st Workshop on NLP for COVID-19 (Part 2) at EMNLP 2020. Association for Computational Linguistics.

John P. A. Ioannidis. 2005. Why most published research findings are false. PLOS Medicine, 2(8):e124.

Wura Jacobs, Ann O. Amuta, and Kwon Chan Jeon. 2017. Health information seeking in the digital age: An analysis of health information seeking behavior among US adults. Cogent Social Sciences, 3(1):1302785.

Sylvie D. Lambert and Carmen G. Loiselle. 2007. Health Information-Seeking Behavior. Qualitative Health Research, 17:1006–1019.

Zhenzhong Lan, Mingda Chen, Sebastian Goodman, Kevin Gimpel, Piyush Sharma, and Radu Soricut. 2020. ALBERT: A Lite BERT for Self-supervised Learning of Language Representations. In 8th International Conference on Learning Representations ICLR 2020. OpenReview.net.

Yinhan Liu, Myle Ott, Naman Goyal, Jingfei Du, Mandar Joshi, Danqi Chen, Omer Levy, Mike Lewis, Luke Zettlemoyer, and Veselin Stoyanov. 2019. RoBERTa: A Robustly Optimized BERT Pretraining Approach. ArXiv, abs/1907.11692.

Association of Health Care Journalists. 2007. Statement of Principles of the Association of Health Care Journalists. https://healthjournalism.org/secondarypage-details.php?id=56. Last accessed: March 14, 2021.

Philip M. Massey. 2016. Where Do U.S. Adults Who Do Not Use the Internet Get Health Information? Examining Digital Health Information Disparities From 2008 to 2013. Journal of Health Communication, 21(1):118–124.

Alexa T. McCray. 2005. Promoting Health Literacy. Journal of the American Medical Informatics Association, 12(2):152–163.

Stephanie Medlock, Saeid Eslami, Marjan Askari, Derk L Arts, Danielle Sent, Sophia E de Rooij, and Ameen Abu-Hanna. 2015. Health information-seeking behavior of seniors who use the internet: A survey. J Med Internet Res, 17(1):e10.

Annette Mills and Nelly Todorova. 2016. An Integrated Perspective on Factors Influencing Online Health-Information Seeking Behaviours Information Seeking Behaviours. In ACIS 2016 Proc., page 83. Association for Information Systems.

Ray Moynihan, Lisa Bero, Dennis Ross-Degnan, David Henry, Kirby Lee, Judy Watkins, Connie Mah, and Stephen B. Soumerai. 2000. Coverage by the News Media of the Benefits and Risks of Medications. New England Journal of Medicine, 342(22):1645–1650.

Preslav Nakov, Alberto Barrón-Cedeno, Tamer Elsayed, Reem Suwaileh, Lluís Màrquez, Wajdi Zaghouani, Pepa Atanasova, Spas Kyuchukov, and Giovanni Da San Martino. 2018. Overview of the CLEF-2018 CheckThat! Lab on Automatic Identification and Verification of Political Claims. In International Conference of the Cross-Language Evaluation Forum for European Languages, pages 372–387. Springer.

Patrick Cheong-Iao Pang, Shanton Chang, Jon M Pearce, and Karin Verspoor. 2014. Online Health Information seeking Behaviour: Understanding Different Search Approaches. In PACIS 2014 Proc., page 229. Association for Information Systems.

Patrick Cheong-Iao Pang, Karin Verspoor, Jon Pearce, and Shanton Chang. 2015. Better Health Explorer: Designing for Health Information Seekers. In Proc. of the Annual Meeting of the Australian Special Interest Group for Computer Human Interaction, pages 588–597.

Dean Pomerleau and Delip Rao. 2017. Fake news challenge. http://fakenewschallenge.org/.

Horst Pöttker. 2003. News and its communicative quality: The inverted pyramid – when and why did it appear? Journalism Studies, 4(4):501–511.

Victor Sanh, Lysandre Debut, Julien Chaumond, and Thomas Wolf. 2019. Distilbert, a distilled version of BERT: smaller, faster, cheaper and lighter. CoRR, abs/1910.01108.

Gary Schwitzer. 2006. Health News Review. https://www.healthnewsreview.org. Last accessed: March 22, 2021.

Juan Carlos Medina Serrano, Orestis Papakyriakopoulos, and Simon Hegelich. 2020. NLP-based Feature Extraction for the Detection of COVID-19 Misinformation Videos on YouTube. In Proc. of the 1st Workshop on NLP for COVID-19 at ACL 2020.

Brian G. Southwell, Jeff Niederdeppe, Joseph N. Cappella, Anna Gaysynsky, Dannielle E. Kelley, Emily B. Oh, April Peterson, and Wen-Ying Sylvia Chou. 2019. Misinformation as a Misunderstood Challenge to Public Health. American Journal of Preventive Medicine, 57.

James Thorne and Andreas Vlachos. 2018. Automated fact checking: Task formulations, methods and future directions. In Proc. of the 27th International Conference on Computational Linguistics, pages 3346–3359. Association for Computational Linguistics.

William Y. Wang. 2017. "Liar, Liar Pants on Fire": A New Benchmark Dataset for Fake News Detection. In Proc. of the 55th Annual Meeting of the Association for Computational Linguistics (Volume 2: Short Papers), pages 422–426, Vancouver, Canada. Association for Computational Linguistics.

Maike Winters, Ben Oppenheim, Jonas Pick, and Helena Nordenstedt. 2020. Creating misinformation: how a headline in The BMJ about covid-19 spread virally. BMJ, 369:m2384.

Howard Wolinsky. 2005. Disease mongering and drug marketing: Does the pharmaceutical industry manufacture diseases as well as drugs? EMBO reports, 6(7):612–614.

Zhilin Yang, Zihang Dai, Yiming Yang, Jaime Carbonell, Russ R Salakhutdinov, and Quoc V Le. 2019. XLNet: Generalized Autoregressive Pretraining for Language Understanding. In H. Wallach, H. Larochelle, A. Beygelzimer, F. d'Alché Buc, E. Fox, and R. Garnett, editors, Advances in Neural Information Processing Systems 32, pages 5753–5763. Curran Associates, Inc.

A Yavchitz, I Boutron, A Bafeta, I Marroun, P Charles, J Mantz, and P Ravaud. 2012. Misrepresentation of Randomized Controlled Trials in Press Releases and News Coverage: A Cohort Study. PLoS Medicine, 9(9):e1001308..

Findings of the NLP4IF-2021 Shared Tasks on Fighting the COVID-19 Infodemic and Censorship Detection

Shaden Shaar,[1] **Firoj Alam,**[1] **Giovanni Da San Martino,**[2] **Alex Nikolov,**[3]
Wajdi Zaghouani,[4] **Preslav Nakov,** [1] and **Anna Feldman**[5]
[1] Qatar Computing Research Institute, HBKU, Qatar
[2] University of Padova, Italy, [3] Sofia University "St. Kliment Ohridski", Bulgaria,
[4] Hamad bin Khalifa University, Qatar, [5] Montclair State University, USA
{sshaar,fialam,wzaghouani,pnakov}@hbku.edu.qa
dasan@math.unipd.it feldmana@montclair.edu

Abstract

We present the results and the main findings of the NLP4IF-2021 shared tasks. Task 1 focused on fighting the COVID-19 infodemic in social media, and it was offered in Arabic, Bulgarian, and English. Given a tweet, it asked to predict whether that tweet contains a verifiable claim, and if so, whether it is likely to be false, is of general interest, is likely to be harmful, and is worthy of manual fact-checking; also, whether it is harmful to society, and whether it requires the attention of policy makers. Task 2 focused on censorship detection, and was offered in Chinese. A total of ten teams submitted systems for task 1, and one team participated in task 2; nine teams also submitted a system description paper. Here, we present the tasks, analyze the results, and discuss the system submissions and the methods they used. Most submissions achieved sizable improvements over several baselines, and the best systems used pre-trained Transformers and ensembles. The data, the scorers and the leaderboards for the tasks are available at `http://gitlab.com/NLP4IF/nlp4if-2021`.

1 Introduction

Social media have become a major communication channel, enabling fast dissemination and consumption of information. A lot of this information is true and shared in good intention; however, some is false and potentially harmful. While the so-called "fake news" is not a new phenomenon, e.g., the term was coined five years ago, the COVID-19 pandemic has given rise to the first global social media infodemic. The infodemic has elevated the problem to a whole new level, which goes beyond spreading fake news, rumors, and conspiracy theories, and extends to promoting fake cure, panic, racism, xenophobia, and mistrust in the authorities, among others. Identifying such false and potentially malicious information in tweets is important to journalists, fact-checkers, policy makers, government entities, social media platforms, and society.

A number of initiatives have been launched to fight this infodemic, e.g., by building and analyzing large collections of tweets, their content, source, propagators, and spread (Leng et al., 2021; Medford et al., 2020; Mourad et al., 2020; Karami et al., 2021). Yet, these efforts typically focus on a specific aspect, rather than studying the problem from a holistic perspective. Here we aim to bridge this gap by introducing a task that asks to predict whether a tweet contains a verifiable claim, and if so, whether it is likely to be false, is of general interest, is likely to be harmful, and is worthy of manual fact-checking; also, whether it is harmful to society, and whether it requires the attention of policy makers. The task follows an annotation schema proposed in (Alam et al., 2020, 2021b).

While the COVID-19 infodemic is characterized by insufficient attention paid to the problem, there are also examples of the opposite: tight control over information. In particular, freedom of expression in social media has been supercharged by a new and more effective form of digital authoritarianism. Political censorship exists in many countries, whose governments attempt to conceal or to manipulate information to make sure their citizens are unable to read or to express views that are contrary to those of people in power. One such example is Sina Weibo, a Chinese microblogging website with over 500 million monthly active users, which sets strict control over its content using a variety of strategies to target censorable posts, ranging from keyword list filtering to individual user monitoring: among all posts that are eventually censored, nearly 30% are removed within 5–30 minutes, and for 90% this is done within 24 hours (Zhu et al., 2013). We hypothesize that the former is done automatically, while the latter involves human censors. Thus, we propose a shared task that aims to study the potential for automatic sensorship, which asks participating systems to predict whether a Sina Weibo post will be censored.

Proceedings of the 4th NLP4IF Workshop on NLP for Internet Freedom, pages 82–92
June 6, 2021.

2 Related Work

In this section, we discuss studies relevant to the COVID-19 infodemic and to censorship detection.

2.1 COVID-19 Infodemic

Disinformation, misinformation, and "fake news" thrive in social media. Lazer et al. (2018) and Vosoughi et al. (2018) in *Science* provided a general discussion on the science of "fake news" and the process of proliferation of true and false news online. There have also been several interesting surveys, e.g., Shu et al. (2017) studied how information is disseminated and consumed in social media. Another survey by Thorne and Vlachos (2018) took a fact-checking perspective on "fake news" and related problems. Yet another survey (Li et al., 2016) covered truth discovery in general. Some very recent surveys focused on stance for misinformation and disinformation detection (Hardalov et al., 2021), on automatic fact-checking to assist human fact-checkers (Nakov et al., 2021a), on predicting the factuality and the bias of entire news outlets (Nakov et al., 2021c), on multimodal disinformation detection (Alam et al., 2021a), and on abusive language in social media (Nakov et al., 2021b).

A number of Twitter datasets have been developed to address the COVID-19 infodemic. Some are without labels, other use distant supervision, and very few are manually annotated. Cinelli et al. (2020) studied COVID-19 rumor amplification in five social media platforms; their data was labeled using distant supervision. Other datasets include a multi-lingual dataset of 123M tweets (Chen et al., 2020), another one of 383M tweets (Banda et al., 2020), a billion-scale dataset of 65 languages and 32M geo-tagged tweets (Abdul-Mageed et al., 2021), and the GeoCoV19 dataset, consisting of 524M multilingual tweets, including 491M with GPS coordinates (Qazi et al., 2020). There are also Arabic datasets, both with (Haouari et al., 2021; Mubarak and Hassan, 2021) and without manual annotations (Alqurashi et al., 2020). We are not aware of Bulgarian datasets.

Zhou et al. (2020) created the ReCOVery dataset, which combines 2,000 news articles about COVID-19, annotated for their factuality, with 140,820 tweets. Vidgen et al. (2020) studied COVID-19 prejudices using a manually labeled dataset of 20K tweets with the following labels: hostile, criticism, prejudice, and neutral.

Song et al. (2021) collected a dataset of false and misleading claims about COVID-19 from IFCN Poynter, which they manually annotated with the following ten disinformation-related categories: (1) Public authority, (2) Community spread and impact, (3) Medical advice, self-treatments, and virus effects, (4) Prominent actors, (5) Conspiracies, (6) Virus transmission, (7) Virus origins and properties, (8) Public reaction, and (9) Vaccines, medical treatments, and tests, and (10) Cannot determine.

Another related dataset study by (Pulido et al., 2020) analyzed 1,000 tweets and categorized them based on factuality into the following categories: *(i)* False information, *(ii)* Science-based evidence, *(iii)* Fact-checking tweets, *(iv)* Mixed information, *(v)* Facts, *(vi)* Other, and *(vii)* Not valid. Ding et al. (2020) have a position paper discussing the challenges in combating the COVID-19 infodemic in terms of data, tools, and ethics. Hossain et al. (2020) developed the COVIDLies dataset by matching a known misconceptions with tweets, and manually annotated the tweets with stance: whether the target tweet agrees, disagrees, or has no position with respect to a known misconception. Finally, (Shuja et al., 2020) provided a comprehensive survey categorizing the COVID-19 literature into four groups: diagonisis related, transmission and mobility, social media analysis, and knowledge-based approaches.

The most relevant previous work is (Alam et al., 2021b, 2020), where tweets about COVID-19 in Arabic and English were annotated based on an annotation schema of seven questions. Here, we adopt the same schema (but with binary labels only), but we have a larger dataset for Arabic and English, and we further add an additional language: Bulgarian.

2.2 Censorship Detection

There has been a lot of research aiming at developing strategies to detect and to evade censorship. Most work has focused on exploiting technological limitations with existing routing protocols (Leberknight et al., 2012; Katti et al., 2005; Levin et al., 2015; Weinberg et al., 2012; Bock et al., 2020). Research that pays more attention to the linguistic properties of online censorship in the context of censorship evasion includes Safaka et al. (2016), who applied linguistic steganography to circumvent censorship.

Other related work is that of Lee (2016), who used parodic satire to bypass censorship in China and claimed that this stylistic device delays and often evades censorship. Hiruncharoenvate et al. (2015) showed that the use of homophones of censored keywords on Sina Weibo could help extend the time for which a Weibo post could remain available online. All these methods require significant human effort to interpret and to annotate texts to evaluate the likelihood of censorship, which might not be practical to carry out for common Internet users in real life.

King et al. (2013) in turn studied the relationship between political criticism and the chance of censorship. They came to the conclusion that posts that have a Collective Action Potential get deleted by the censors even if they support the state. Zhang and Pan (2019) introduced a system, Collective Action from Social Media (CASM), which uses convolutional neural networks on image data and recurrent neural networks with long short-term memory on text data in a two-stage classifier to identify social media posts about offline collective action. Zhang and Pan (2019) found that despite online censorship in China suppressing the discussion of collective action in social media, censorship does not have a large impact on the number of collective action posts identified through CASM-China. Zhang and Pan (2019) claimed that the system would miss collective action taking place in ethnic minority regions, such as Tibet and Xinjiang, where social media penetration is lower and more stringent Internet control is in place, e.g., Internet blackouts.

Finally, there has been research that uses linguistic and content clues to detect censorship. Knockel et al. (2015) and Zhu et al. (2013) proposed detection mechanisms to categorize censored content and to automatically learn keywords that get censored. Bamman et al. (2012) uncovered a set of politically sensitive keywords and found that the presence of some of them in a Weibo blogpost contributed to a higher chance of the post being censored. Ng et al. (2018b) also targeted a set of topics that had been suggested to be sensitive, but unlike Bamman et al. (2012), they covered areas not limited to politics. Ng et al. (2018b), Ng et al. (2019), and Ng et al. (2020) investigated how the textual content might be relevant to censorship decisions when both censored and uncensored blogposts include the same sensitive keyword(s).

3 Tasks

Below, we describe the two tasks: their setup and their corresponding datasets.

3.1 Task 1: COVID-19 Infodemic

Task Setup: The task asks to predict several binary properties for an input tweet about COVID-19. These properties are formulated in seven questions as briefly discussed below:

1. **Verifiable Factual Claim:** *Does the tweet contain a verifiable factual claim?* A verifiable factual claim is a statement that something is true, and this can be verified using factual, verifiable information such as statistics, specific examples, or personal testimony. Following (Konstantinovskiy et al., 2018), factual claims could be (*a*) stating a definition, (*b*) mentioning a quantity in the present or in the past, (*c*) making a verifiable prediction about the future, (*d*) reference laws, procedures, and rules of operation, and (*e*) reference images or videos (e.g., "*This is a video showing a hospital in Spain.*"), (*f*) implying correlation or causation (such correlation/-causation needs to be explicit).

2. **False Information:** *To what extent does the tweet appear to contain false information?* This annotation determines how likely the tweet is to contain false information without fact-checking it, but looking at things like its style, metadata, and the credibility of the sources cited, etc.

3. **Interesting for the General Public:** *Will the tweet have an impact on or be of interest to the general public?* In general, claims about topics such as healthcare, political news and findings, and current events are of higher interest to the general public. Not all claims should be fact-checked, for example "*The sky is blue.*", albeit being a claim, is not interesting to the general public and thus should not be fact-checked.

4. **Harmfulness:** *To what extent is the tweet harmful to the society/person(s)/company(s)/product(s)?* The purpose of this question is to determine whether the content of the tweet aims to and can negatively affect the society as a whole, a specific person(s), a company(s), a product(s), or could spread rumors about them.[1]

[1]A rumor is a form of a statement whose veracity is not quickly or ever confirmed.

	Train	Dev	Test	Total
Arabic	520	2,536	1,000	4,056
Bulgarian	3,000	350	357	3,707
English	867	53	418	1,338

Table 1: **Task 1**: Statistics about the dataset.

	Train	Dev	Test	Total
censored	762	93	98	953
uncensored	750	96	91	937
Total	1,512	189	189	1,890

Table 2: **Task 2**: Statistics about the dataset.

5. **Need to Fact-Check:** *Do you think that a professional fact-checker should verify the claim in the tweet?* Not all factual claims are important or worth fact-checking by a professional fact-checker as this is a time-consuming process. For example, claims that could be fact-checked with a very simple search on the Internet probably do not need the attention of a professional fact-checker.

6. **Harmful to Society:** *Is the tweet harmful for the society?* The purpose of this question is to judge whether the content of the tweet is could be potentially harmful for the society, e.g., by being weaponized to mislead a large number of people. For example, a tweet might not be harmful because it is a joke, or it might be harmful because it spreads panic, rumors or conspiracy theories, promotes bad cures, or is xenophobic, racist, or hateful.

7. **Requires Attention:** *Do you think that this tweet should get the attention of government entities?* A variety of tweets might end up in this category, e.g., such blaming the authorities, calling for action, offering advice, discussing actions taken or possible cures, asking important questions (e.g., "*Will COVID-19 disappear in the summer?*"), etc.

Data: For this task, the dataset covers three different languages (Arabic, Bulgarian, and English), annotated with yes/no answers to the above questions. More details about the data collection and the annotation process, as well as statistics about the corpus can be found in (Alam et al., 2021b, 2020), where an earlier (and much smaller) version of the corpus is described. We annotated additional tweets for Arabic and Bulgarian for the shared task using the same annotation schema. Table 1 shows the distribution of the examples in the training, development and test sets for the three languages. Note that, we have more data for Arabic and Bulgarian than for English.

3.2 Task 2: Censorship Detection

Task Setup: For this task, we deal with a particular type of censorship – when a post gets removed from a social media platform semi-automatically based on its content. The goal is to predict which posts on Sina Weibo, a Chinese microblogging platform, will get removed from the platform, and which posts will remain on the website.

Data: Tracking censorship topics on Sina Weibo is a challenging task due to the transient nature of censored posts and the scarcity of censored data from well-known sources such as FreeWeibo[2] and WeiboScope[3]. The most straightforward way to collect data from a social media platform is to make use of its API. However, Sina Weibo imposes various restrictions on the use of its API[4] such as restricted access to certain endpoints and restricted number of posts returned per request. Above all, their API does not provide any endpoint that allows easy and efficient collection of the target data (posts that contain sensitive keywords). Therefore, Ng et al. (2019) and Ng et al. (2020) developed an alternative method to track censorship for our purposes. The reader is referred to the original articles to learn more details about the data collection. In a nutshell, the dataset contains censored and uncensored tweets, and it includes no images, no hyperlinks, no re-blogged content, and no duplicates.

For the present shared task 2, we use the balanced dataset described in (Ng et al., 2020) and (Ng et al., 2019). The data is collected across ten topics for a period of four months: from August 29, 2018 till December 29, 2018. Table 2 summarizes the datasets in terms of number of censored and uncensored tweets in the training, development, and testing sets, while Table 3 shows the main topics covered by the dataset.

[2] `http://freeweibo.com`

[3] `http://weiboscope.jmsc.hku.hk`

[4] http://open.weibo.com/wiki/API文档/en

Topic	Censored	Uncensored
cultural revolution	55	60
human rights	53	67
family planning	15	25
censorship & propaganda	32	54
democracy	119	107
patriotism	70	105
China	186	194
Trump	320	244
Meng Wanzhou	55	76
kindergarten abuse	48	5
Total	**953**	**937**

Table 3: **Task 2**: Topics featured in the dataset.

4 Task Organization

In this section, we describe the overall task organization, phases, and evaluation measures.

4.1 Task Phases

We ran the shared tasks in two phases:

Development Phase In the first phase, only training and development data were made available, and no gold labels were provided for the latter. The participants competed against each other to achieve the best performance on the development set.

Test Phase In the second phase, the test set (unlabeled input only) was released, and the participants were given a few days to submit their predictions.

4.2 Evaluation Measures

The official evaluation measure for task 1 was the average of the weighted F1 scores for each of the seven questions; for task 2, it was accuracy.

5 Evaluation Results for Task 1

Below, we describe the baselines, the evaluation results, and the best systems for each language.

5.1 Baselines

The baselines for Task 1 are (*i*) majority class, (*ii*) ngram, and (*iii*) random. The performance of these baselines on the official test set is shown in Tables 4, 5, and 6.

5.2 Results and Best Systems

The results on the official test set for English, Arabic, and Bulgarian are reported in Tables 4, 5, and 6, respectively. We can see that most participants managed to beat all baselines by a margin.

Below, we give a brief summary of the best performing systems for each language.

The English Winner: Team **TOKOFOU** (Tziafas et al., 2021) performed best for English. They gathered six BERT-based models pre-trained in relevant domains (e.g., Twitter and COVID-themed data) or fine-tuned on tasks, similar to the shared task's topic (e.g., hate speech and sarcasm detection). They fine-tuned each of these models on the task 1 training data, projecting a label from the sequence classification token for each of the seven questions in parallel. After model selection on the basis of development set F1 performance, they combined the models in a majority-class ensemble.

The Arabic Winner: Team **R00** had the best performing system for Arabic. They used an ensemble of the follwoing fine-tuned Arabic transformers: AraBERT (Antoun et al., 2020), Asafaya-BERT (Safaya et al., 2020), ARBERT. In addition, they also experimented with MARBERT (Abdul-Mageed et al., 2020).

The Bulgarian Winner: We did not receive a submission for the best performing team for Bulgarian. The second best team, **HunterSpeech-Lab** (Panda and Levitan, 2021), explored the cross-lingual generalization ability of multitask models trained from scratch (logistic regression, transformer encoder) and pre-trained models (English BERT, and mBERT) for deception detection.

5.3 Summary of All Systems

DamascusTeam (Hussein et al., 2021) used a two-step pipeline, where the first step involves a series of pre-processing procedures to transform Twitter jargon, including emojis and emoticons, into plain text. In the second step, a version of AraBERT is fine-tuned and used to classify the tweets. Their system was ranked 5th for Arabic.

Team dunder_mifflin (Suhane and Kowshik, 2021) built a multi-output model using task-wise multi-head attention for inter-task information aggregation. This was built on top of the representations obtained from RoBERTa. To tackle the small size of the dataset, they used back-translation for data augmentation. Their loss function was weighted for each output, in accordance with the distribution of the labels for that output. They were the runners-up in the English subtask with a mean F1-score of 0.891 on the test set, without the use of any task-specific embeddings or ensembles.

Rank	Team	F1	P	R	Q1	Q2	Q3	Q4	Q5	Q6	Q7
1	TOKOFOU	**0.897**	0.907	**0.896**	0.835	0.913	0.978	**0.873**	**0.882**	0.908	**0.889**
2	dunder_mifflin	0.891	0.907	0.878	0.807	0.923	0.966	0.868	0.852	**0.940**	0.884
3	NARNIA	0.881	0.900	0.879	0.831	0.925	0.976	0.822	0.854	0.909	0.849
4	InfoMiner	0.864	0.897	0.848	0.819	0.886	0.946	0.841	0.803	0.884	0.867
5	advex	0.858	0.882	0.864	0.784	**0.927**	0.987	0.858	0.703	0.878	0.866
6	LangResearchLabNC	0.856	**0.909**	0.827	**0.842**	0.873	0.914	0.829	0.792	0.894	0.849
	majority_baseline	0.830	0.786	0.883	0.612	**0.927**	**1.000**	0.770	0.807	0.873	0.821
	ngram_baseline	0.828	0.819	0.868	0.647	0.904	0.992	0.761	0.800	0.873	0.821
7	HunterSpeechLab	0.736	0.874	0.684	0.738	0.822	0.824	0.744	0.426	0.878	0.720
8	spotlight	0.729	0.907	0.676	0.813	0.822	0.217	0.764	0.701	0.905	0.877
	random_baseline	0.496	0.797	0.389	0.552	0.480	0.457	0.473	0.423	0.563	0.526

Table 4: **Task 1, English:** Evaluation results. For Q1 to Q7, the results are in terms of weighted F1 score.

Rank	Team	F1	P	R	Q1	Q2	Q3	Q4	Q5	Q6	Q7
1	R00	**0.781**	**0.842**	**0.763**	0.843	0.762	0.890	0.799	**0.596**	**0.912**	0.663
*	iCompass	0.748	0.784	0.737	0.797	0.746	0.881	0.796	0.544	0.885	0.585
2	HunterSpeechLab	0.741	0.804	0.700	0.797	0.729	0.878	0.731	0.500	0.861	**0.690**
3	advex	0.728	0.809	0.753	0.788	**0.821**	**0.981**	**0.859**	0.573	0.866	0.205
4	InfoMiner	0.707	0.837	0.639	**0.852**	0.704	0.774	0.743	0.593	0.698	0.588
	ngram_baseline	0.697	0.741	0.716	0.410	0.762	0.950	0.767	0.553	0.856	0.579
5	DamascusTeam	0.664	0.783	0.677	0.169	0.754	0.915	0.783	0.583	0.857	0.589
	majority_baseline	0.663	0.608	0.751	0.152	0.786	**0.981**	0.814	0.475	0.857	0.579
6	spotlight	0.661	0.805	0.632	0.843	0.703	0.792	0.647	0.194	0.828	0.620
	random_baseline	0.496	0.719	0.412	0.510	0.444	0.487	0.442	0.476	0.584	0.533

Table 5: **Task 1, Arabic:** Evaluation results. For Q1 to Q7, the results are in terms of weighted F1 score (The team iCompass submitted their system after the deadline, and thus we rank them with a $*$).

Rank	Team	F1	P	R	Q1	Q2	Q3	Q4	Q5	Q6	Q7
1	advex	**0.837**	**0.860**	**0.861**	0.887	**0.955**	0.980	0.834	**0.819**	**0.678**	**0.706**
2	HunterSpeechLab	0.817	0.819	0.837	**0.937**	0.943	0.968	**0.835**	0.748	0.605	0.686
	majority_baseline	0.792	0.742	0.855	0.876	0.951	**0.986**	0.822	0.672	0.606	0.630
	ngram_baseline	0.778	0.790	0.808	0.909	0.919	0.949	0.803	0.631	0.606	0.630
3	spotlight	0.686	0.844	0.648	0.832	0.926	0.336	0.669	0.687	0.650	0.700
4	InfoMiner	0.578	0.826	0.505	0.786	0.749	0.419	0.599	0.556	0.303	0.631
	random_baseline	0.496	0.768	0.400	0.594	0.502	0.470	0.480	0.399	0.498	0.528

Table 6: **Task 1, Bulgarian:** Evaluation results. For Q1 to Q7 results are in terms of weighted F1 score.

Team HunterSpeechLab (Panda and Levitan, 2021) participated in all three languages. They explored the cross-lingual generalization ability of multitask models trained from scratch (logistic regression, transformers) and pre-trained models (English BERT, mBERT) for deception detection. They were 2nd for Arabic and Bulgarian.

Team iCompass (Henia and Haddad, 2021) had a late submission for Arabic, and would have ranked 2nd. They used contextualized text representations from ARBERT, MARBERT, AraBERT, Arabic ALBERT and BERT-base-arabic, which they fine-tuned on the training data for task 1. They found that BERT-base-arabic performed best.

Team InfoMiner (Uyangodage et al., 2021) participated in all three subtasks, and were ranked 4th on all three. They used pre-trained transformer models, specifically BERT-base-cased, RoBERTa-base, BERT-multilingual-cased, and AraBERT. They optimized these transformer models for each question separately and used undersampling to deal with the fact that the data is imbalanced.

Team NARNIA (Kumar et al., 2021) experimented with a number of Deep Learning models, including different word embeddings such as Glove and ELMo, among others. They found that the BERTweet model achieved the best overall F1-score of 0.881, securing them the third place on the English subtask.

Team R00 (Qarqaz et al., 2021) had the best performing system for the Arabic subtask. They used an ensemble of neural networks combining a linear layer on top of one out of the following four pre-trained Arabic language models: AraBERT, Asafaya-BERT, ARBERT. In addition, they also experimented with MARBERT.

Team TOKOFOU (Tziafas et al., 2021) participated in English only and theirs was the winning system for that language. They gathered six BERT-based models pre-trained in relevant domains (e.g., Twitter and COVID-themed data) or fine-tuned on tasks, similar to the shared task's topic (e.g., hate speech and sarcasm detection). They fine-tuned each of these models on the task 1 training data, projecting a label from the sequence classification token for each of the seven questions in parallel. After carrying out model selection on the basis of the F1 score on the development set, they combined the models in a majority-class ensemble in order to counteract the small size of the dataset and to ensure robustness.

5.4 Summary of the Approaches

Tables 7, 8 and 9 offer a high-level comparison of the approaches taken by the participating systems for English, Arabic and Bulgarian, respectively (unfortunately, in these comparisons, we miss two systems, which did not submit a system description paper). We can see that across all languages, the participants have used transformer-based models, monolingual or multilingual. In terms of models, SVM and logistic regression were used. Some teams also used ensembles and data augmentation.

Ranks Team	Trans.		Models		Repres.		Misc		
	BERT	RoBERTa	Logistic Regression	SVM	ELMo	GloVe	Ensemble	Under/Over-Sampling	Data Augmentation
1. TOKOFOU	☑						☑		
2. dunder_mifflin		☑							☑
3. NARNIA	☑			✓	✓	✓	✓		
4. InfoMiner	☑	✓						☑	
7. HunterSpeechLab	☑		☑						

1 (Tziafas et al., 2021)
2 (Suhane and Kowshik, 2021)
3 (Kumar et al., 2021)
4 (Uyangodage et al., 2021)
7 (Panda and Levitan, 2021)

Table 7: **Task 1:** Overview of the approaches used by the participating systems for **English**. ☑=part of the official submission; ✓=considered in internal experiments; *Trans.* is for Transformers; *Repres.* is for Representations. References to system description papers are shown below the table.

Ranks Team	Trans.						Models	Misc	
	BERT multilingual	AraBERT	Asafaya-BERT	ARBERT	ALBERT	MARBERT	Logistic Regression	Ensemble	Under/Over-Sampling
1. R00		☑	☑	☑		☑		☑	
* iCampass		☑		✓	✓	✓			
2. HunterSpeechLab	☑						☑		
4. InfoMiner	✓	☑							☑
5. DamascusTeam				☑					

1 (Qarqaz et al., 2021)
∗ (Henia and Haddad, 2021)
2 (Panda and Levitan, 2021)
4 (Uyangodage et al., 2021)
5 (Hussein et al., 2021)

Table 8: **Task 1:** Overview of the approaches used by the participating systems for **Arabic**.

Ranks Team	Trans.	Models	Misc
	BERT multilingual	Logistic Regression	Under/Over-Sampling
2. HunterSpeechLab	☑	☑	
4. InfoMiner	☑		☑

2 (Panda and Levitan, 2021)
4 (Uyangodage et al., 2021)

Table 9: **Task 1:** Overview of the approaches used by the participating systems for **Bulgarian**.

Team	P	R	F1	A
NITK_NLP	c: 0.69 u: 0.61	c: 0.56 u: 0.73	c: 0.62 u: 0.66	0.64
Baseline from (Ng et al., 2020)	c: 0.82 u: 0.76	c: 0.79 u: 0.79	c: 0.80 u: 0.77	0.80
Majority baseline				0.50
Human baseline (Ng et al., 2020)				0.24

Table 10: **Task 2:** the NITK_NLP team's results. Here: *c* is censored and *u* is uncensored.

6 Evaluation Results for Task 2

Below, we report the results for the baselines and for the participating system.

6.1 Baselines

For task 2, we have three baselines as shown in Table 10: a majority class baseline, as before, and two additional baselines described in (Ng et al., 2020). The first additional baseline is a human baseline based on crowdsourcing. The second additional baseline is a multilayer perceptron (MLP) using linguistic features as well as such measuring the complexity of the text, e.g., in terms of its readability, ambiguity, and idiomaticity. These features are motivated by observations that censored texts are typically more negative, more idiomatic, contain more content words and more complex semantic categories. Moreover, censored tweets use more verbs, which indirectly points to the Collective Action Potential. In contrast, uncensored posts are generally more positive, and contain words related to leisure, reward, and money.

6.2 Results

Due to the unorthodox application, and perhaps to the sensitivity of the data, task 2 received only one submission: from team NITK_NLP. The team used a pre-trained XLNet-based Chinese model by Cui et al. (2020), which they fine-tuned for 20 epochs, using the Adam optimizer. The evaluation results for that system are shown in Table 10. We can see that while the system outperformed both the human baseline and the majority class baseline by a large margin, it could not beat the MLP baseline. This suggests that capturing the linguistic fingerprints of censorship might indeed be important, and thus probably should be considered, e.g., in combination with deep contextualized representations from transformers (Ng et al., 2018a, 2019, 2020).

7 Conclusion and Future Work

We have presented the NLP4IF-2021 shared tasks on fighting the COVID-19 infodemic in social media (offered in Arabic, Bulgarian, and English) and on censorship detection (offered in Chinese).

In future work, we plan to extend the dataset to cover more examples, e.g., from more recent periods when the attention has shifted from COVID-19 in general to vaccines. We further plan to develop similar datasets for other languages.

Ethical Considerations

While our datasets do not contain personally identifiable information, creating systems for our tasks could face a "dual-use dilemma," as they could be misused by malicious actors. Yet, we believe that the need for replicable and transparent research outweigh concerns about dual-use in our case.

Acknowledgments

We would like to thank Akter Fatema, Al-Awthan Ahmed, Al-Dobashi Hussein, El Messelmani Jana, Fayoumi Sereen, Mohamed Esraa, Ragab Saleh, and Shurafa Chereen for helping with the Arabic data annotations.

This research is part of the Tanbih mega-project, developed at the Qatar Computing Research Institute, HBKU, which aims to limit the impact of "fake news," propaganda, and media bias by making users aware of what they are reading.

This material is also based upon work supported by the US National Science Foundation under Grants No. 1704113 and No. 1828199.

This publication was also partially made possible by the innovation grant No. 21 – Misinformation and Social Networks Analysis in Qatar from Hamad Bin Khalifa University's (HBKU) Innovation Center. The findings achieved herein are solely the responsibility of the authors.

References

Muhammad Abdul-Mageed, AbdelRahim Elmadany, and El Moatez Billah Nagoudi. 2020. ARBERT & MARBERT: Deep bidirectional transformers for Arabic. *arXiv/2101.01785*.

Muhammad Abdul-Mageed, AbdelRahim Elmadany, El Moatez Billah Nagoudi, Dinesh Pabbi, Kunal Verma, and Rannie Lin. 2021. Mega-COV: A billion-scale dataset of 100+ languages for COVID-19. In *Proceedings of the 16th Conference of the European Chapter of the Association for Computational Linguistics*, EACL '21, pages 3402–3420.

Firoj Alam, Stefano Cresci, Tanmoy Chakraborty, Fabrizio Silvestri, Dimiter Dimitrov, Giovanni Da San Martino, Shaden Shaar, Hamed Firooz, and Preslav Nakov. 2021a. A survey on multimodal disinformation detection. *arXiv/2103.12541*.

Firoj Alam, Fahim Dalvi, Shaden Shaar, Nadir Durrani, Hamdy Mubarak, Alex Nikolov, Giovanni Da San Martino, Ahmed Abdelali, Hassan Sajjad, Kareem Darwish, and Preslav Nakov. 2021b. Fighting the COVID-19 infodemic in social media: A holistic perspective and a call to arms. In *Proceedings of the International AAAI Conference on Web and Social Media*, ICWSM '21.

Firoj Alam, Shaden Shaar, Fahim Dalvi, Hassan Sajjad, Alex Nikolov, Hamdy Mubarak, Giovanni Da San Martino, Ahmed Abdelali, Nadir Durrani, Kareem Darwish, and Preslav Nakov. 2020. Fighting the COVID-19 infodemic: Modeling the perspective of journalists, fact-checkers, social media platforms, policy makers, and the society. *arXiv/2005.00033*.

Sarah Alqurashi, Ahmad Alhindi, and Eisa Alanazi. 2020. Large Arabic Twitter dataset on COVID-19. *arXiv/2004.04315*.

Wissam Antoun, Fady Baly, and Hazem Hajj. 2020. AraBERT: Transformer-based model for Arabic language understanding. In *Proceedings of the 4th Workshop on Open-Source Arabic Corpora and Processing Tools*, OSACT '20, pages 9–15, Marseille, France.

David Bamman, Brendan O'Connor, and Noah A. Smith. 2012. Censorship and deletion practices in Chinese social media. *First Monday*, 17(3).

Juan M Banda, Ramya Tekumalla, Guanyu Wang, Jingyuan Yu, Tuo Liu, Yuning Ding, and Gerardo Chowell. 2020. A large-scale COVID-19 Twitter chatter dataset for open scientific research – an international collaboration. *arXiv:2004.03688*.

Kevin Bock, Yair Fax, Kyle Reese, Jasraj Singh, and Dave Levin. 2020. Detecting and evading censorship-in-depth: A case study of Iran's protocol whitelister. In *Proceedings of the 10th USENIX Workshop on Free and Open Communications on the Internet*, FOCI '20.

Emily Chen, Kristina Lerman, and Emilio Ferrara. 2020. Tracking social media discourse about the COVID-19 pandemic: Development of a public coronavirus Twitter data set. *JMIR*, 6(2):e19273.

Matteo Cinelli, Walter Quattrociocchi, Alessandro Galeazzi, Carlo Michele Valensise, Emanuele Brugnoli, Ana Lucia Schmidt, Paola Zola, Fabiana Zollo, and Antonio Scala. 2020. The COVID-19 social media infodemic. *Sci. Reports*, 10(1):1–10.

Yiming Cui, Wanxiang Che, Ting Liu, Bing Qin, Shijin Wang, and Guoping Hu. 2020. Revisiting pretrained models for Chinese natural language processing. In *Findings of the Association for Computational Linguistics: EMNLP 2020*, pages 657–668.

Kaize Ding, Kai Shu, Yichuan Li, Amrita Bhattacharjee, and Huan Liu. 2020. Challenges in combating COVID-19 infodemic – data, tools, and ethics. *arXiv/2005.13691*.

Fatima Haouari, Maram Hasanain, Reem Suwaileh, and Tamer Elsayed. 2021. ArCOV19-rumors: Arabic COVID-19 Twitter dataset for misinformation detection. In *Proceedings of the Sixth Arabic Natural Language Processing Workshop*, ANLP '21, pages 72–81, Kyiv, Ukraine (Virtual).

Momchil Hardalov, Arnav Arora, Preslav Nakov, and Isabelle Augenstein. 2021. A survey on stance detection for mis- and disinformation identification. *arXiv/2103.00242*.

Wassim Henia and Hatem Haddad. 2021. iCompass at NLP4IF-2021–Fighting the COVID-19 infodemic. In *Proceedings of the Fourth Workshop on Natural Language Processing for Internet Freedom: Censorship, Disinformation, and Propaganda*, NLP4IF@NAACL' 21.

Chaya Hiruncharoenvate, Zhiyuan Lin, and Eric Gilbert. 2015. Algorithmically bypassing censorship on Sina Weibo with nondeterministic homophone substitutions. In *Proceedings of the Ninth International Conference on Web and Social Media*, ICWSM '15, pages 150–158, Oxford, UK.

Tamanna Hossain, Robert L Logan IV, Arjuna Ugarte, Yoshitomo Matsubara, Sean Young, and Sameer Singh. 2020. COVIDLies: Detecting COVID-19 misinformation on social media. In *Proceedings of the 1st Workshop on NLP for COVID-19 (Part 2) at EMNLP 2020*.

Ahmad Hussein, Nada Ghneim, and Ammar Joukhadar. 2021. DamascusTeam at NLP4IF2021: Fighting the Arabic COVID-19 Infodemic on Twitter using AraBERT. In *Proceedings of the Fourth Workshop on Natural Language Processing for Internet Freedom: Censorship, Disinformation, and Propaganda*, NLP4IF@NAACL' 21.

Amir Karami, Morgan Lundy, Frank Webb, Gabrielle Turner-McGrievy, Brooke W McKeever, and Robert

McKeever. 2021. Identifying and analyzing health-related themes in disinformation shared by conservative and liberal Russian trolls on Twitter. *Int. J. Environ. Res. Public Health*, 18(4):2159.

Sachin Katti, Dina Katabi, and Katarzyna Puchala. 2005. Slicing the onion: Anonymous routing without PKI. Technical report, MIT CSAIL Technical Report 1000.

Gary King, Jennifer Pan, and Margaret E Roberts. 2013. How censorship in China allows government criticism but silences collective expression. *American Political Science Review*, 107(2):1–18.

Jeffrey Knockel, Masashi Crete-Nishihata, Jason Q. Ng, Adam Senft, and Jedidiah R. Crandall. 2015. Every rose has its thorn: Censorship and surveillance on social video platforms in China. In *Proceedings of the 5th USENIX Workshop on Free and Open Communications on the Internet*, FOCI '15, Washington, D.C., USA.

Lev Konstantinovskiy, Oliver Price, Mevan Babakar, and Arkaitz Zubiaga. 2018. Towards automated factchecking: Developing an annotation schema and benchmark for consistent automated claim detection. *arXiv/1809.08193*.

Ankit Kumar, Naman Jhunjhunwala, Raksha Agarwal, and Niladri Chatterjee. 2021. NARNIA at NLP4IF-2021: Identification of misinformation in COVID-19 tweets using BERTweet. In *Proceedings of the Fourth Workshop on Natural Language Processing for Internet Freedom: Censorship, Disinformation, and Propaganda*, NLP4IF@NAACL' 21.

David M.J. Lazer, Matthew A. Baum, Yochai Benkler, Adam J. Berinsky, Kelly M. Greenhill, Filippo Menczer, Miriam J. Metzger, Brendan Nyhan, Gordon Pennycook, David Rothschild, Michael Schudson, Steven A. Sloman, Cass R. Sunstein, Emily A. Thorson, Duncan J. Watts, and Jonathan L. Zittrain. 2018. The science of fake news. *Science*, 359(6380):1094–1096.

Christopher S. Leberknight, Mung Chiang, and Felix Ming Fai Wong. 2012. A taxonomy of censors and anti-censors: Part I: Impacts of internet censorship. *International Journal of E-Politics (IJEP)*, 3(2).

Siu-yau Lee. 2016. Surviving online censorship in China: Three satirical tactics and their impact. *The China Quarterly*, 228:1061–1080.

Yan Leng, Yujia Zhai, Shaojing Sun, Yifei Wu, Jordan Selzer, Sharon Strover, Hezhao Zhang, Anfan Chen, and Ying Ding. 2021. Misinformation during the COVID-19 outbreak in China: Cultural, social and political entanglements. *IEEE Trans. on Big Data*, 7(1):69–80.

Dave Levin, Youndo Lee, Luke Valenta, Zhihao Li, Victoria Lai, Cristian Lumezanu, Neil Spring, and Bobby Bhattacharjee. 2015. Alibi routing. In *Proceedings of the 2015 ACM Conference of the Special Interest Group on Data Communication*, SIGCOMM '15, pages 611–624, London, UK.

Yaliang Li, Jing Gao, Chuishi Meng, Qi Li, Lu Su, Bo Zhao, Wei Fan, and Jiawei Han. 2016. A survey on truth discovery. *SIGKDD Explor. Newsl.*, 17(2):1–16.

Richard J Medford, Sameh N Saleh, Andrew Sumarsono, Trish M Perl, and Christoph U Lehmann. 2020. An "Infodemic": Leveraging high-volume Twitter data to understand early public sentiment for the coronavirus disease 2019 outbreak. *OFID*, 7(7).

Azzam Mourad, Ali Srour, Haidar Harmanai, Cathia Jenainati, and Mohamad Arafeh. 2020. Critical impact of social networks infodemic on defeating coronavirus COVID-19 pandemic: Twitter-based study and research directions. *IEEE TNSM*, 17(4):2145–2155.

Hamdy Mubarak and Sabit Hassan. 2021. ArCorona: Analyzing Arabic tweets in the early days of coronavirus (COVID-19) pandemic. In *Proceedings of the 12th International Workshop on Health Text Mining and Information Analysis*, pages 1–6.

Preslav Nakov, David Corney, Maram Hasanain, Firoj Alam, Tamer Elsayed, Alberto Barrón-Cedeño, Paolo Papotti, Shaden Shaar, and Giovanni Da San Martino. 2021a. Automated fact-checking for assisting human fact-checkers. *arXiv/2103.07769*.

Preslav Nakov, Vibha Nayak, Kyle Dent, Ameya Bhatawdekar, Sheikh Muhammad Sarwar, Momchil Hardalov, Yoan Dinkov, Dimitrina Zlatkova, Guillaume Bouchard, and Isabelle Augenstein. 2021b. Detecting abusive language on online platforms: A critical analysis. *arXiv/2103.00153*.

Preslav Nakov, Husrev Taha Sencar, Jisun An, and Haewoon Kwak. 2021c. A survey on predicting the factuality and the bias of news media. *arXiv/2103.12506*.

Kei Yin Ng, Anna Feldman, and Chris Leberknight. 2018a. Detecting censorable content on Sina Weibo: A pilot study. In *Proceedings of the 10th Hellenic Conference on Artificial Intelligence*, SETN '18, Patras, Greece.

Kei Yin Ng, Anna Feldman, and Jing Peng. 2020. Linguistic fingerprints of internet censorship: the case of Sina Weibo. In *Proceedings of the Thirty-Fourth AAAI Conference on Artificial Intelligence*, AAAI '20, pages 446–453.

Kei Yin Ng, Anna Feldman, Jing Peng, and Chris Leberknight. 2018b. Linguistic characteristics of censorable language on SinaWeibo. In *Proceedings of the First Workshop on Natural Language Processing for Internet Freedom*, NLP4IF '18, pages 12–22, Santa Fe, New Mexico, USA.

Kei Yin Ng, Anna Feldman, Jing Peng, and Chris Leberknight. 2019. Neural network prediction of censorable language. In *Proceedings of the Third Workshop on Natural Language Processing and Computational Social Science*, pages 40–46, Minneapolis, Minnesota, USA.

Subhadarshi Panda and Sarah Ita Levitan. 2021. Detecting multilingual COVID-19 misinformation on social media via contextualized embeddings. In *Proceedings of the Fourth Workshop on Natural Language Processing for Internet Freedom: Censorship, Disinformation, and Propaganda*, NLP4IF@NAACL' 21.

Cristina M Pulido, Beatriz Villarejo-Carballido, Gisela Redondo-Sama, and Aitor Gómez. 2020. COVID-19 infodemic: More retweets for science-based information on coronavirus than for false information. *International Sociology*, 35(4):377–392.

Ahmed Qarqaz, Dia Abujaber, and Malak A. Abdullah. 2021. R00 at NLP4IF-2021: Fighting COVID-19 infodemic with transformers and more transformers. In *Proceedings of the Fourth Workshop on Natural Language Processing for Internet Freedom: Censorship, Disinformation, and Propaganda*, NLP4IF@NAACL' 21.

Umair Qazi, Muhammad Imran, and Ferda Ofli. 2020. GeoCoV19: A dataset of hundreds of millions of multilingual COVID-19 tweets with location information. *SIGSPATIAL Special*, 12(1):6–15.

Iris Safaka, Christina Fragouli, and Katerina Argyraki. 2016. Matryoshka: Hiding secret communication in plain sight. In *Proceedings of the 6th USENIX Workshop on Free and Open Communications*, FOCI '16.

Ali Safaya, Moutasem Abdullatif, and Deniz Yuret. 2020. KUISAIL at SemEval-2020 task 12: BERT-CNN for offensive speech identification in social media. In *Proceedings of the Fourteenth Workshop on Semantic Evaluation*, SemEval '20, pages 2054–2059, Barcelona, Spain.

Kai Shu, Amy Sliva, Suhang Wang, Jiliang Tang, and Huan Liu. 2017. Fake news detection on social media: A data mining perspective. *SIGKDD Explor. Newsl.*, 19(1):22–36.

Junaid Shuja, Eisa Alanazi, Waleed Alasmary, and Abdulaziz Alashaikh. 2020. COVID-19 open source data sets: A comprehensive survey. *Applied Intelligence*, pages 1–30.

Xingyi Song, Johann Petrak, Ye Jiang, Iknoor Singh, Diana Maynard, and Kalina Bontcheva. 2021. Classification aware neural topic model for COVID-19 disinformation categorisation. *PLOS ONE*, 16(2).

Ayush Suhane and Shreyas Kowshik. 2021. Multi output learning using task wise attention for predicting binary properties of tweets: Shared-task-on-fighting the COVID-19 infodemic. In *Proceedings of the Fourth Workshop on Natural Language Processing for Internet Freedom: Censorship, Disinformation, and Propaganda*, NLP4IF@NAACL' 21.

James Thorne and Andreas Vlachos. 2018. Automated fact checking: Task formulations, methods and future directions. In *Proceedings of the 27th International Conference on Computational Linguistics*, COLING '18, pages 3346–3359, Santa Fe, New Mexico, USA.

Giorgos Tziafas, Konstantinos Kogkalidis, and Tommaso Caselli. 2021. Fighting the COVID-19 infodemic with a holistic BERT ensemble. In *Proceedings of the Fourth Workshop on Natural Language Processing for Internet Freedom: Censorship, Disinformation, and Propaganda*, NLP4IF@NAACL' 21.

Lasitha Uyangodage, Tharindu Ranasinghe, and Hansi Hettiarachchi. 2021. Transformers to fight the COVID-19 infodemic. In *Proceedings of the Fourth Workshop on Natural Language Processing for Internet Freedom: Censorship, Disinformation, and Propaganda*, NLP4IF@NAACL' 21.

Bertie Vidgen, Scott Hale, Ella Guest, Helen Margetts, David Broniatowski, Zeerak Waseem, Austin Botelho, Matthew Hall, and Rebekah Tromble. 2020. Detecting East Asian prejudice on social media. In *Proceedings of the Workshop on Online Abuse and Harms*, pages 162–172.

Soroush Vosoughi, Deb Roy, and Sinan Aral. 2018. The spread of true and false news online. *Science*, 359(6380):1146–1151.

Zachary Weinberg, Jeffrey Wang, Vinod Yegneswaran, Linda Briesemeister, Steven Cheung, Frank Wang, and Dan Boneh. 2012. StegoTorus: A camouflage proxy for the Tor anonymity system. In *Proceedings of the 2012 ACM Conference on Computer and Communications Security*, CCS '12, page 109–120, Raleigh, North Carolina, USA.

Han Zhang and Jennifer Pan. 2019. CASM: A deep-learning approach for identifying collective action events with text and image data from social media. *Sociological Methodology*, 49(1):1–57.

Xinyi Zhou, Apurva Mulay, Emilio Ferrara, and Reza Zafarani. 2020. ReCOVery: A multimodal repository for COVID-19 news credibility research. In *Proceedings of the 29th ACM International Conference on Information & Knowledge Management*, CIKM '20, page 3205–3212, Galway, Ireland (Virtual Event).

Tao Zhu, David Phipps, Adam Pridgen, Jedidiah R. Crandall, and Dan S. Wallach. 2013. The velocity of censorship: High-fidelity detection of microblog post deletions. In *Proceedings of the 22nd USENIX Conference on Security*, SEC'13, pages 227–240, Washington, D.C., USA.

DamascusTeam at NLP4IF2021: Fighting the Arabic COVID-19 Infodemic on Twitter Using AraBERT

Ahmad Hussein[1], Nada Ghneim[2], and Ammar Joukhadar[1]

[1]Faculty of Information Technology Engineering, Damascus University, Damascus, Syria
ahmadhussein.ah7gmail.com, ajoukhadar@el-ixir.com
[2]Faculty of Informatics&Communication Engineering, Arab International University, Damascus, Syria
n-ghneim@aiu.edu.sy

Abstract

In the modern era of computing, the news ecosystem has transformed from old traditional print media to social media outlets. Social media platforms allow us to consume news much faster, with less restricted editing results in the spread of infodemic misinformation at an incredible pace and scale. Consequently, the research on the infodemic of the post's misinformation is becoming more important than ever before. In this paper, we present our approach using AraBERT (Transformer-based Model for Arabic Language Understanding) to predict 7 binary properties of an Arabic tweet about COVID-19. To train our classification models, we use the dataset provided by NLP4IF 2021. We ranked 5th in the Fighting the COVID-19 Infodemic task results with an F1 of 0.664.

1 Introduction

In the past few years, various social media platforms such as Twitter, Facebook, Instagram, etc. have become very popular since they facilitate the easy acquisition of information and provide a quick platform for information sharing (Vicario et al., 2016; Kumar et al., 2018). The work presented in this paper primarily focuses on Twitter. Twitter is a micro-blogging web service with over 330 million Active Twitter Users per month, and has gained popularity as a major news source and information dissemination agent over the last years. Twitter provides the ground information and helps in reaching out to people in need, thus it plays an important role in aiding crisis management teams as the researchers have shown (Ntalla et al., 2015). The availability of unauthentic data on social media platforms has gained massive attention among researchers and become a hot-spot for sharing misinformation (Gorrell et al., 2019; Vosoughi et al., 2017). Infodemic misinformation has been an important issue due to its tremendous negative impact (Gorrell et al., 2019; Vosoughi et al., 2017; Zhou et al., 2018), it has increased attention among researchers, journalists, politicians and the general public. In the context of writing style, misinformation is written or published with the intent to mislead the people and to damage the image of an agency, entity, person, either for financial or political benefits (Zhou et al., 2018; Ghosh et al., 2018; Ruchansky et al., 2017; Shu et al., 2020).

This paper is organized as follows: Section 2 describes the related work in this domain; Section 3 gives our methodology in detail; Section 4 discusses the evaluation of our proposed solution and finally, the last section gives the conclusion and describes future works.

2 Related Works

There are various techniques used to solve the problem of infodemic misinformation on Online Social Media, especially in English content. This section briefly summarizes the work in this field. Allcott et al. (2017) have focused on a quantitative report to understand the impact of misinformation on social media in the 2016 U.S. Presidential General Election and its effect upon U.S. voters.

Proceedings of the 4th NLP4IF Workshop on NLP for Internet Freedom, pages 93–98
June 6, 2021.

Authors have investigated the authentic and unauthentic URLs related to misinformation from the BuzzFeed dataset. Shu et al. (2019) have investigated a way for robotization process through hashtag recurrence. Authors have also presented a comprehensive review of detecting misinformation on social media, false news classifications on psychology and social concepts, and existing algorithms from a data mining perspective. Ghosh et al. (2018) have investigated the impact of web-based social networking on political decisions. Quantity research (Zhou et al., 2018; Allcott et al., 2017; Zubiaga et al., 2018) has been done in the context of detecting political-news-based articles. Authors have investigated the effect of various political gatherings related to the discussion of any misinformation as agenda. Authors have also explored the Twitter-based data of six Venezuelan government officials with a specific end goal to investigate bot collaboration. Their discoveries recommend that political bots in Venezuela tend to imitate individuals from political gatherings or basic natives. In one of the studies, Zhou et al. (2018) have investigated the ability of social media to aggregate the judgments of a large community of users. In their further investigation, they have explained machine learning approaches with the end goal to develop a better rumors detection. They have investigated the difficulties for the spread of rumors, rumors classification, and deception for the advancement of such frameworks. They have also investigated the utilization of such useful strategies towards creating fascinating structures that can help individuals in settling on choices towards evaluating the integrity of data gathered from various social media platforms. In one of the studies, Jwa et al. (2019) have explored the approach towards automatic misinformation detection. They have used Bidirectional Encoder Representations from Transformers model (BERT) model to detect misinformation by analyzing the relationship between the headline and the body text of the news story. Their results improve the 0.14 F-score over existing state-of-the-art models. Williams et al. (2020) utilized BERT and RoBERTa models to identify claims in social media text a professional fact-checker should review. For the English language, they fine-tuned a RoBERTa model and added an extra mean pooling layer and a dropout layer to enhance generalizability to unseen text. For the Arabic language, they fine-tuned Arabic-language BERT models and demonstrate the use of back-translation to amplify the minority class and balance the dataset. Hussein et al. (2020) presented their approach to analyze the worthiness of Arabic information on Twitter. To train the classification model, they annotated for worthiness a dataset of 5000 Arabic tweets -corresponding to 4 high impact news events of 2020 around the world, in addition to a dataset of 1500 tweets provided by CLEF 2020. They proposed two models to classify the worthiness of Arabic tweets: BI-LSTM model, and a CNN-LSTM model. Results show that BI-LSTM model can extract better the worthiness of tweets.

3 Methodology

In this section, we will present our methodology by explaining the different steps of building the models, we use the same architecture for building them: Data Set, Data Preprocessing, AraBERT System Architecture, and Model Training.

3.1 Data Set

We used a dataset of 2556 tweets provided by NLP4IF 2021 (Shaar et al., 2021), which includes tweets about COVID-19. The dataset includes besides the tweet text and the tweet Id. Each tweet annotates with binary properties about COVID-19: whether it contains a verifiable claim (Q1), whether it appears to contain false information (Q2), whether it may be of interest to the general public (Q3), whether it is harmful (Q4), whether it needs to verification (Q5), whether it is harmful to society (Q6) and whether it requires attention of government entities (Q7). Each question has a Yes/No (binary) annotation. However, the answers to Q2, Q3, Q4 and Q5 are all "nan" if the answer to Q1 is No. Table 1 shows the statistics of the class labels for each property in the dataset.

Classifier	Yes	No	Not Sure
Q1	1926	610	0
Q2	376	1545	635
Q3	1895	22	639
Q4	351	1566	639
Q5	936	990	630
Q6	2075	459	0
Q7	2208	328	0

Table 1: Dataset with the class labels

3.2 Data Preprocessing

Tweets have certain special features, i.e., emojis, emoticons, hashtags and user mentions, coupled with typical web constructs, such as email addresses and URLs, and other noisy sources, such as phone numbers, percentages, money amounts, time, date, and generic numbers. In this work, a set of pre-processing procedures, which has been tailored to translate tweets into a more conventional form sentences, is adopted. Most of the noisy entities are normalized because their particular instances generally do not contribute to the identification of the class within a sentence. Regarding date, email addresses, money amounts, numbers, percentages, phone numbers and time, this process is performed by using the ekphrasis tool[1] (Baziotis et al., 2017), which enables to individuate regular expressions and replace them with normalized forms.

3.3 AraBERT System Architecture

Among modern language modeling architectures, AraBERT (Antoun et al., 2020) is one of the most popular for Arabic language. Its generalization capability is such that it can be adapted to different down-stream tasks according to different needs, be it NER or relation extraction, question answering or sentiment analysis. The core of the architecture is trained on particularly large text corpora and, consequently, the parameters of the most internal layers of the architecture are frozen. The outermost layers are instead those that adapt to the task and on which the so-called fine-tuning is performed. An overview is shown in Figure 1.

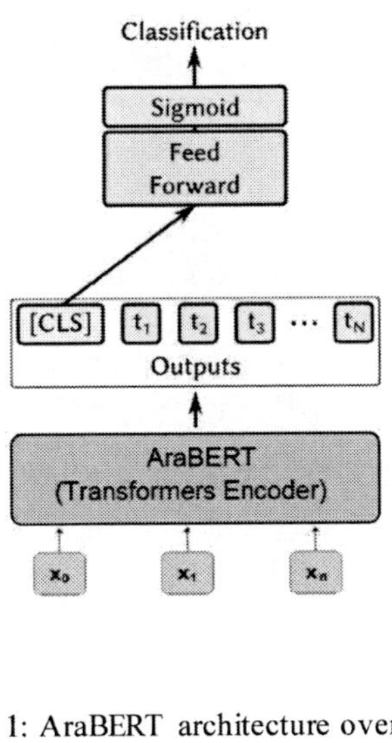

Figure 1: AraBERT architecture overview.

Going into details, one can distinguish two main architectures of AraBERT, the base and the large. The architectures differ mainly in four fundamental aspects: the number of hidden layers in the transformer encoder, also known as transformer blocks (12 vs. 24), the number of attention heads, also known as self-attention (Vaswani et al., 2017) (12 vs. 16), the hidden size of the feed-forward networks (768 vs. 1024) and finally the maximum sequence length parameter (512 vs. 1024), i.e., the maximum accepted input vector size. In this work, the base architecture is used, and the corresponding hyper-parameters are reported in Table 2.

Hyperparameter	Value
Attention heads	12
Batch size	6
Epochs	10
Gradient accumulation steps	16
Hidden size	768
Hidden layers	12
Learning rate	0.00002
Maximum sequence length	128
Parameters	136 M

Table 2: Hyper-parameters of the model

In addition, the AraBERT architecture employs two special tokens: [SEP] for segment separation and [CLS] for classification, used as the first input token for any classifier, representing the whole sequence and from which an output vector of the same size as the hidden size H is derived. Hence, the output of the transformers, i.e., the final hidden state of this first token used as input, can be denoted as a vector $C \in R^H$. The vector C is used as input of the final fully-connected classification layer. Given the parameter matrix $W \in R^{KxH}$ of the classification layer, where K is the number of

[1] https://github.com/cbaziotis/ekphrasis

categories, the probability of each category P can be calculated by the softmax function as:

$$P = softmax(CW^T)$$

3.4 Model Training

The whole classification model has been trained in two steps, involving firstly the pre-training of the AraBERT language model and then the fine-tuning of the outermost classification layer. The AraBERTv0.2-base (Antoun et al., 2020) is pre-trained on five corpora: OSCAR unshuffled and filtered, Arabic Wikipedia dump, the 1.5B words, Arabic corpus, the OSIAN corpus and Assafir news articles with a final corpus size equal to about 77 GB. The cased version was chosen, being more suitable for the proposed pre-processing method. The fine-tuning of the model was performed by using labeled tweets comprising the training set provided for the shared task. In particular, the fully connected classification layer was learned accordingly. During training, the loss function used was categorical cross-entropy. For this study, the hyper-parameters used are shown in Table 1. The maximum sequence length was reduced to 128, due to the short length of the tweets.

4 Evaluation and Results

To validate the results, we used the NLP4IF tweets dataset. The training and testing sets contain 90% and 10% of total samples, respectively. We split the training data set into 90% for training and 10% for validation.
In this section, we will introduce the different evaluation experiments of our implemented model on the test data. In Table 3, we present the accuracy, precision, recall, F1-score of each evaluation experiment on the test dataset.

Results show that our model can detect if the tweet is "harmfull to society" or "requires attention of government entities" with high accuracy (90% and 92% respectively), if the tweet "may be of interest to the general public" or "contains false information" with a very good accuracy (84% and 86% respectively), and if the tweet is "Harmfull", "needs verification", or "Verifiable" with fairly good accuracy (76%, 75%, and 74% respectively).

Evaluation Experiment	Recall	Precision	F1-score	Accuracy
Q1	73%	75%	70%	74%
Q2	87%	87%	87%	86%
Q3	83%	84%	84%	84%
Q4	76%	76%	76%	76%
Q5	74%	76%	71%	75%
Q6	91%	90%	90%	90%
Q7	93%	92%	90%	92%

Table 3: The evaluation results of our models on the test data.

In Table 4, we represent the evaluation results of our implementation models, which was conducted by the organizers based on our submitted predicted labels for the blind test set.

Recall	Precision	F1-score	Accuracy
67.7%	78.7%	66.4%	67.7%

Table 4: The evaluation results of our models on the blind test data.

5 Conclusions

The objective of this work was the introduction of an effective approach based on the AraBERT language model for fighting Tweets COVID-19 Infodemic. It was arranged in the form of a two-step pipeline, where the first step involved a series of pre-processing procedures to transform Twitter jargon, including emojis and emoticons, into plain text, and the second step exploited a version of AraBERT, which was pre-trained on plain text, to fine-tune and classify the tweets with respect to their Label.
Future work will be directed to investigate the specific contributions of each pre-processing procedure, as well as other settings associated with the tuning, so as to further characterize the language model for the purposes of COVID-19 Infodemic. Finally, the proposed approach will also be tested and assessed with respect to other datasets, languages and social media sources, such as Facebook posts, in order to further estimate its applicability and generalizability.

References

Hadeer Ahmed, Issa Traore, Sherif Saad. 2017. Detection of online fake news using N-gram analysis and machine learning techniques. In *International conference on intelligent, secure, and dependable systems in distributed and cloud environments*. Springer, Cham, pages 127–138.

Hunt Allcott, and Matthew Gentzkow. 2017. Social Media and Fake News in the 2016 Election. In *Journal of Economic Perspectives*. 31 (2): 211-36.

Wissam Antoun, Fady Baly, and Hazem Hajj. 2020. AraBERT: Transformer-based Model for Arabic Language Understanding. In *LREC 2020 Workshop Language Resources and Evaluation Conference*. pages 11-16.

Christos Baziotis, Nikos Pelekis, and Christos Doulkeridis. 2017. DataStories at SemEval-2017 Task 4: Deep LSTM with Attention for Message-level and Topic-based Sentiment Analysis. In *Proceedings of the 10th International Workshop on Semantic Evaluation, SemEval@NAACL-HLT 2016*. San Diego, CA, USA, 16–17 June 2016; pages 747–754.

Alessandro Bondielli, and F. Marcelloni. 2019. A survey on fake news and rumour detection techniques. In *Inf. Sci. 497*. pages 38-55.

Linda Cappellato, Carsten Eickhoff, Nicola Ferro, and Aurélie Névéol. 2020. CLEF 2020 Working Notes. In *CEUR Workshop Proceedings, CEUR-WS.org*.

Souvick Ghosh, and Chirag Shah. 2018. Towards automatic fake news classification. *Proceedings of the Association for Information Science and Technology*. 55(1): pages 805–807.

Genevieve Gorrell, Elena Kochkina, Maria Liakata, Ahmet Aker, Arkaitz Zubiaga, Kalina Bontcheva, and Leon Derczynski. 2019. SemEval-2019 task 7: RumourEval, determining rumour veracity and support for rumours. In *Proceedings of the 13th International Workshop on Semantic Evaluation*, pages 845–854.

Maram Hasanain, Fatima Haouari, Reem Suwaileh, Zien Sheikh Ali,Bayan Hamdan, Tamer Elsayed , Alberto Barrón-Cedeño, Giovanni Da San Martino , and Preslav Nakov. 2020. Overview of CheckThat! 2020 Arabic: Automatic Identi-fication and Verification of Claims in Social Media. In *arXiv:2007.07997*.

Ahmad Hussein, Abdulkarim Hussein, Nada Ghneim, and Ammar Joukhadar. 2020. DamascusTeam at CheckThat! 2020: Check worthiness on Twitter with hybrid CNN and RNN models. In *Cappellato et al. (2020)*.

Heejung Jwa, Dongsuk Oh, Kinam Park, Jang Mook Kang, and Heuiseok Lim. 2019. exBAKE: Automatic fake news detection model based on Bidirectional Encoder Representations from Transformers (BERT). In *Applied Sciences (Switzerland), 9(19), [4062]*.

Srijan Kumar, and Neil Shah.2018. False Information on Web and Social Media: A Survey. In *arXiv:arXiv-1804*.

Athanasia Ntalla, and Stavros T. Ponis. (2015). Twitter as an instrument for crisis response: The Typhoon Haiyan case study. In *The 12th International Conference on Information Systems for Crisis Response and Management*.

Natali Ruchansky, Sungyong Seo, and Yan Liu. 2017. CSI: A Hybrid Deep Model for Fake News Detection. In *Proceedings of the 2017 ACM on Conference on Information and Knowledge Management (CIKM '17)*. Association for Computing Machinery, New York, NY, USA, pages 797–806.

Shaden Shaar, Firoj Alam, Giovanni Da San Martino, Alex Nikolov, Wajdi Zaghouani, Preslav Nakov,and Anna Feldman. 2021. Findings of the {NLP4IF}-2021 Shared Task on Fighting the {COVID}-19 Infodemic and Censorship Detection. In *Proceedings of the Fourth Workshop on Natural Language Processing for Internet Freedom: Censorship, Disinformation, and Propaganda*.

Jieun Shin, Lian Jian, Kevin Driscoll, and Franois Bar. 2018. The diffusion of misinformation on social media. *Comput. Hum. Behav*. 83, C (June 2018), pages 278–287.

Kai Shu, Deepak Mahudeswaran, Suhang Wang, Dongwon Lee, Huan Liu. 2020. FakeNewsNet: A Data Repository with News Content, Social Context, and Spatiotemporal Information for Studying Fake News on Social Media. In *Big Data. 8. 171-188*. 10.1089/big.2020.0062.

Kai Shu, Limeng Cui, Suhang Wang, Dongwon Lee, and Huan Liu. 2019. Defend: Explainable fake news detection. In *KDD 2019 - Proceedings of the 25th ACM SIGKDD International Conference on Knowledge Discovery and Data Mining*. pages 395-405.

Ashish Vaswani, Noam Shazeer, Niki Parmar, Jakob Uszkoreit, Llion Jones, Aidan N. Gomez, Lukasz Kaiser, Illia Polosukhin. 2017. Attention is All you Need. In *Proceedings of the Advances in Neural Information Processing Systems 30: Annual Conference on Neural Information Processing Systems 2017*.

Michela Del Vicario, Alessandro Bessi, Fabiana Zollo, Fabio Petroni, Antonio Scala, Guido Caldarelli, H. Eugene Stanley, and Walter Quattrociocchi. 2016.

The spreading of misinformation online. In *Proceedings of the National Academy of Sciences Jan 2016*, 113 (3) pages 554-559; DOI: 10.1073/pnas.1517441113.

Soroush Vosoughi, Mostafa 'Neo' Mohsenvand, and Deb Roy. 2017. Rumor Gauge: Predicting the Veracity of Rumors on Twitter. In *ACM Trans. Knowl. Discov*. Data 11, 4, Article 50 (August 2017), 36 pages.

Evan Williams, Paul Rodrigues, and Valerie Novak. 2020. Accenture at CheckThat! 2020: If you say so: Post-hoc fact-checking of claims using transformer-based models. In *Cappellato et al. (2020).*

Xinyi Zhou, and Reza Zafarani. 2018. A Survey of Fake News: Fundamental Theories, Detection Methods, and Opportunities. In *arXiv:arXiv-1812.*

Arkaitz Zubiaga, Ahmet Aker, Kalina Bontcheva, Maria Liakata, and Rob Procter. 2018. Detection and Resolution of Rumours in Social Media.In *ACM Computing Surveys.* 51(2): pages 1–36.

NARNIA at NLP4IF-2021: Identification of Misinformation in COVID-19 Tweets Using BERTweet

Ankit Kumar*, Naman Jhunjhunwala*, Raksha Agarwal, Niladri Chatterjee
Indian Institute of Technology Delhi
Hauz Khas, Delhi-110016, India
{mt1170727, mt1170737, maz178296, niladri}@maths.iitd.ac.in

Abstract

The spread of COVID-19 has been accompanied with widespread misinformation on social media. In particular, Twitterverse has seen a huge increase in dissemination of distorted facts and figures. The present work aims at identifying tweets regarding COVID-19 which contains harmful and false information. We have experimented with a number of Deep Learning based models, including different word embeddings, such as Glove, ELMo, among others. BERTweet model achieved the best overall F1-score of 0.881 and secured the third rank on the above task.

1 Introduction

Rapid propagation of social media has revolutionized the way information is consumed by general public. The ability of web platforms, such as Twitter, Instagram and Facebook, to quickly and broadly disseminate huge volumes of information has encouraged any user to be a (super) conduit of information. This can be helpful for problem solving in stressful and uncertain circumstances. However, this has also raised serious concerns about the disability of naive internet users in distinguishing truth from widespread misinformation.

As the world reacts to the COVID-19 pandemic, we are confronted with an overabundance of virus-related material. Some of this knowledge may be misleading and dangerous. The wildfire of Fake News in the times of COVID-19 has been popularly referred to as an 'infodemic' by the WHO chief. Also, in literature, we see terms such as 'pandemic populism' and 'covidiocy' (Hartley and Vu, 2020). Distorted facts and figures formed by drawing false equivalence between scientific evidence and uninformed opinions and doctored videos of public figures have flooded the online space since the onset of COVID. In order to ensure safety and well being of online information consumers, it is crucial to identify and curb the spread of false information. Twitter should mark content that is demonstrably inaccurate or misleading and poses a serious risk of damage (such as increased virus transmission or negative impacts on public health systems). Hence, developing and improving classification methods for tweets is need of the hour.

In the present work, Fighting with Covid19 infodemic dataset (Shaar et al., 2021) comprising English tweets about COVID-19 has been utilised for identifying false tweets. Many Deep Learning models have been trained to predict several properties of a tweet as described in Section 3.

The rest of the paper is organized as follows. Section 2 discusses related research work. Section 3 describes the dataset and Section 4 describes the language models we have used for our predictions. Sections 5 and 6 report the results of the experiments we conducted for the different language models and the error analysis respectively. Finally, in Section 7, we discuss future work that can be done in this area and conclude our paper.

2 Related Work

Classification of tweets has been studied widely by many researchers. Most of the methods use traditional Machine Learning classifiers on the features extracted from individual tweets, such as POS, unigrams, bigrams. Gamallo and Garcia (2014) built a Naive Bayes classifier for detecting sentiment of tweets. They considered Lemmas, Polarity Lexicons, and Multiword from different sources and Valence Shifters as input features to the classifier.

In recent times, the advancement of deep learning approaches (e.g., neural networks and transformer-based pre-trained language models like BERT and GPT) have taken precedence over feature-based classifiers (e.g., Naive-Bayes, SVM, among others). Classification problems have primarily been tackled in two ways - Feature

* Joint First Author

Proceedings of the 4th NLP4IF Workshop on NLP for Internet Freedom, pages 99–103
June 6, 2021. ©2021 Association for Computational Linguistics

based and by Fine-tuning of parameters. Feature based approaches use word-embeddings, such as Word2Vec (Mikolov et al., 2013), GloVe (Pennington et al., 2014), ELMO (Peters et al., 2018), and feed them into some Deep Learning model to perform downstream task. On the other hand, parameter fine-tuning based approach fine tunes all the pre-trained parameters on downstream tasks. We have experimented with both these approaches.

Recently, language models such as BERT (Devlin et al., 2018), pre-trained on large amount of unlabelled data and fine tuned on downstream task, have given state-of-the-art results in numerous NLP tasks. BERTweet (Nguyen et al., 2020) is one such model which is pre-trained on English tweets. It has been found that BERTweet outperforms other state-of-the art language models, e.g RoBERTa, XLM-R (Conneau et al., 2019) with respect to several NLP tasks, viz. text classification, NER etc. This motivates us to use BERTweet based approach for this task.

3 Dataset Description

The dataset used in this task contains English tweets, and the corresponding labels (which are mainly "yes"/"no"), that are the answers to the following questions:

1. Does the tweet contain a verifiable claim?
2. Does the tweet appear to contain any false information?
3. Will the tweet be of any interest to the public?
4. Can the claim made be harmful to society?
5. Does the claim need any verification?
6. Is the tweet harmful or misleading the society?
7. Should the govt pay any attention to the tweet?

As per the dataset specifications, Q2 to Q5 will be NaN if and only if Q1 is "no". Further, Q1, Q6 and Q7 are never supposed to be NaN. If there are some instances where this condition is violated, we have dropped the corresponding tweets (independently for all the questions) during training or validation. Finally, for the final predictions, we first obtain the predictions for Q1, and the tweets are checked for the labels Q2 to Q5 only when Q1 is "yes".

The given dataset has 869 tweets in the train dataset. We randomly split the dataset for training and in-sample validation purposes, with the splits having 695 and 174 tweets respectively ($80-20$ split). For validation, we are given a dev dataset with 53 tweets. The test dataset on which we submit our final predictions contains 418 tweets.

4 Model Description

A vast number of Language Models have been developed in the last decade. We used a number of them to solve the given problem, and they are described in the following subsections.

4.1 Pre-trained Embeddings

BERT and its variants have successfully produced state-of-the-art performance results for various NLP tasks. BERTweet is one such variant, which has been pre-trained for English tweets. It has three variants, that differ on the data they are trained on:

1. **Base:** This model has been trained on 845M (cased) English tweets along with 5M COVID-19 tweets.
2. **Cased:** It has been trained on additional 23M COVID-19 (cased) English Tweets
3. **Uncased:** It has been trained on additional 23M COVID-19 (uncased) English Tweets

However, using the pre-trained embeddings provided by BERTweet may not give the best results since they have been trained for a different dataset. So, to fine-tune the model for our task, we plug the BERTweet model to a fully connected neural network. We vary the number of hidden layers, optimization function (Adam and AdaFactor), learning rate and the number of epochs. Thus, for each label, we try all three of the BERTweet variants, and choose the best one depending upon the F1-score obtained.

Additionally, we have experimented with GloVe and ELMo embeddings. We have used the GloVe Twitter embeddings, which have been pre-trained on 2B tweets. To obtain the embeddings for the entire tweet from GloVe, we have taken average of the embeddings of the words present in the tweet. The pre-trained ELMo model available on the Tensorflow hub has also been utilised to obtain tweet embeddings. This model, however, was not trained on a tweet dataset. After obtaining the embeddings, the subsequent model used is the same as that for BERTweet.

4.2 SVM

In this method, we first trained our BERTweet based model (Section 4.1) and stored the output of the last fully connected layer for each dataset

Models	Q1	Q2	Q3	Q4	Q5	Q6	Q7
BERTweet	**0.94**	**0.84**	**0.92**	**0.96**	**0.76**	**0.84**	**0.76**
GloVe	0.83	0.23	0.90	0.53	0.50	0.17	0.15
ELMo	0.76	0.35	0.83	0.49	0.63	0.54	0.52
SVM	0.90	0.78	0.88	0.85	0.71	0.34	0.74
3-BERT Ensemble	0.91	0.84	0.85	0.84	0.73	0.75	0.71
5-BERT Ensemble	0.87	0.84	0.81	0.82	0.72	0.69	0.62

Table 1: Comparison of F1-score of different models

Q1	Q2	Q3	Q4	Q5	Q6	Q7	Overall
0.831	0.925	0.976	0.822	0.854	0.909	0.849	0.881

Table 2: F1-score on official test dataset

(training, validation and test). We used these stored values as input features for training and testing SVM for each label separately.

4.3 Ensemble

Finally, we created two ensemble models with BERTweet. Among the different models we obtained by fine-tuning BERTweet, we chose the best 3 and best 5 models for the ensembles.

5 Performance Evaluation

This section describes the evaluation scheme, followed by the results obtained for the different models.

5.1 Evaluation Scheme

We have used F1-score as the main evaluation scheme. Apart from Q2 to Q5, we have assumed the labels to be independent of each other (because Q2 to Q5 only need to be checked when Q1 is "yes"). Thus, we first train a model for Q1 and obtain the predictions on the dev/test dataset. Then, we pick the tweets for which Q1 is "yes", and assign Q2 to Q5 to be NaN for the rest of the tweets. Subsequently, we have treated all the models for all the questions to be independent of each other. Due to this, it may be possible that while some model performs extremely well on one label, its performance may not be that good for some other label(s). Thus, we can have different models for different labels. So, we calculate label-wise F1-score to compare different models, and choose the best one.

5.2 Evaluation of Different Models

Performance of different systems for the present task are described in the following subsections.

5.2.1 BERTweet

As was expected, in all our experiments, models based on BERTweet outperform all the other models that we described in Section 4. Detailed results (F1-score) for all the labels (along with results for all the different models) are given in Table 1.

5.2.2 GloVe

Although the dataset used in Glove Twitter is bigger than the one over which BERTweet was trained (2B vs 850M tweets), the GloVe vectors are "fixed", and unlike BERTweet, no Transfer Learning was involved for GloVe. As a result, GloVe performed much worse compared to BERTweet for most of the labels. The closest performance obtained is in Q3, when the GloVe based model was simply predicting all 1s (for Q3, the number of 1s is $> 90\%$ in the dataset (excluding NaNs)).

5.2.3 ELMo

Since we did not use an ELMo model pre-trained on the twitter dataset, it did not perform as well as BERTweet. But, as it was possible to use transfer learning here to fine-tune the weights of ELMo, it was mostly performing better than GloVe. On an average, the difference between the F1-scores of BERTweet and GloVe is 0.39, while for ELMo it is 0.28. Further, ELMo performs better than GloVe for four labels, namely, Q2, Q5, Q6 and Q7. Even on the labels when the F1-score of ELMo is lesser than that of GloVe (Q1, Q3 and Q4), the difference between their scores is low (average difference of 0.06), but that is not true for the labels when ELMo beats GloVe (average difference of 0.2475).

5.2.4 SVM

Since this method takes last fully connected layer output of our BERTweet based model as input features, it performes better than Glove and ELMo for almost all questions (except for ELMO for Q6).

5.2.5 Ensemble

For all the labels, the 3-BERTweet Ensemble (3BE) is atleast as good as 5-BERTweet Ensemble (5BE). Further, BERTweet is atleast as good as 3BE. In fact, BERTweet is better than 3BE, which is better than 5BE, for all labels other than Q2. For Q2, all the three models have the same F1-score: 0.84.

5.2.6 Best Model

In view of the results described in Table 1, we decided to use BERTweet for our final predictions. We combined the train + in-sample + dev splits to obtain a dataset with 912 tweets. Early stopping callback has been used with 10% validation split. Testing was done for the best five models we had for each label. We submitted two models (see Table 3). Their average F1-scores over the (new) validation dataset are 0.813 and 0.827, respectively. Even though Model 1 has a lesser F1-score on validation than Model 2, it has the final score of 0.881 (2), beating the latter (0.856).

	Model Specs	Q1	Q2	Q3	Q4	Q5	Q6	Q7
Model 1	BERTweet	Base	Cased	Base	Uncased	Uncased	Cased	Base
	Optimizer	AdaF	Adam	Adam	AdaF	Adam	Adam	AdaF
	Learning Rate	5e-5	1e-5	1e-5	1e-4	2e-5	1e-5	1e-4
	F1-Score	0.83	0.88	0.98	0.86	0.72	0.69	0.73
Model 2	BERTweet	Uncased	Cased	Base	Uncased	Uncased	Uncased	Base
	Optimizer	Adam	Adam	Adam	Adam	Adam	AdaF	AdaF
	Learning Rate	2e-5	1e-5	1e-5	1e-5	2e-5	5e-5	1e-4
	F1-Score	0.86	0.85	0.98	0.86	0.71	0.80	0.73

Table 3: Hyperparameters corresponding to the best models

Labels	Example 1	Example 2
Q1	(452) Instead of prioritizing regular Americans who need tests for #coronavirus, or paid sick leave because they live paycheck to paycheck, @realDonaldTrump wants to bail out oil billionaires. Thank goodness the House of Representatives, and not @POTUS, has the Power of the Purse. URL"	(490) We love this handwashing dance from Vietnamese dancer, Quang ng. Washing your hands with soap and water is one of the first steps to protect yourself from #coronavirus.
Q2	(491) Just like all the other fake stuff they do, the COVID-19 over-hype will backfire on the Democrats. The economy will come roaring backs with China's grip on trade weakened and Trump's high approval on handling the virus will only help.	(498) But, but...Trump didn't prepare for the coronavirus...his admin still doesn't have a clue...we are just not ready to combat a pandemic...Trump ignored the HHS, CDC? #FakeNews WATCH ?? #coronavirus #RepMarkGreen thank you! URL"
Q4	(461) The Italian COVID-19 outbreak has just been explosive... look at the numbers & timeframe. Time is not a luxury we have! Feb 18: 3 cases Feb 21: 20 cases Feb 24: 231 cases Feb 27: 655 cases Mar 1: 1,694 cases Mar 4: 3,089 cases Mar 7: 5,883	(462) A Youtuber who recently made a racist remark regarding BTS by relating them to Corona virus will now be making a video about them where he roasts the band and our fandom I request ARMYs to pls block him and report his channel, Ducky Bhai on YouTube URL

Table 4: Example tweets (from dev data) on which the BERTweet model fails. For each tweet the preceding number in parenthesis denotes the tweet number in the database

6 Error Analysis

For Q1, only three tweets in the dev data (452, 490, 492: all having a verifiable claim) are predicted wrong by our model. Similarly, for Q2, three examples (491, 498, 500), which also have a positive label (denoting that the tweet appears to contain false information), have been predicted wrong while for Q4, four examples (461, 462, 484, 485), all having negative labels (denoting that the claim made in the tweet cannot be harmful to the society), are predicted wrong by our model. Some of these tweets (as described above) can be found in Table 4. Rest of the labels do not have such pattern.

7 Conclusion and Future Work

We implemented five models, described in section 4, and showed that the BERTweet based models outperforms the rest. However, apart from the dependence of Q2 to Q5 on Q1 (refer section 3), we have assumed all questions to be independent. But, by the definitions of questions (section 3), it is evident that Q4 & Q6 and Q5 & Q7 have some dependence on each other. This can be seen in the dataset labels as well, because Q4 & Q6 have the same label for 87.6% of the tweets. Similarly, Q5 and Q7 have the same label 83.3% of the times. Since correlation does not imply causation, this property can be further explored to see if there is some dependence between the labels, which can possibly be incorporated in the model to improve the predictions for Q4 to Q7. Moreover, in this work, we have not experimented with Multi-class classification techniques, which can be further explored for a possible improvement.

Acknowledgments

Raksha Agarwal acknowledges Council of Scientific and Industrial Research (CSIR), India for supporting the research under Grant no: SPM-06/086(0267)/2018-EMR-I.

References

Alexis Conneau, Kartikay Khandelwal, Naman Goyal, Vishrav Chaudhary, Guillaume Wenzek, Francisco Guzmán, Edouard Grave, Myle Ott, Luke Zettlemoyer, and Veselin Stoyanov. 2019. Unsupervised cross-lingual representation learning at scale. *arXiv preprint arXiv:1911.02116*.

Jacob Devlin, Ming-Wei Chang, Kenton Lee, and Kristina Toutanova. 2018. BERT: pre-training of deep bidirectional transformers for language understanding. *CoRR*, abs/1810.04805.

Pablo Gamallo and Marcos Garcia. 2014. Citius: A naivebayes strategy for sentiment analysis on english tweets. In *Proceedings of the 8th International Workshop on Semantic Evaluation*, pages 171–175.

Kris Hartley and Minh Khuong Vu. 2020. Fighting fake news in the covid-19 era: policy insights from an equilibrium model. *Policy Sciences*, 53(4):735–758.

Tomas Mikolov, Kai Chen, Greg Corrado, and Jeffrey Dean. 2013. Efficient estimation of word representations in vector space. *arXiv preprint arXiv:1301.3781*.

Dat Quoc Nguyen, Thanh Vu, and Anh Tuan Nguyen. 2020. BERTweet: A pre-trained language model for English Tweets. In *Proceedings of the 2020 Conference on Empirical Methods in Natural Language Processing: System Demonstrations*, pages 9–14.

Jeffrey Pennington, Richard Socher, and Christopher Manning. 2014. GloVe: Global vectors for word representation. In *Proceedings of the 2014 Conference on Empirical Methods in Natural Language Processing (EMNLP)*, pages 1532–1543, Doha, Qatar. Association for Computational Linguistics.

Matthew E. Peters, Mark Neumann, Mohit Iyyer, Matt Gardner, Christopher Clark, Kenton Lee, and Luke Zettlemoyer. 2018. Deep contextualized word representations. *CoRR*, abs/1802.05365.

Shaden Shaar, Firoj Alam, Giovanni Da San Martino, Alex Nikolov, Wajdi Zaghouani, Preslav Nakov, and Anna Feldman. 2021. Findings of the NLP4IF-2021 shared task on fighting the COVID-19 infodemic and censorship detection. In *Proceedings of the Fourth Workshop on Natural Language Processing for Internet Freedom: Censorship, Disinformation, and Propaganda*, NLP4IF@NAACL' 21, Online. Association for Computational Linguistics.

R00 at NLP4IF-2021: Fighting COVID-19 Infodemic with Transformers and More Transformers

Ahmed Qarqaz **Dia Abujaber** **Malak A. Abdullah**
Jordan University of Science and Technology
Irbid, Jordan
afalqarqaz17, daabujaber17@cit.just.edu.jo
mabdullah@just.edu.jo

Abstract

This paper describes the winning model in the Arabic NLP4IF shared task for fighting the COVID-19 infodemic. The goal of the shared task is to check disinformation about COVID-19 in Arabic tweets. Our proposed model has been ranked 1st with an F1-Score of 0.780 and an Accuracy score of 0.762. A variety of transformer-based pre-trained language models have been experimented with through this study. The best-scored model is an ensemble of AraBERT-Base, Asafya-BERT, and ARBERT models. One of the study's key findings is showing the effect the pre-processing can have on every model's score. In addition to describing the winning model, the current study shows the error analysis.

1 Introduction

Social media platforms are highly used for expressing and delivering ideas. Most people on social media platforms tend to spread and share posts without fact-checking the story or the source. Consequently, the propaganda is posted to promote a particular ideology to create further confusion in understanding an event. Of course, it does not apply to all posts. However, there is a line between propaganda and factual news, blurred for people engaged in these platforms (Abedalla et al., 2019). And thus, social media can act as a distortion for critical and severe events. The COVID-19 pandemic is one such event.

Several previous works were published for using language models and machine learning techniques for detecting misinformation. Authors in Haouari et al. (2020b) presented a twitter data set for COVID-19 misinformation detection called "ArCOV19-Rumors". It is an extension of the "ArCOV-19" (Haouari et al., 2020a), which is a data set of Twitter posts with "Propagation Networks". Propagation networks refer to a post's retweets and conversational threads. Other authors in Shahi et al. (2021) performed an exploratory study of COVID-19 misinformation on Twitter. They collected data from Twitter and identified misinformation, rumors on Twitter, and misinformation propagation. Authors in Müller et al. (2020) presented CT-BERT, a transformer-based model pre-trained on English Twitter data. Other works that used Deep Learning models to detect propaganda in news articles (Al-Omari et al., 2019; Altiti et al., 2020).

The NLP4IF (Shaar et al., 2021) shared-task offers an annotated data set of tweets to check disinformation about COVID-19 in each tweet. The task asked the participants to propose models that can predict the disinformation in these tweets. This paper describes the winning model in the shared task, an ensemble of AraBERT-Base, Asafya-BERT, and ARBERT pre-trained language models. The team R00's model outperformed the other teams and baseline models with an F1-Score of 0.780 and an Accuracy score of 0.762. This paper describes the Dataset and the shared task in section 2. The Data Preprocessing step is presented in section 3. The experiments with the pre-trained language models are provided in section 4. Finally, the proposed winning model and methodology are discussed in section 5.

2 Dataset

The Data provided by the organizers Shaar et al., 2021 comprised of tweets, which are posts from the Twitter social media platform "twitter.com". The posts are related to the COVID-19 pandemic and have been annotated in a "Yes or No" question style annotation. The annotator was asked to read the post/tweet and go to an affiliated weblink (if the tweet contains one). For each tweet, the seven main questions that were asked are:

1. Verifiable Factual Claim: *Does the tweet contain a verifiable factual claim?*

Proceedings of the 4th NLP4IF Workshop on NLP for Internet Freedom, pages 104–109
June 6, 2021.

2. False Information: *To what extent does the tweet appear to contain false information?*

3. Interest to General Public: *Will the tweet affect or be of interest to the general public?*

4. Harmfulness: *To what extent is the tweet harmful to the society/person(s)/company(s)/product(s)?*

5. Need of Verification: *Do you think that a professional fact-checker should verify the claim in the tweet?*

6. Harmful to Society: *Is the tweet harmful the society and why?*

7. Require attention: *Do you think that this tweet should get the attention of government entities?*

For each question, the answer can be "Yes" or "No". However the questions two through five **depend** on the first question. If the first question (Verifiable Factual Claim) is answered "No", questions two through five will be labeled as "NaN". "NaN" is interpreted as there's no need to ask the question. For example, for the following tweet:

> *"maybe if i develop feelings for covid-19 it will leave".*

This tweet is not a verifiable factual claim. Therefore asking whether it's False Information or is in Need of Verification is unnecessary. Moreover, our model modified the values to be " No" for all text samples with labels annotated as "NaN".

Task Our team participated in the Arabic text shared task. The Arabic data set consists of 2,536 tweets for the training data, 520 tweets for the development (validation) data, and 1,000 tweets for the test data. It has been observed that the label distribution in the training data is unbalanced, as shown in Figure 1.

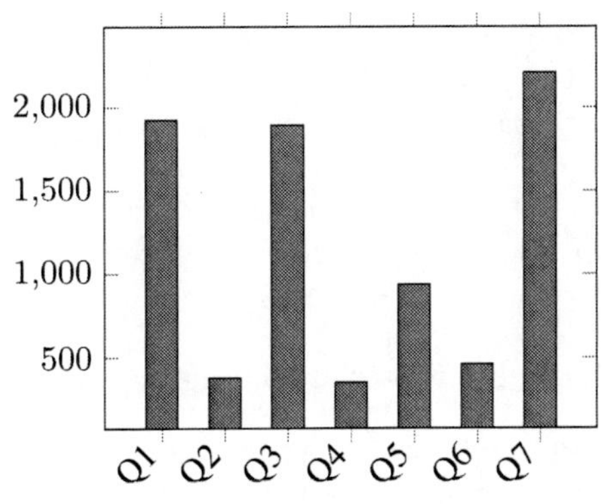

Figure 1: label distribution in data. Unbalance labels for questions.

3 Data Pre-Processing

Social media posts can contain noisy features, particularly the special characters (#, @, emojis, weblinks, etc..). Many elements within Arabic text can act as distortions for the model. We Tokenize the Arabic text [1], and for each sequence of tokens, we remove stop-words, numbers, and punctuation from the text. We also remove any non-Arabic terms in the text. Stemming and Segmentation are two common pre-processing operations done in Arabic Natural Language Processing. However, we do not apply them here, except in the case of AraBERT, where segmentation was applied.

4 Fine-tuning Pre-Trained Language Models

We approach the problem as a multi-label classification problem. For each label in a text sample, the label's value can be one (yes) or zero (no). In the training phase, we load the pre-trained language model (along with its corresponding tokenizer) and stack a linear classifier on top of the model.

This section describes the pre-trained Arabic language models that have been used in the study. The hyperparameters' fine-tuning is also detailed in this section in addition to the experiments' results.

4.1 Pre-trained Arabic Language Models

This section goes over the pre-trained language models experimented with through the study: AraBERT, Asafaya-BERT, ARBERT, and MARBERT.

- **AraBERT** (Antoun et al.) follows the original BERT pre-training (Devlin et al., 2018), employing the Masked Language Modelling task. It was pre-trained on roughly 70-million sentences amounting to 24GB of text data. There are four variations of the model: *AraBERTv0.2-base, AraBERTv0.2-large, AraBERTv2-base, AraBERTv2-large.* The difference is that the *v2* variants were trained on the pre-segmented text where prefixes and suffixes were split, whereas the *v0.2* were not. The models we used are the *v0.2* variants. the Authors recommended using the Arabert-Preprocessor powered by the farasapy[2] python package for the *v2* versions. Although the *v0.2* models don't require it, we

[1] Preprocessing was done using the NLTK Library

[2] farasapy

have found that the Arabert-Preprocessor improves the performance significantly for some experiments. So, we have used it with all the AraBERT models only.

- **Asafaya-BERT** (Safaya et al., 2020) is a model also based on the BERT architecture. This model was pre-trained on 8.2B words, with a vocabulary of 32,000 word-pieces. The corpus the model was pre-trained on was not restricted to Modern Standard Arabic, as they contain some dialectal Arabic, and as such Safaya et al. (2020) argue that this boosts the model's performance on data gathered from social media platforms. There are four variants of the model: Large, Base, Medium, and Mini. We only used Large and Base.

- **ARBERT** (Abdul-Mageed et al., 2020) is a pre-trained model focused on Modern Standard Arabic (MSA). It was trained on 61GB of text data, with a vocabulary of 100K WordPieces. There is only one variation of this model, which follows the BERT-Base architecture. It uses 12-attention layers (each with 12-attention heads) and 768 hidden-dimension. We use this model to possibly write some tweets (such as news updates) formally following MSA.

- **MARBERT** (Abdul-Mageed et al., 2020) argues that since AraBERT and ARBERT are trained on MSA text, these models are not well suited for tasks involving dialectal Arabic, which is what social media posts often are. MARBERT was trained on a large Twitter data set comprised of 6B tweets, making up about 128GB of text data. MARBERT follows the BERT-Base architecture but without sentence prediction. MARBERT uses the same vocabulary as ARBERT (100K Word-Pieces).

4.2 Fine-Tuning

Each model has been trained for 20 epochs. We found that after the 10th epoch, most of the model scores start to plateau. This is, of course, highly dependent on the learning rate used for each model. We have not tuned the models' learning rates, and rather we chose the learning rate we found best after doing multiple experiments with each model. We use a **Training Batch-Size** of 32 and a **Validation Batch-Size** of 16 for all the models. For each model's tokenizer we choose a **Max Sequence-length** of 100.

Each model has been trained on two versions of the data set, one that has not been pre-processed (We refer to it as "Raw") and one that has been pre-processed (we refer to it as "Cleaned"). A model that has been trained on cleaned data in training time will also receive cleaned text at validation and testing time. We apply the post-processing step, where for the labels Question-2, 3, 4, and Question-5, if a model predicts that Question-1 is "No" then the values of the mentioned Questions (Q2 through Q5) will be "NaN" Unconditionally. This, of course, assumes that the model can perform well on the first question. We report the results in Table 1.

Note: It is worth noting that, initially, we save the model on the first epoch along with its score as the "best-score". After each epoch, we compare the score of the model on that epoch with the best score. If the model's current score is higher than the best score, the model will be saved, and the model's best score will be overwritten as the current model's score. And as such, saying we train a model for 20 epochs is **not an accurate description** of the model's training. The score we used as criteria for saving was the Weighted F1-Score.

4.3 Results

We see (in Table 1) that generally, training on cleaned data either gave slightly better scores or no significant improvement, with ARBERT 4.1 being the exception. This is because ARBERT was specifically trained on Arabic text that followed the Modern Standard Arabic. Cleaning has normalized text for the model and removed features in the text that may otherwise act as noise. Furthermore, we conclude that Asafya-BERT 4.1 has a better performance when trained on Raw data, proving that a model pre-trained on Twitter data would perform better. Lastly, we observe that using a larger model (deeper network) does provide a slight improvement over using the Base version. [3]

5 Ensemble Pre-trained language Models

To maximize the scores, we resort to ensembling some of the models we fine-tuned on the data set. Ensemble models are known to improve accuracy

[3]Results and scores were generated using the Scikit-learn library

ID	Model	Data	Learning Rate	F1-Weighted	F1-Micro	Accuracy
(1)	AraBERT-Base	Raw	$3e^{-6}$	0.703	0.727	0.338
(2)	AraBERT-Base	Cleaned	$3e^{-5}$	0.735	0.725	0.394
(3)	AraBERT-Large	Raw	$3e^{-5}$	0.733	0.737	0.390
(4)	AraBERT-Large	Cleaned	$3e^{-5}$	0.747	0.749	0.425
(5)	MARBERT	Raw	$4e^{-5}$	0.737	0.741	0.382
(6)	MARBERT	Cleaned	$4e^{-6}$	0.735	0.735	0.413
(7)	ARBERT	Raw	$8e^{-6}$	0.715	0.728	0.407
(8)	ARBERT	Cleaned	$3e^{-5}$	0.734	0.745	0.398
(9)	Asafaya-Base	Raw	$5e^{-6}$	0.750	0.749	0.413
(10)	Asafaya-Base	Cleaned	$3e^{-5}$	0.707	0.743	0.382
(11)	**Asafaya-Large**	Raw	$5e^{-6}$	**0.750**	**0.752**	**0.436**
(12)	Asafaya-Large	Cleaned	$5e^{-6}$	0.737	0.743	0.373

Table 1: Shows model scores on the validation data set. The Weighted F1-Score and the Micro F1-Score are the average F1-Scores of the labels.

ID	Model	Q1	Q2	Q3	Q4	Q5	Q6	Q7
(1)	AraBERT-Base	0.73	0.11	0.71	0.22	0.37	0.43	0.84
(2)	AraBERT-Base	0.76	**0.26**	0.75	0.38	0.42	**0.55**	0.83
(4)	AraBERT-Large	**0.81**	0.16	**0.79**	0.32	0.42	0.50	**0.85**
(5)	MARBERT	0.78	0.12	0.78	0.36	0.43	0.44	0.84
(6)	MARBERT	0.75	0.10	0.74	**0.52**	**0.48**	0.54	0.84
(8)	ARBERT	0.78	0.19	0.78	0.36	0.44	0.53	0.83
(10)	Asafya-Base	0.78	0.11	0.77	0.30	0.22	0.39	0.84
(12)	Asafya-Large	0.79	0.18	0.78	0.40	0.35	0.48	0.84

Table 2: Shows models F1-Scores for the labels on the validation data set.

under the right conditions. If two models can detect different data patterns, then ensembling these two models would perhaps (in theory) give a better prediction. Of course, the process of finding a good ensemble is an empirical one. It involves a process of trial-and-error of combining different models and choosing the best one. However, as we show in Table 1 various combinations can be done, and as a result, trying all combinations would perhaps be impractical. We mention in Section-2 that the label distribution in the data set is unbalanced, and hence for labels like Question-2 (False Information), the model can give poor predictions for the answer to that label. However, suppose we were to acquire a model (through experimentation) that tends to perform well in predicting that label. In that case, we could ensemble this model with one that generally performs well to get a better overall score.

Strategy Through experimentation and for each label, train a model that performs well on that label and save it for an ensemble. Then, train a model that generally performs well on all labels (relative to the models at hand) and save it for an ensemble. After collecting several models, ensemble these models through various combinations. And for each ensemble, record the combination and its score (performance on validation data). Choose the best performing ensemble.

Weighted-Average Our approach for an ensemble is to take the weighted average of each's model predictions for each sample. Each model produces a vector of probabilities (whose length is equal to the number of labels) for each tweet. We take the weighted average point-wise and then apply a 0.5-threshold to decide if a label is one (yes) or zero (no). We suggest using the weighted average rather than a normal average with equal weights to

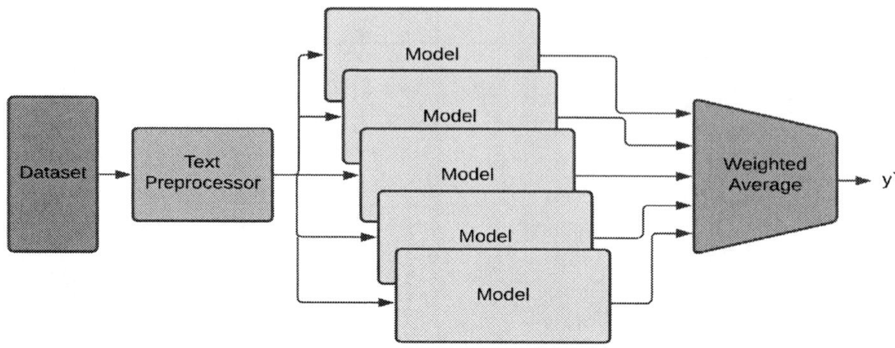

Figure 2: Shows Ensemble architecture. Each model has its classifier stacked on top. The models receive the text pre-processed and produce logits. Logits are then inserted into a Sigmoid layer making predictions. Prediction vectors are multiplied with a scalar (the weight), and the weighted average is calculated point-wise.

give higher confidence to the generally performing model as opposed to the less generally performing one. The intuition is that you would want the model to be the deciding factor in predicting better overall performance. The models with the lesser weights are merely there to increase the models' confidence in predicting some labels. The optimal weights for an ensemble are obtainable through experimentation. As a hyperparameter, they can be tuned.

Proposed Model We ensemble five models as shown in Figure 2, all of them were trained on cleaned data. And so, the models were tested on cleaned data. The models are:

1. Model (2): AraBERT-Base, with a weight of 3.
2. Model (4): Asafya-BERT-Large, with a weight of 3
3. Model (10): Asafya-BERT-Base, with a weight of 1.
4. Model (12): AraBERT-Large, with a weight of 1.
5. Model (8): ARBERT, with a weight of 3.

Our model achieved an F1-Weighted Score of 0.749, an F1-Micro Score of 0.763, and an Accuracy of 0.405 on validation data. It also earned an F1-Weighted Score of 0.781 and an Accuracy of 0.763 on the Test data. These results made the model ranked the first mode since it is the top-performing model in the shared task. Figure 3 presents the confusion matrix for the Ensemble-model predictions on the labels.

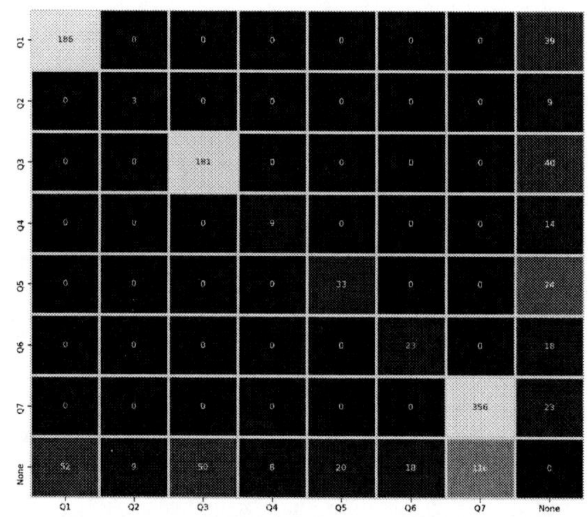

Figure 3: Shows confusion matrix for the Ensemble-model predictions on the labels. The Y-axis represents the *True*-Label while the X-axis represents the *Predicted*-label.

6 Conclusion

This paper described the winning model in the NLP4IF 2021 shared task. The task aimed to check disinformation about COVID-19 in Arabic tweets. We have ensembled five pre-trained language models to obtain the highest F1-score of 0.780 and an Accuracy score of 0.762. We have shown the performances of every pre-trained language model on the data set. We also have shown some of the models' performances on each label. Moreover, we have demonstrated the confusion matrix for the ensemble model. We have illustrated that a pre-trained model on Twitter data (Asafya-Bert in Section 4.1) will perform better relative to a model that hasn't.

References

Muhammad Abdul-Mageed, AbdelRahim Elmadany, and El Moatez Billah Nagoudi. 2020. Arbert & marbert: Deep bidirectional transformers for arabic. *arXiv preprint arXiv:2101.01785*.

Ayat Abedalla, Aisha Al-Sadi, and Malak Abdullah. 2019. A closer look at fake news detection: A deep learning perspective. In *Proceedings of the 2019 3rd International Conference on Advances in Artificial Intelligence*, pages 24–28.

Hani Al-Omari, Malak Abdullah, Ola AlTiti, and Samira Shaikh. 2019. JUSTDeep at NLP4IF 2019 task 1: Propaganda detection using ensemble deep learning models. In *Proceedings of the Second Workshop on Natural Language Processing for Internet Freedom: Censorship, Disinformation, and Propaganda*, pages 113–118, Hong Kong, China. Association for Computational Linguistics.

Ola Altiti, Malak Abdullah, and Rasha Obiedat. 2020. JUST at SemEval-2020 task 11: Detecting propaganda techniques using BERT pre-trained model. In *Proceedings of the Fourteenth Workshop on Semantic Evaluation*, pages 1749–1755, Barcelona (online). International Committee for Computational Linguistics.

Wissam Antoun, Fady Baly, and Hazem Hajj. Arabert: Transformer-based model for arabic language understanding. In *LREC 2020 Workshop Language Resources and Evaluation Conference 11–16 May 2020*, page 9.

Jacob Devlin, Ming-Wei Chang, Kenton Lee, and Kristina Toutanova. 2018. Bert: Pre-training of deep bidirectional transformers for language understanding. *arXiv preprint arXiv:1810.04805*.

Fatima Haouari, Maram Hasanain, Reem Suwaileh, and Tamer Elsayed. 2020a. Arcov-19: The first arabic covid-19 twitter dataset with propagation networks. *arXiv preprint arXiv:2004.05861*, 3(1).

Fatima Haouari, Maram Hasanain, Reem Suwaileh, and Tamer Elsayed. 2020b. Arcov19-rumors: Arabic covid-19 twitter dataset for misinformation detection. *arXiv preprint arXiv:2010.08768*.

Martin Müller, Marcel Salathé, and Per E Kummervold. 2020. Covid-twitter-bert: A natural language processing model to analyse covid-19 content on twitter. *arXiv preprint arXiv:2005.07503*.

Ali Safaya, Moutasem Abdullatif, and Deniz Yuret. 2020. Kuisail at semeval-2020 task 12: Bert-cnn for offensive speech identification in social media.

Shaden Shaar, Firoj Alam, Giovanni Da San Martino, Alex Nikolov, Wajdi Zaghouani, Preslav Nakov, and Anna Feldman. 2021. Findings of the NLP4IF-2021 shared task on fighting the COVID-19 infodemic and censorship detection. In *Proceedings of the Fourth Workshop on Natural Language Processing for Internet Freedom: Censorship, Disinformation, and Propaganda*, NLP4IF@NAACL' 21, Online. Association for Computational Linguistics.

Gautam Kishore Shahi, Anne Dirkson, and Tim A Majchrzak. 2021. An exploratory study of covid-19 misinformation on twitter. *Online Social Networks and Media*, 22:100104.

Multi Output Learning using Task Wise Attention for Predicting Binary Properties of Tweets : Shared-Task-On-Fighting the COVID-19 Infodemic

Ayush Suhane*
IIT Kharagpur
Kharagpur, India
ayushsuhane99@iitkgp.ac.in

Shreyas Kowshik*
IIT Kharagpur
Kharagpur, India
shreyaskowshik@iitkgp.ac.in

Abstract

In this paper, we describe our system for the shared task on Fighting the COVID-19 Infodemic in the English Language. Our proposed architecture consists of a multi-output classification model for the seven tasks, with a task-wise multi-head attention layer for inter-task information aggregation. This was built on top of the Bidirectional Encoder Representations obtained from the RoBERTa Transformer. Our team, dunder_mifflin, was able to achieve a mean F1 score of 0.891 on the test data, leading us to the second position on the test-set leaderboard.

1 Introduction

In recent years, the spread of misinformation on social media has been growing rapidly. Amid the global pandemic, the spread of misinformation has had serious consequences. Covid-19 misinformation caused mass hysteria and panic; reluctance to use masks and follow social distancing norms; denial of the existence of Covid-19, anti-vaxxers, etc. There is a need for automatic detection and flagging of tweets spreading misinformation.

Automatic detection of misinformation is an open research problem in NLP. Misinformation is intentionally written to deceive and pass as factual which makes detecting it a difficult task.

(Silva et al., 2020) analyzed a dataset of 505k tweets. They used sentiment analysis, polarity scores, and LIWC to build features. They used ML models such as RandomForest, AdaBoost, SVM, etc to classify tweets as factual/misinformation.

Predicting answers to multiple questions, which is the setup of our current problem statement, can be modeled as a multi-task-learning problem. (Crawshaw, 2020) have highlighted different methods for sharing information among tasks, for task-specific performance boosts, such as cross-stitching and soft-parameter-sharing. They also highlight ways for loss weighting based on task-dependent uncertainty and learning-speed.

(Liu et al., 2019) have highlighted the use of attention mechanisms for the multi-task learning problem and show that it performs competitively with other approaches.

Inspired by this idea, we propose an Attention-Based architecture **RoBERTa Multihead Attn** for our task by incorporating inter-task information for task-specific performance enhancement. With a test-set F1 score of **0.891**, our approach shows the superiority of combining information among tasks over modeling them independently and shows the effectiveness of multihead-attention for this purpose.

2 Task Description and Dataset

The objective of this task (Shaar et al., 2021) is to predict various binary properties of tweets. We were given several tweets where we had to predict answers to 7 questions. These questions pertain to whether the tweet is harmful, whether it contains a verifiable claim, whether it may be of interest to the general public, whether it appears to contain false information, etc. There were three tracks of languages on English, Arabic, and Bulgarian and a team was free to choose any subset of the languages.

For the English Language, the training dataset consisted of 862 tweets [1] The dev set consisted of 53 tweets and the testing set consisted of 418. The training dataset statistics are shown in Table 1.

* Denotes Equal Contribution

[1] In the training dataset (869 tweets) provided by the organizers, 7 tweets were mislabeled and had "Nan" in Q6 or Q7 (which only have classes "yes" and "no"). As instructed by the organizers, we dropped those tweets from the dataset and were left with 862 tweets, which were used for further analysis.

Proceedings of the 4th NLP4IF Workshop on NLP for Internet Freedom, pages 110–114
June 6, 2021.

Question-Id	No	Yes	Nan
Q1	298	564	-
Q2	457	39	366
Q3	50	506	306
Q4	407	153	302
Q5	383	181	298
Q6	726	136	-
Q7	634	228	-

Table 1: Training dataset statistics

3 Methodology

We explored different base embeddings inspired by (Devlin et al., 2019) and (Liu et al., 2020). These are state-of-the-art language models which when used with task-specific fine-tuning, perform well on a wide variety of tasks. The embeddings are passed to our task-specific architecture for further processing and the whole model is trained end-to-end.

We hypothesize that the prediction for one question may benefit from the use of information needed to predict another question. For instance, questions Q4 ("Harmfulness: To what extent is the tweet harmful to the society/person/company/product?") and Q6 ("Harmful to Society: Is the tweet harmful to the society and why?") in the task have a deduction process that may have several common steps. To model this, we add an inter-task multi-head attention layer before our prediction heads.

3.1 Preprocessing

Before feeding the tweets to the RoBERTa tokenizer, we performed the following operations:

1. We observed that there were a lot of non-ASCII characters in the tweets, so we stripped these characters.

2. We then replaced the emojis with their text description using the demoji python package.

3. We replaced all the links in the tweets with "URL" and mentions with "USER" tokens.

3.2 Data Augmentation

Due to the small size of the dataset, we used data augmentation to improve generalization. Back-Translation was used for this purpose. Given an input, the text is first translated into a destination language to obtain a new sentence. This new sentence is then translated back into the source language. This process creates a slightly modified version of the original sentence, while still preserving the original meaning. We carried this out using 3 destination languages (French, Spanish, German) using the MarianMT (Neural Machine Translation Model)[2]. As an example :

Original Tweet

For the average American the best way to say if you have covid-19 is coughing in a rich person face and waiting for their test results

Augmented Tweet

For the average American the best way to tell if you have covid-19 is to cough in a rich person's face and wait for their test results

3.3 Task-Wise Multi-head Attention Architecture

Multi-Head-Attention (Vaswani et al., 2017) has shown to capture representations across different subspaces, thus being more diverse in its modeling compared to Single-Head-Attention. Inspired by this, we added a multi-head-attention layer to aggregate information among different tasks.

Our entire architecture is shown in Figure 1. The input sentences are encoded using the RoBERTa tokenizer. These are then forward propagated to get the embedding vectors. This vector is passed through a linear-block[3] and then branched out using 7 different linear layers, one for each task. These are further processed to obtain the 7 task-specific vectors (we will refer to these as task vectors).

Each of these vectors is then passed through a multi-head-attention layer with the vector itself being the query vector, and the concatenated task vectors being the key and value vectors. The attention weights captured through this method signify what proportion of information the model would want to propagate further from each of the task-specific vectors. The information from all the task vectors is thus aggregated as their weighted sum to get the penultimate layers for each task. Note that the projection matrices for multihead-attention for all tasks are independent of each other. A final linear layer maps these to the prediction layers on which softmax is applied for per-task prediction.

[2]MarianMT

[3]Linear-Block is a linear-layer+ReLU

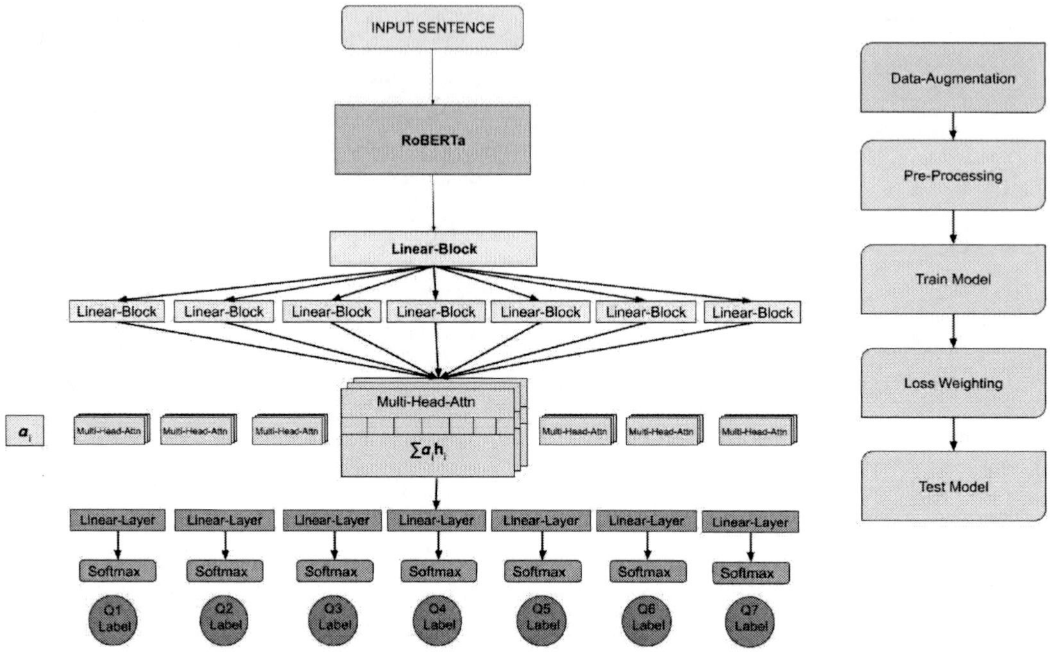

Figure 1: (Towards Left) Our proposed architecture for Roberta-Multihead-Attention. h_i denotes the embedding after projecting the value vector (the ith task vector) using the multihead-attention layer's value-projection matrix. α_i denotes the attention weight for i^{th} task vector, which is the amount of information to propagate forward from that task vector. (Towards Right) Preprocessing and training pipeline

Model	Mean F1	F1 Q1	F1 Q2	F1 Q3	F1 Q4	F1 Q5	F1 Q6	F1 Q7
ngram_baseline	0.828	0.647	0.904	0.992	0.761	0.800	0.873	0.821
majority_baseline	0.830	0.612	**0.927**	**1.000**	0.770	0.807	0.873	0.821
RoBERTa Multihead Attn	**0.891**	**0.807**	0.923	0.966	**0.868**	**0.852**	**0.940**	**0.884**

Table 2: Evaluation results on official test set. Baselines provided by the organizers

Model	Mean F1
Vanilla BERT	0.786
BERT Multihead Attn	0.812
RoBERTa Multihead Attn	**0.823**

Table 3: Evaluation results on official dev set.

3.4 Loss Weighting

The input data is skewed in the distribution of labels for each question. A natural approach to tackle this issue is to use a weighted loss. For each task, we use the following scheme for assigning weights :

$$w_c = \frac{N_{samples}}{N_{classes} * N_c}$$

where $N_{samples}$ is the number of input data samples, $N_{classes}$ is the number of classes and N_c is the number of samples for class c for a particular task. This weighting was done independently for each task, based on the label distribution for that particular task.

4 Experiments

We conducted our experiments with $\text{Bert}_{\text{BASE}}$ and $\text{Roberta}_{\text{BASE}}$. All our code is open-source and available on Github [4].
The different architectures are explained below:

- **Vanilla BERT** : The input sentence is passed through the $\text{BERT}_{\text{BASE-UNCASED}}$ model. The output is first processed through a couple of linear blocks and finally branched out for task-wise linear layers for predictions for each of the 7 questions.

[4]https://github.com/shreyas-kowshik/nlp4if

Model	Language	Mean F1
Vanilla BERT	Arabic	0.706
BERT Multihead Attn	Arabic	**0.726**
Vanilla BERT	Bulgarian	0.819
BERT Multihead Attn	Bulgarian	**0.825**

Table 4: Evaluation results on official dev set for Arabic and Bulgarian

- **Bert Multihead Attn** : Figure 1 shows this architecture, with RoBERTa replaced by BERT. The input sentence is passed through the BERT transformer to obtain the bidirectional encoder representations. These are passed through a couple of linear-blocks and then branched out to 7 linear layers, each one corresponding to a task. For each branch, the output from the seven linear layers is then fed into a separate multi-head attention layer, with 3 heads. The output from the multihead attention for each task is finally passed through a linear layer and softmax and is used for predictions.

- **RoBERTa Multihead Attn** : This model is the same as Bert Multihead Attn except that the transformer used is $\text{RoBERTa}_{\text{BASE}}$.

All models were finetuned end-to-end, with weights also being updated for the embedding layers of BERT and RoBERTa. The loss function was weighted-cross-entropy for each task, and the final loss was the sum of losses for the 7 tasks. The learning rates followed a linear decay schedule starting from an initial learning rate. The models were trained in PyTorch with the HuggingFace library (Wolf et al., 2020).

Regarding the results in Table 3, we see that RoBERTa Multihead Attn performs the best overall on the development set. We obtain a significant boost in performance, over Vanilla-BERT, by using our proposed Multihead-Attention layers. Using RoBERTa embeddings further brings about a slight improvement over this. We thus finalize Roberta Multihead Attn as our final model for submission.

For this particular experiment, we used a learning rate of 5e-5 for the task-specific layer and 5e-6 for the RoBERTa fine-tuning layers. The model was trained for 60 epochs with the number of attention-heads set to 3. All layers except the penultimate, attention, and RoBERTa layers had a 0.1 dropout probability.

Roberta Multihead Attn beats the baselines by a significant margin overall as shown in Table 2 and ranks 2nd on the test-set leaderboard for the English Language sub-task, with a test-set mean F1-Score of 0.891.

Upon request from the reviewers, we also show the results on the development set for the given architecture on the Arabic and Bulgarian datasets. The bert-base-multilingual-cased embeddings were used as the base embeddings for these experiments. With reference to Table 4 we see that our proposed architecture outperforms the Vanilla BERT architecture on both the Arabic and Bulgarian datasets, further illustrating it's effectiveness across languages.

5 Conclusion and Future Work

In this paper, we have described our system for predicting different binary properties of a tweet, on the English sub-task of the Shared Task On Fighting the Covid Infodemic in NLP4IF'21. Our approach uses the $\text{RoBERTa}_{\text{BASE}}$ architecture for the initial embeddings and builds on top of that using task-wise multi-head attention layers. Our results show that using a multi-head attention approach for aggregating information from different tasks leads to an overall improvement in performance.

Possible developments in this task can include the incorporation of additional contextual information in our models using tweet-related features like the #(number) of URLs in a tweet, the # of user mentions and the # of hashtags, etc. Also, user-related features such as the # of followers, account age, account type (verified or not) can be included. These features contain a lot of auxiliary information that can aid in fine-grained classification. Sociolinguistic Analysis such as Linguistic Inquiry and Word Count (LIWC) can also be used to gather emotional and cognitive components from the tweet.

6 Acknowledgements

We would like to thank everyone in the organizing committee and the reviewers for reviewing our paper and providing their valuable feedback. We would also like to thank Chinmay Singh and Prakhar Sharma for proof-reading the paper and providing other valuable suggestions towards improving the paper.

References

Michael Crawshaw. 2020. Multi-Task Learning with Deep Neural Networks: A Survey. *arXiv e-prints*, page arXiv:2009.09796.

Jacob Devlin, Ming-Wei Chang, Kenton Lee, and Kristina Toutanova. 2019. BERT: Pre-training of deep bidirectional transformers for language understanding. In *Proceedings of the 2019 Conference of the North American Chapter of the Association for Computational Linguistics: Human Language Technologies, Volume 1 (Long and Short Papers)*, pages 4171–4186, Minneapolis, Minnesota. Association for Computational Linguistics.

Shikun Liu, Edward Johns, and Andrew J. Davison. 2019. End-to-end multi-task learning with attention. In *2019 IEEE/CVF Conference on Computer Vision and Pattern Recognition (CVPR)*, pages 1871–1880.

Yinhan Liu, Myle Ott, Naman Goyal, Jingfei Du, Mandar Joshi, Danqi Chen, Omer Levy, Mike Lewis, Luke Zettlemoyer, and Veselin Stoyanov. 2020. Ro{bert}a: A robustly optimized {bert} pretraining approach.

Shaden Shaar, Firoj Alam, Giovanni Da San Martino, Alex Nikolov, Wajdi Zaghouani, Preslav Nakov, and Anna Feldman. 2021. Findings of the NLP4IF-2021 shared task on fighting the COVID-19 infodemic and censorship detection. In *Proceedings of the Fourth Workshop on Natural Language Processing for Internet Freedom: Censorship, Disinformation, and Propaganda*, NLP4IF@NAACL' 21, Online. Association for Computational Linguistics.

Mirela Silva, Fabrício Ceschin, Prakash Shrestha, Christopher Brant, Juliana Fernandes, Catia Silva, André Grégio, Daniela Oliveira, and Luiz Giovanini. 2020. Predicting misinformation and engagement in covid-19 twitter discourse in the first months of the outbreak.

Ashish Vaswani, Noam Shazeer, Niki Parmar, Jakob Uszkoreit, Llion Jones, Aidan N Gomez, Ł ukasz Kaiser, and Illia Polosukhin. 2017. Attention is all you need. In *Advances in Neural Information Processing Systems*, volume 30. Curran Associates, Inc.

Thomas Wolf, Lysandre Debut, Victor Sanh, Julien Chaumond, Clement Delangue, Anthony Moi, Pierric Cistac, Tim Rault, Remi Louf, Morgan Funtowicz, Joe Davison, Sam Shleifer, Patrick von Platen, Clara Ma, Yacine Jernite, Julien Plu, Canwen Xu, Teven Le Scao, Sylvain Gugger, Mariama Drame, Quentin Lhoest, and Alexander Rush. 2020. Transformers: State-of-the-art natural language processing. pages 38–45.

iCompass at NLP4IF-2021–Fighting the COVID-19 Infodemic

Wassim Henia
Oumayma Rjab
iCompass, Tunisia
{wassim.henia, oumayma.rjab}
@etudiant-isi.utm.tn

Hatem Haddad
Chayma Fourati
iCompass, Tunisia
{Hatem, Chayma}
@icompass.degital

Abstract

This paper provides a detailed overview of the system and its outcomes, which were produced as part of the NLP4IF Shared Task on Fighting the COVID-19 Infodemic at NAACL 2021. This task is accomplished using a variety of techniques. We used state-of-the-art contextualized text representation models that were fine-tuned for the down-stream task in hand. ARBERT, MARBERT,AraBERT, Arabic ALBERT and BERT-base-arabic were used. According to the results, BERT-base-arabic had the highest 0.748 F1 score on the test set.

1 Introduction

In recent years, there has been a massive increase in the number of people using social media (such as Facebook and Twitter) to share, post information, and voice their thoughts. The increasing number of users has resulted in the development of an enormous number of posts on Twitter. Although social media networks have enhanced information exchange, they have also created a space for antisocial and illegal activities such as spreading false information, rumors, and abuse. These anti-social behaviors intensify in a massive way during crisis cases, creating a toxic impact on society, either purposely or accidentally. The COVID-19 pandemic is one such situation that has impacted people's lives by locking them down to their houses and causing them to turn to social media. Since the beginning of the pandemic, false information concerning Covid-19 has circulated in a variety of languages, but the spread in Arabic is especially harmful due to a lack of quality reporting. For example, the tweet "مسائكم أخبار جميلة عن #كورونا 40 ثانية فقط م صاحب مبادرة تجميع العلماء لإيجاد علاج ضد #كرونا يعلنها على الهواء مباشرة أن فريق كامل من ضمنهم طبيب فرنسي اسمه "راولت" اكتشفوا أن دواء الملاريا هو الذي يعالج # كورونا_الجديد بنسبة 100% وتم تجربته على 40 مريض #ترجمات_عبدالله_الخريف" is translated as follows: "Good evening, good news, 40 seconds, the owner of the initiative to gather scientists to find a treatment against Corona announces on the air that an entire team, including a French doctor named "Raoult", discovered that the malaria treatment is the one that treats the new Corona, and it has been tried on 40 patients". This tweet contains false information that is harmful to the society and people believing it could be faced with real danger. Basically, we are not only fighting the coronavirus, but there is a war against infodemic which makes it crucial to identify this type of false information. For instance, the NLP4IF Task 2 is fighting the COVID-19 Infodemic by predicting several binary properties of a tweet about COVID-19 as follows: whether it is harmful, whether it contains a verifiable claim, whether it may be of interest to the general public, whether it appears to contain false information, whether it needs verification or/and requires attention. This is why we performed a multi-label classification using Arabic pretrained models including ALBERT Arabic (Lan et al., 2019), BERT-base-arabic (Devlin et al., 2018), AraBERT (Antoun et al., 2020), ARBERT(Abdul-Mageed et al., 2020), and MARBERT (Abdul-Mageed et al., 2020) with different hyper-parameters. The paper is structured as follows: Section 2 provides a concise description of the used dataset. Section 3 describes the used systems and the experimental setup to build models for Fighting the COVID-19 Infodemic. Section 4 presents the obtained results. Section 5 presents the official submission results. Finally, section 6 concludes and points to possible directions for future work.

2 Dataset description

The provided training dataset of the competition, fighting the COVID-19 Infodemic Arabic, consists of 2536 tweets and the development dataset con-

Proceedings of the 4th NLP4IF Workshop on NLP for Internet Freedom, pages 115–118
June 6, 2021. ©2021 Association for Computational Linguistics

sists of 520 tweets (Shaar et al., 2021). The data was labelled as yes/no questions answering seven questions:

1. Verifiable Factual Claim: Does the tweet contain a verifiable factual claim?
2. False Information: To what extent does the tweet appear to contain false information?
3. Interest to General Public: Will the tweet have an effect on or be of interest to the general public?
4. Harmfulness: To what extent is the tweet harmful to the society/person(s)/company(s)/product(s)?
5. Need of Verification: Do you think that a professional fact-checker should verify the claim in the tweet?
6. Harmful to Society: Is the tweet harmful for society and why?
7. Require attention: Do you think that this tweet should get the attention of government entities?

Questions 2,3,4 and 5 will be labelled as nan if the answer to the first question is no. The tweets are in Modern Standard Arabic (MSA) and no other Arabic dialect was observed. Data was preprocessed by removing emojis, URLs, punctuation, duplicated characters in a word, diacritics, and any non Arabic words.
We present an example sentence before and after preprocessing:

- Before preprocessing: : #وزارة_الصحة تلزم المشاركين من منسوبيها في حج 1442[1] باخذ لقاح كوفيد_19
- After preprocessing: وزاره_الصحه تلزم المشاركين من منسوبيها في حج 1442 باخذ لقاح كوفيد 19

3 System description

Pretrained contextualized text representation models have shown to perform effectively in order to make a natural language understandable by machines. Bidirectional Encoder Representations from Transformers (BERT) (Devlin et al., 2018) is, nowadays, the state-of-the-art model for language understanding, outperforming previous models and opening new perspectives in the Natural Language Processing (NLP) field. Recent similar work was conducted for Arabic which is increasingly gaining attention. In our work, we used three BERT Arabic variants: AraBERT (Antoun et al., 2020), ARBERT (Abdul-Mageed et al., 2020), MARBERT (Abdul-Mageed et al., 2020) and Arabic BERT (Safaya et al., 2020). Added-on, we used the xlarge version Arabic Albert[2].

3.1 AraBERT

AraBERT (Antoun et al., 2020), was trained on 70 million sentences, equivalent to 24 GB of text, covering news in Arabic from different media sources. It achieved state-of-the-art performances on three Arabic tasks including Sentiment Analysis. Yet, the pre-training dataset was mostly in MSA and therefore can't handle dialectal Arabic as much as official Arabic.

3.2 ARBERT

ARBERT (Abdul-Mageed et al., 2020) is a large-scale pretrained language model using BERT base's architecture and focusing on MSA. It was trained on 61 GB of text gathered from books, news articles, crawled data and the Arabic Wikipedia. The vocabulary size was equal to 100k WordPieces which is the largest compared to AraBERT (60k for Arabic out of 64k) and mBERT (5k for Arabic out of 110k).

3.3 MARBERT

MARBERT, also by (Abdul-Mageed et al., 2020), is a large-scale pretrained language model using BERT base's architecture and focusing on the various Arabic dialects. It was trained on 128 GB of Arabic Tweets. The authors chose to keep the Tweets that have at least three Arabic words. Therefore, Tweets that have three or more Arabic words and some other non-Arabic words are kept. This is because dialects are often times mixed with other foreign languages. Hence, the vocabulary size is equal to 100k WordPieces. MARBERT enhances the language variety as it focuses on representing the previously underrepresented dialects and Arabic variants.

[1] https://t.co/6MEMHFMQj2

[2] https://github.com/KUIS-AI-Lab/Arabic-ALBERT

3.4 Arabic ALBERT

Arabic ALBERT[2] by (KUIS-AI-Lab) models were pretrained on 4.4 Billion words: Arabic version of OSCAR (unshuffled version of the corpus) filtered from Common Crawl and Recent dump of Arabic Wikipedia. Also, the corpus and vocabulary set are not restricted to MSA, but contain some dialectical Arabic too.

3.5 Arabic BERT

Arabic BERT (Safaya et al., 2020) is a set of BERT language models that consists of four models of different sizes trained using masked language modeling with whole word masking (Devlin et al., 2018). Using a corpus that consists of the unshuffled version of OSCAR data (Ortiz Suárez et al., 2020) and a recent data dump from Wikipedia, which sums up to 8.2B words, a vocabulary set of 32,000 Wordpieces was constructed. The final version of corpus contains some non-Arabic words inlines. The corpus and the vocabulary set are not restricted to MSA, they contain some dialectical (spoken) Arabic too, which boosted models performance in terms of data from social media platforms.

3.6 Fine-tuning

We use these pretrained language models and build upon them to obtain our final models. Other than outperforming previous techniques, huge amounts of unlabelled text have been used to train general purpose models. Fine-tuning them on much smaller annotated datasets achieves good results thanks to the knowledge gained during the pretraining phase, which is expensive especially in terms of computational power. Hence, given our relatively small dataset, we chose to fine-tune these pretrained models. The fine-tuning actually consists of adding an untrained layer of neurons on top of the pretrained model and only tweaking the weights of the last layers to adjust them to the new labelled dataset.
We chose to train our models on a Google Cloud GPU using Google Colaboratory. The average training time of one model is around 10 minutes.
We experimented with Arabic ALBERT, Arabic BERT, AraBERT, ARBERT and MARBERT with different hyperparameters.
The final model that we used to make the submission is a model based on BERT-base-arabic, trained for 10 epochs with a learning rate of 5e-5, a batch size of 32 and max sequence length of 128.

4 Development dataset results

We have validated our models through the development dataset as mentioned in the data section. The results of all models were close but the BERT-base-arabic achieved the best results performing 78.27% F1 score. For reference, and to compare with other models, we also showcase the results obtained with ARBERT, AraBERT, and Arabic ALBERT in Table 1.

- The best ARBERT model was achieved using 2e-5 learning rate, 32 batch size, 10 epochs, 128 max length.
- The best MARBERT model was achieved using 6e-5 learning rate, 32 batch size, 10 epochs, 128 max length.
- The best AraBERT model was achieved using 4e-5 learning rate, 32 batch size, 10 epochs, 128 max length.
- The best ALBERT Arabic model was achieved using 2e-5 learning rate, 16 batch size, 8 epochs, 128 max length.

5 Official submission results

Table 1 presents the results obtained over development data for Fighting COVID-19 Infodemic. The result of all the models used are very close. However, bert-base-arabic outperformed all other models. This may be due to the pretrained data for bert-base-arabic. The final version has some non-Arabic words inlines. Also, the corpus of bert-base-arabic and vocabulary set are not restricted to MSA, they contain some dialectical Arabic too which can boost the model performance in terms of data from social media.
Table 2 reviews the official results of iCompass system against the top three ranked systems.
Table 3 presents the official results per class of iCompass system.

6 Conclusion

This paper describes the system built in the NLP4IF 2021 shared Task , along with comprehensive results. Various learning techniques have been investigated using five language models (Arabic ALBERT, AraBERT, ARBERT, MARBERT, and BERT-base-arabic) to accomplish the task of Fighting the COVID-19 Infodemic. The results show

Model	F1 Score	Precision	Recall
ARBERT	0.7734	0.8153	0.7502
MARBERT	0.7654	0.7879	0.7662
AraBERT	0.7635	0.8223	0.7403
ALBERT-Arabic	0.7603	0.8202	0.7399
BERT-base-Arabic	**0.7827**	**0.8255**	**0.7712**

Table 1: Models performances on the Dev dataset.

Team	Rank	F1 Score
R00	1	0.781
iCompass	**2**	**0.748**
HunterSpeechLab	3	0.741
advex	4	0.728

Table 2: Official Results on Test set and ranking as reported by the task organisers (Shaar et al., 2021).

Questions	F1 Score
Q1	0.797
Q2	0.746
Q3	0.881
Q4	0.796
Q5	0.544
Q6	0.885
Q7	0.585

Table 3: Official Results for each classifier as reported by the task organisers (Shaar et al., 2021).

that BERT-base-arabic outperforms all of the previously listed models in terms of overall performance, and was chosen for the final submission. Future work will include developing larger contextualized pretrained models and improving the current COVID-19 Infodemic Detection .

References

Muhammad Abdul-Mageed, AbdelRahim Elmadany, and El Moatez Billah Nagoudi. 2020. Arbert & marbert: Deep bidirectional transformers for arabic. *arXiv preprint arXiv:2101.01785*.

Wissam Antoun, Fady Baly, and Hazem Hajj. 2020. Arabert: Transformer-based model for arabic language understanding. *arXiv preprint arXiv:2003.00104*.

Jacob Devlin, Ming-Wei Chang, Kenton Lee, and Kristina Toutanova. 2018. Bert: Pre-training of deep bidirectional transformers for language understanding. *arXiv preprint arXiv:1810.04805*.

Zhenzhong Lan, Mingda Chen, Sebastian Goodman, Kevin Gimpel, Piyush Sharma, and Radu Soricut. 2019. Albert: A lite bert for self-supervised learning of language representations. *arXiv preprint arXiv:1909.11942*.

Pedro Javier Ortiz Suárez, Laurent Romary, and Benoît Sagot. 2020. A monolingual approach to contextualized word embeddings for mid-resource languages. In *Proceedings of the 58th Annual Meeting of the Association for Computational Linguistics*, pages 1703–1714, Online. Association for Computational Linguistics.

Ali Safaya, Moutasem Abdullatif, and Deniz Yuret. 2020. Kuisail at semeval-2020 task 12: Bert-cnn for offensive speech identification in social media.

Shaden Shaar, Firoj Alam, Giovanni Da San Martino, Alex Nikolov, Wajdi Zaghouani, Preslav Nakov, and Anna Feldman. 2021. Findings of the NLP4IF-2021 shared task on fighting the COVID-19 infodemic and censorship detection. In *Proceedings of the Fourth Workshop on Natural Language Processing for Internet Freedom: Censorship, Disinformation, and Propaganda*, NLP4IF@NAACL' 21, Online. Association for Computational Linguistics.

Fighting the COVID-19 Infodemic with a Holistic BERT Ensemble

Giorgos Tziafas[◇], **Konstantinos Kogkalidis**[♣], **Tommaso Caselli**[◇]
[◇]University of Groningen, [♣]Utrecht University
Groningen The Netherlands, Utrecht The Netherlands
g.tziafas@student.rug.nl, k.kogkalidis@uu.nl, t.caselli@rug.nl

Abstract

This paper describes the TOKOFOU system, an ensemble model for misinformation detection tasks based on six different transformer-based pre-trained encoders, implemented in the context of the COVID-19 Infodemic Shared Task for English. We fine tune each model on each of the task's questions and aggregate their prediction scores using a majority voting approach. TOKOFOU obtains an overall F1 score of 89.7%, ranking first.

1 Introduction

Social media platforms, e.g., Twitter, Instagram, Facebook, TikTok among others, are playing a major role in facilitating communication among individuals and sharing of information. Social media, and in particular Twitter, are also actively used by governments and health organizations to quickly and effectively communicate key information to the public in case of disasters, political unrest, and outbreaks (Househ, 2016; Stefanidis et al., 2017; LaLone et al., 2017; Daughton and Paul, 2019; Rogers et al., 2019).

However, there are dark sides to the use of social media. The removal of forms of gate-keeping and the democratization process of the production of information have impacted the quality of the content that becomes available. Misinformation, i.e., the spread of false, inaccurate, misleading information such as rumors, hoaxes, false statements, is a particularly dangerous type of low quality content that affects social media platforms. The dangers of misinformation are best illustrated by considering the combination of three strictly interconnected factors: (i) the diminishing abilities to discriminate between trustworthy sources and information from hoaxes and malevolent agents (Hargittai et al., 2010); (ii) a faster, deeper, and broader spread than true information, especially for topics such as disasters and science (Vosoughi et al., 2018); (iii) the elicitation of fears and suspicions in the population, threatening the texture of societies.

The COVID-19 pandemic is the perfect target for misinformation: it is the first pandemic of the Information Age, where social media platforms have a primary role in the information-sphere; it is a natural disaster, where science plays a key role to understand and cure the disease; knowledge about the SARS-CoV-2 virus is limited and the scientific understanding is continually developing. To monitor and limit the threats of COVID-19 misinformation, different initiatives have been activated (e.g., #CoronaVirusFacts Alliance[1], EUvsDisinfo[2]), while social media platforms have been enforcing more stringent policies. Nevertheless, the amount of produced misinformation is such that manual intervention and curation is not feasible, calling for the development of automatic solutions grounded on Natural Language Processing.

The proposed shared task on COVID-19 misinformation presents innovative aspects mirroring the complexity and variation of phenomena that accompanies the spread of misinformation about COVID-19, including fake news, rumors, conspiracy theories, racism, xenophobia and mistrust of science, among others. To embrace the variation of the phenomena, the task organizers have developed a rich annotation scheme based on seven questions (Shaar et al., 2021). Participants are asked to design a system capable of automatically labeling a set of messages from Twitter with a binary value (i.e., *yes/no*) for each of the seven questions. Train and test data are available in three languages, namely English, Arabic, and Bulgarian. Our team, TOKOFOU, submitted predictions only for the English data by developing an ensemble model based on a combination of different transformer-based pre-trained language encoders. Each pre-trained model has been selected to match the language va-

[1]https://bit.ly/3uGjwEr
[2]https://bit.ly/3wPqsBg

Proceedings of the 4th NLP4IF Workshop on NLP for Internet Freedom, pages 119–124
June 6, 2021. ©2021 Association for Computational Linguistics

riety of the data (i.e., tweet) and the phenomena entailed by each of the questions. With an overall F1 score of 89.7 our system ranked first[3].

2 Data

The English task provides both training and development data. The data have been annotated using a in-house crowdsourcing platform following the annotation scheme presented in Alam et al. (2020).

The scheme covers in a very extensive way the complexity of the phenomena that surrounds COVID-19 misinformation by means of seven key questions. The annotation follows a specific pattern after the first question (Q1), that aims at checking whether a message is a verifiable factual claim. In case of a positive answer, the annotator is presented with an additional set of four questions (Q2–Q5) addressing aspects such as presence of false information, interest for the public, presence of harmful content, and check-worthiness. After this block, the annotator has two further questions. Q6 can be seen as a refinement of the presence of harmful content (i.e, the content is intended to harm society or weaponized to mislead the society), while Q7 asks the annotator whether the message should receive the attention of a government authority. In case of a negative answer to Q1, the annotator jumps directly to Q6 and Q7. Quite interestingly, Q6 lists a number of categories to better identify the nature of the harm (e.g., satire, joke, rumor, conspiracy, xenophobic, racist, prejudices, hate speech, among others).

The labels of the original annotation scheme present fine-grained categories for each questions, including a *not sure* value. For the task, the set of labels has been simplified to three: *yes*, *no*, and *nan*, with this latter corresponding in some cases to the *not sure* value. Indeed, due to the dependence of Q2–Q5 to a positive answer to Q1, some *nan* values for this set of questions can also correspond to *not applicable* rather than to *not sure* making the task more challenging than one would expect.

For English, the organisers released 869 annotated messages for training, 53 for development, and 418 for testing. The distribution of the labels for each question in the training data is reported in Figure 1. As the figures show, the dataset is unbalanced for all questions. While the majority of messages present potential factual claims (Q1), only a tiny minority has been labelled as containing false information (Q2) with a very high portion re-

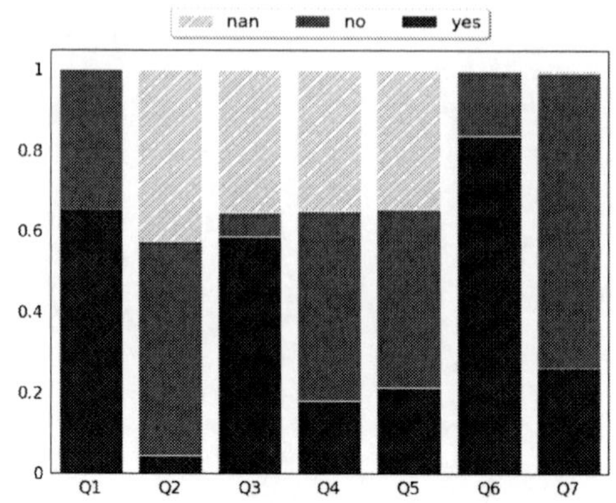

Figure 1: Distribution of the categories for each question in the training data.

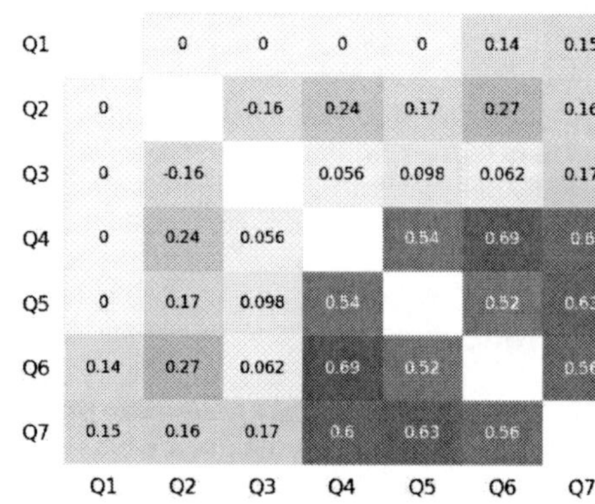

Figure 2: ϕ coefficients between question pairs, excluding *nan* values.

ceiving a *nan* label, suggesting that discriminating whether a claim is false or not is a difficult task for human annotators. Similar observations hold for Q3–Q5. Q6 is a refinement of Q4 about the nature of the harm. The low amount of *nan* values indicates a better reliability of the annotators in deciding the specific type of harms. Q7 also appears to elicit more clear-cut judgements. Finally, with the exception of questions Q4–Q7 which exhibit a weak pairwise covariance, no noteworthy correlation is discernible (refer to Figure 2).

3 System Overview

Our system is a majority voting ensemble model based on a combination of six different transformer-based pre-trained encoders, each selected targeting a relevant aspect of the annotated data such as domain, topic, and specific sub-tasks.

[3]Source code is available at https://git.io/JOtpH.

3.1 BERT Models

Preliminary data analysis and manual inspection of the input texts strongly hint at the notable difficulty of the problem. The questions our model will be called to answer are high-level semantic tasks that sometimes go beyond sentential understanding, seemingly also relying on external world knowledge. The limited size of the dataset also rules out the possibility for a task-specific architecture, even more so if one considers the effective loss of data from *nan* labels and the small proportion of development samples, factors that increase the risk of overfitting. Knowledge grounding with a static external source becomes impractical in view of the rapid pace of events throughout the COVID-19 pandemic: a claim would need to be contrasted against a distinct version of the knowledge base depending on when it was expressed, inserting significant overhead and necessitating an additional timestamp input feature.[4]

In light of the above, we turn our attention to pretrained BERT-like models (Devlin et al., 2019). BERT-like models are the workhorses in NLP, boasting a high capacity for semantic understanding while acting as implicit rudimentary knowledge bases, owing to their utilization of massive amounts of unlabeled data (Petroni et al., 2019; Rogers et al., 2020). Among the many candidate models, the ones confined within the twitter domain make for the most natural choices. Language use in twitter messages differs from the norm, in terms of style, length, and content. A twitter-specific model should then already be accustomed to the particularities of the domain, relieving us from either having to account for domain adaptation, or relying on external data. We obtain our final set of models by filtering our selection in accordance with a refinement of the tasks, as expressed by the questions of the annotation schemes, and the domain. In particular, we focus our selection of models according to the following criteria: (i) models that have been pre-trained on the language domain (i.e, Twitter); (ii) models that have been pre-trained on data related to the COVID-19 pandemic; and (iii) models that have been pre-trained or fine tuned for high-level tasks (e.g., irony and hate speech detection) expressed by any of the target questions. In this way, we identified and used six variations of three pre-trained models, detailed in the following paragraphs.

[4]This is especially relevant in the task's context, where the training/development and test data are temporally offset by about a year.

BERTWEET (Nguyen et al., 2020) is a RoBERTa$_{base}$ model (Liu et al., 2019) trained from scratch on 850M tweets. It is a strong baseline that, fine tuned, achieves state-of-the-art benchmarks on the SemEval 2017 sentiment analysis and the SemEval 2018 irony detection shared tasks (Rosenthal et al., 2017; Van Hee et al., 2018). Here, we use a variant of the model, additionally trained on 23M tweets related to the COVID-19 pandemic, collected prior to September 2020.

CT-BERT (Müller et al., 2020) is a pre-trained BERT$_{large}$ model, adapted for use in the twitter setting and specifically the COVID-19 theme by continued unsupervised training on 160M tweets related to the COVID-19 pandemic and collected between January and April 2020. Fine tuned and evaluated on a small range of tasks, it has been shown to slightly outperform the original.

TWEETEVAL (Barbieri et al., 2020) is a pre-trained RoBERTa$_{base}$ model, further trained with 60M tweets, randomly collected, resulting in a Twitter-domain adapted version. We use a selection of four TWEETEVAL models, each fine tuned for a twitter-specific downstream task: hate speech-, emotion- and irony-detection, and offensive language identification.

3.2 Fine-tuning

The affinity between the above models and the task at hand allows us to use them for sentence vectorization as-is, requiring only an inexpensive fine tuning pass. We attach a linear projection on top of each model, which maps its `[CLS]` token representation to $||Q|| = 7$ outputs, one per question. The sigmoid-activated outputs act as independent logits for binary classification of each question and the entire network is trained through summing their cross-entropy losses. We train for 15 epochs on batches of 16 tweets, using the *AdamW* (Loshchilov and Hutter, 2017) optimizer with a learning rate of $3 \cdot 10^{-5}$ and weight decay of 0.01, without penalizing predictions corresponding to *nan* gold labels. We add dropout layers of rate 0.5 in each model's classification head. We perform model selection on the basis of mean F1-score on the development set, and report results in Table 1. As the figures show, no single model outperforms the rest. Indeed, performance largely varies both across models and questions, with best scores scattered over the table. Similar results occur when repeating the experiments with different random seeds.

Models	average	Q1	Q2	Q3	Q4	Q5	Q6	Q7
BERTWEET	83.6	86.5	78.4	86.9	88.8	73.4	87.9	**83.0**
CT-BERT	81.3	**92.4**	76.5	88.5	90.5	68.1	80.5	72.4
TWEETEVAL-hate	84.8	88.6	84	85.3	90.6	**82.7**	85.8	70.7
TWEETEVAL-emotion	84.5	78.2	85.9	**91.8**	89.0	81.4	85.0	80.0
TWEETEVAL-irony	**85.7**	86.5	**96.1**	85.2	81.6	81.5	**88.7**	76.7
TWEETEVAL-offensive	82.9	90.5	74.5	84.1	**92.2**	72.6	84.4	81.5
average	83.8	87.1	82.6	87.0	88.8	76.6	85.4	77.4
Ensemble	84.6	90.6	78.4	**91.8**	**92.2**	76.9	**90.9**	78.5

Table 1: Best mean F1-scores (%) reported in the development set individually for each question as well as their average (with implicit exclusion of *nan* labels for Q2-Q5). Best scores are in bold.

3.3 Aggregation

The proposed ensemble model aggregates predictions scores along the model axis by first rounding them (into positive or negative labels) and then selecting the final outcome by a majority rule. The ensemble performs better or equally to all individual models in 3 out of 7 questions in the development set, and its metrics lie above the average for 6 of them. Keeping in mind the small size of the development set, we refrain from altering the voting scheme, expecting the majority-based model to be the most robust.

During training, we do not apply any preprocessing of the data and rely on the respective tokenizer of each model, but homogenize test data by removing URLs.

4 Results and Discussion

Results on the test data are illustrated in Table 2. Two of the three organizers' baselines, namely the majority voting and the ngram baseline, provide already competitive scores. Our ensemble model largely outperforms all of them. The delta with the second best performing system is 0.6 points in F1 score, with a better Recall for TOKOFOU of 3 points.

System	Precision	Recall	F1
TOKOFOU	90.7	89.6	89.7
Majority Baseline	78.6	88.3	83.0
Ngram Baseline	81.9	86.8	82.8
Random Baseline	79.7	38.9	49.6

Table 2: Results on English test data - average on all questions - and comparison with organizers' baselines.

When looking at the results per question,[5] TOKOFOU achieves an F1 higher than 90 on Q2 (91.3), Q3 (97.8), and Q6 (90.8). With the exclusion of Q6, the majority baseline on Q2 and Q3 is 92.7 and 100, respectively. This indicates that label imbalance affects the test data as well. At the same time, the performance of ngram baseline suggest that lexical variability is limited. This is not expected given the large variety of misinformation topics that seems affect the discussion around the COVID-19 pandemic. These results justify both our choice of models for the ensemble and majority voting as a robust aggregation method.

5 Conclusion

We participated in the COVID-19 misinformation shared task with an ensemble of pre-trained BERT-based encoders, fine-tuning each model for predictions in all questions and aggregating them into a final answer through majority voting. Our system is indeed a strong baseline for this task showing the effectiveness of available pre-trained language models for Twitter data, mixed with variants fine tuned for a specific topic (COVID-19) and multiple downstream tasks (emotion detection, hate-speech, etc.). Results indicate that this holistic approach to transfer learning allows for a data-efficient and compute-conscious methodology, omitting the often prohibitive computational requirement of re-training a model from scratch for a specific task, in favour of an ensemble architecture based on task/domain-similar solutions from a large ecosystem of publicly available models.

With appropriate scaling of the associated dataset, a system as proposed by this paper can be suitably integrated into a human-in-the-loop scenario, serving as an effective assistant in (semi-) automated annotation of Twitter data for misinformation.

[5]Leaderboard is available here: https://tinyurl.com/2drvruc

Acknowledgments

The authors would like to acknowledge the RUG university computer cluster, Peregrine, for providing the computational infrastructure which allowed the implementation of the current work.

References

Firoj Alam, Fahim Dalvi, Shaden Shaar, Nadir Durrani, Hamdy Mubarak, Alex Nikolov, Giovanni Da San Martino, Ahmed Abdelali, Hassan Sajjad, Kareem Darwish, et al. 2020. Fighting the covid-19 infodemic in social media: A holistic perspective and a call to arms. *arXiv preprint arXiv:2007.07996*.

Francesco Barbieri, Jose Camacho-Collados, Luis Espinosa Anke, and Leonardo Neves. 2020. TweetEval: Unified benchmark and comparative evaluation for tweet classification. In *Findings of the Association for Computational Linguistics: EMNLP 2020*, pages 1644–1650, Online. Association for Computational Linguistics.

Ashlynn R Daughton and Michael J Paul. 2019. Identifying protective health behaviors on twitter: observational study of travel advisories and zika virus. *Journal of medical Internet research*, 21(5):e13090.

Jacob Devlin, Ming-Wei Chang, Kenton Lee, and Kristina Toutanova. 2019. Bert: Pre-training of deep bidirectional transformers for language understanding. In *Proceedings of the 2019 Conference of the North American Chapter of the Association for Computational Linguistics: Human Language Technologies, Volume 1 (Long and Short Papers)*, pages 4171–4186.

Eszter Hargittai, Lindsay Fullerton, Ericka Menchen-Trevino, and Kristin Yates Thomas. 2010. Trust online: Young adults' evaluation of web content. *International journal of communication*, 4:27.

Mowafa Househ. 2016. Communicating ebola through social media and electronic news media outlets: A cross-sectional study. *Health informatics journal*, 22(3):470–478.

Nicolas LaLone, Andrea Tapia, Christopher Zobel, Cornelia Caraega, Venkata Kishore Neppalli, and Shane Halse. 2017. Embracing human noise as resilience indicator: twitter as power grid correlate. *Sustainable and Resilient Infrastructure*, 2(4):169–178.

Yinhan Liu, Myle Ott, Naman Goyal, Jingfei Du, Mandar Joshi, Danqi Chen, Omer Levy, Mike Lewis, Luke Zettlemoyer, and Veselin Stoyanov. 2019. Roberta: A robustly optimized BERT pretraining approach. *CoRR*, abs/1907.11692.

Ilya Loshchilov and Frank Hutter. 2017. Fixing weight decay regularization in adam. *CoRR*, abs/1711.05101.

Martin Müller, Marcel Salathé, and Per E Kummervold. 2020. Covid-twitter-bert: A natural language processing model to analyse covid-19 content on twitter. *arXiv preprint arXiv:2005.07503*.

Dat Quoc Nguyen, Thanh Vu, and Anh Tuan Nguyen. 2020. BERTweet: A pre-trained language model for English Tweets. In *Proceedings of the 2020 Conference on Empirical Methods in Natural Language Processing: System Demonstrations*.

Fabio Petroni, Tim Rocktäschel, Sebastian Riedel, Patrick Lewis, Anton Bakhtin, Yuxiang Wu, and Alexander Miller. 2019. Language models as knowledge bases? In *Proceedings of the 2019 Conference on Empirical Methods in Natural Language Processing and the 9th International Joint Conference on Natural Language Processing (EMNLP-IJCNLP)*, pages 2463–2473, Hong Kong, China. Association for Computational Linguistics.

Anna Rogers, Olga Kovaleva, and Anna Rumshisky. 2019. Calls to action on social media: Detection, social impact, and censorship potential. In *Proceedings of the Second Workshop on Natural Language Processing for Internet Freedom: Censorship, Disinformation, and Propaganda*, pages 36–44, Hong Kong, China. Association for Computational Linguistics.

Anna Rogers, Olga Kovaleva, and Anna Rumshisky. 2020. A primer in BERTology: What we know about how BERT works. *Transactions of the Association for Computational Linguistics*, 8:842–866.

Sara Rosenthal, Noura Farra, and Preslav Nakov. 2017. SemEval-2017 task 4: Sentiment analysis in Twitter. In *Proceedings of the 11th International Workshop on Semantic Evaluation (SemEval-2017)*, pages 502–518, Vancouver, Canada. Association for Computational Linguistics.

Shaden Shaar, Firoj Alam, Giovanni Da San Martino, Alex Nikolov, Wajdi Zaghouani, Preslav Nakov, and Anna Feldman. 2021. Findings of the NLP4IF-2021 shared task on fighting the COVID-19 infodemic and censorship detection. In *Proceedings of the Fourth Workshop on Natural Language Processing for Internet Freedom: Censorship, Disinformation, and Propaganda*, NLP4IF@NAACL' 21, Online. Association for Computational Linguistics.

Anthony Stefanidis, Emily Vraga, Georgios Lamprianidis, Jacek Radzikowski, Paul L Delamater, Kathryn H Jacobsen, Dieter Pfoser, Arie Croitoru, and Andrew Crooks. 2017. Zika in twitter: temporal variations of locations, actors, and concepts. *JMIR public health and surveillance*, 3(2):e22.

Cynthia Van Hee, Els Lefever, and Véronique Hoste. 2018. SemEval-2018 task 3: Irony detection in English tweets. In *Proceedings of The 12th International Workshop on Semantic Evaluation*, pages 39–50, New Orleans, Louisiana. Association for Computational Linguistics.

Soroush Vosoughi, Deb Roy, and Sinan Aral. 2018. The spread of true and false news online. *Science*, 359(6380):1146–1151.

Detecting Multilingual COVID-19 Misinformation on Social Media via Contextualized Embeddings

Subhadarshi Panda
Hunter College
City University of New York
spanda@gc.cuny.edu

Sarah Ita Levitan
Hunter College
City University of New York
sarah.levitan@hunter.cuny.edu

Abstract

We present machine learning classifiers to automatically identify COVID-19 misinformation on social media in three languages: English, Bulgarian, and Arabic. We compared 4 multitask learning models for this task and found that a model trained with English BERT achieves the best results for English, and multilingual BERT achieves the best results for Bulgarian and Arabic. We experimented with zero shot, few shot, and target-only conditions to evaluate the impact of target-language training data on classifier performance, and to understand the capabilities of different models to generalize across languages in detecting misinformation online. This work was performed as a submission to the shared task, NLP4IF 2021: Fighting the COVID-19 Infodemic. Our best models achieved the second best evaluation test results for Bulgarian and Arabic among all the participating teams and obtained competitive scores for English.

1 Introduction

Automatic detection of misinformation online is a crucial problem that has become increasingly necessary in recent years. Misinformation is shared frequently online, especially via social media platforms which generally do not filter content based on veracity. The ongoing COVID-19 pandemic has highlighted the importance of creating tools to automatically identify misinformation online and to help stop the spread of deceptive messages. During a global health crisis, misinformation can cause tremendous damage. A recent study polled Americans about beliefs in COVID-19 misinformation, and found that many conspiracy theories were believed by a substantial percentage of participants. For example, 20% of participants believed that the pandemic is a ruse "to install tracking devices inside our bodies." Such conspiracy theories, when shared widely online, could influence people to make choices based on those beliefs which can jeopardize their own health and safety as well as others around them.

There has been recent work in the NLP community aimed at identifying general misinformation on social media (Shu et al., 2017; Mitra et al., 2017) and particularly COVID-19 misinformation (Hossain et al., 2020). Most of this prior work has focused on data in English. In this paper we address the problem of cross-lingual identification of COVID-19 misinformation. There is a severe data shortage of high quality datasets that are labeled for misinformation in multiple languages. Because of this, we need to develop models of deception and misinformation that can leverage large amounts of training data in a source language, such as English, and generalize to new target languages.

Some prior work on misinformation and deception detection has been applied to a cross-cultural setting (Pérez-Rosas and Mihalcea, 2014) and recently to a cross-lingual setting (Capuozzo et al., 2020b,a). Whereas previous approaches have focused on single task models, in this work we train four different multitask models and demonstrate their performance in cross-lingual settings for identifying misinformation in social media. Two of these models are based on BERT (Devlin et al., 2019). We show that even with no training data in the target language, the multilingual BERT based model can obtain 0.685 F1 in English, 0.81 F1 in Bulgarian and 0.672 F1 in Arabic.

2 Data

Language →	English	Bulgarian	Arabic
Train	451 (869)	3000	198 (2536)
Dev	53	350	20 (520)
Test	418	357	1000
Total	922 (1340)	3707	1218 (4056)

Table 1: Data sizes for the three languages. The numbers within parentheses denote the sizes after adding additional data that was released for the shared task.

Proceedings of the 4th NLP4IF Workshop on NLP for Internet Freedom, pages 125–129
June 6, 2021.

Language	Split	Q1	Q2	Q3	Q4	Q5	Q6	Q7
English	Train	569 Y / 300 N	39 Y / 460 N	510 Y / 51 N	156 Y / 409 N	185 Y / 384 N	138 Y / 729 N	229 Y / 634 N
	Dev	27 Y / 26 N	4 Y / 20 N	22 Y / 5 N	11 Y / 16 N	12 Y / 15 N	6 Y / 47 N	8 Y / 45 N
Bulgarian	Train	1933 Y / 1067 N	64 Y / 1897 N	1910 Y / 55 N	181 Y / 1770 N	392 Y / 1557 N	316 Y / 2680 N	300 Y / 2655 N
	Dev	315 Y / 35 N	5 Y / 316 N	308 Y / 12 N	25 Y / 288 N	62 Y / 254 N	62 Y / 288 N	69 Y / 275 N
Arabic	Train	1926 Y / 610 N	376 Y / 1545 N	1895 Y / 22 N	351 Y / 1566 N	936 Y / 990 N	459 Y / 2075 N	2208 Y / 328 N
	Dev	225 Y / 295 N	12 Y / 210 N	221 Y / 4 N	23 Y / 201 N	107 Y / 118 N	41 Y / 478 N	379 Y / 141 N

Table 2: Distribution of the labels (Yes/No) in the training and dev sets for different languages. The numbers shown are after considering the additional data for train and dev.

We used the tweet data provided for the Fighting the COVID-19 Infodemic shared task (Shaar et al., 2021).[1] The data was created by answering 7 questions about COVID-19 for each tweet (Shaar et al., 2021). Questions include: Q1 – Does the tweet contain a verifiable factual claim? Q2 – Does the tweet appear to contain false information? Each question has a Yes/No (binary) annotation. However, the answers to Q2, Q3, Q4 and Q5 are all "nan" if the answer to Q1 is No. The data includes tweets in three languages: English, Bulgarian and Arabic. An example of an English tweet from the dataset along with its 7 labels is shown below.

> Tweet: *Anyone else notice that COVID-19 seemed to pop up almost immediately after impeachment failed?*
> Labels: *Q1 Yes, Q2 Yes, Q3 Yes, Q4 Yes, Q5 No, Q6 Yes, Q7 No*

The training, development and test data sizes for each of the three languages are shown in Table 1 and the distribution of the Yes/No labels are shown in Table 2.

3 Methodology

The task is to predict 7 properties of a tweet about COVID-19 misinformation based on the corresponding 7 questions mentioned in Section 2. We use four multitask learning models for this task as described below.

Logistic regression The logistic regression model is a linear model where the output is passed through 7 different linear layers for each prediction. The input to logistic regression model is word embeddings for a given sequence of words. The embedding layer is initialized randomly. We represent the sequence of words as the sum of the token level embeddings for a given sentence. The loss is computed as the sum of the cross entropy loss for each of the 7 tasks. This logistic regression model is a simple approach and provides a baseline to compare other more complex models with.

Transformer encoder The logistic regression model ignores the word order in the input sentence and handles the input as a bag of words. To consider word order, models such as LSTMs (Hochreiter and Schmidhuber, 1997) and more recently attention based networks called transformers (Vaswani et al., 2017) have been shown to be effective. A transformer encoder model is an attention based model that uses positional embeddings to incorporate word order. We add a `[CLS]` token in the beginning of each sentence. The classification is done based on the `[CLS]` token's representation. For our multitask objective, the `[CLS]` token's representation is passed through 7 different linear layers separately to produce the logits corresponding to the 7 tasks. As in the case of the logistic regression model, the loss is computed as the sum of the cross-entropy loss for each task.

English BERT BERT (Devlin et al., 2019) is a large language model trained on a gigantic amount of text data from BookCorpus (Zhu et al., 2015) and Wikipedia. Pre-trained BERT has been shown to be effective in a wide range of NLP tasks (Devlin et al., 2019) by fine-tuning on data for a specific task. For our multitask objective, we use the `[CLS]` token's representation of BERT and pass it through 7 separate linear layers to produce the logits corresponding to the 7 tasks. The loss is computed as the sum of the cross entropy loss for each task.

Multilingual BERT Multilingual BERT (m-BERT) (Devlin et al., 2019) is a single large language model pre-trained from monolingual corpora in 104 languages. It has been shown to have strong cross-lingual generalization ability (K et al., 2020). m-BERT also manages to transfer knowledge between languages that have very little or no lexical overlap (Pires et al., 2019). For our multitask objective, similar to BERT we use the `[CLS]` token's representation of BERT and pass it through 7 sepa-

[1] `https://gitlab.com/NLP4IF/nlp4if-2021`

Trg. Lang.	Setup	Src. Lang.: Bulgarian				Src. Lang.: Arabic			
		Log. Reg.	Transf. Enc.	BERT	m-BERT	Log. Reg.	Transf. Enc.	BERT	m-BERT
English	zero	0.523	0.569	0.488	**0.685**	0.436	0.517	0.594	**0.683**
	few50	0.601	0.578	0.643	**0.672**	0.537	0.553	0.63	**0.659**
	few100	0.607	0.619	0.621	**0.659**	0.622	0.609	0.639	**0.663**
	few150	0.635	0.61	0.632	**0.655**	0.627	0.61	**0.729**	0.665
	few200	0.674	0.635	**0.713**	0.696	0.661	0.686	**0.722**	0.68
	full	0.713	0.67	**0.729**	0.7	0.715	0.68	**0.745**	0.712
	trg	0.698	0.686	**0.745**	0.722	0.698	0.686	**0.745**	0.722

Trg. Lang.	Setup	Src. Lang.: English				Src. Lang.: Arabic			
		Log. Reg.	Transf. Enc.	BERT	m-BERT	Log. Reg.	Transf. Enc.	BERT	m-BERT
Bulgarian	zero	0.37	0.804	0.803	**0.81**	0.558	0.805	0.803	**0.808**
	few50	0.776	0.8	0.81	**0.819**	0.794	0.804	0.811	**0.815**
	few100	0.781	0.81	0.816	**0.823**	0.799	0.808	0.818	**0.821**
	few150	0.796	0.819	0.819	**0.821**	0.8	0.816	0.82	**0.821**
	few200	0.807	0.82	0.816	**0.825**	0.8	0.811	**0.822**	0.82
	full	0.812	0.815	0.822	**0.834**	0.821	0.812	0.822	**0.836**
	trg	0.814	0.81	0.822	**0.843**	0.814	0.81	0.822	**0.843**

Trg. Lang.	Setup	Src. Lang.: English				Src. Lang.: Bulgarian			
		Log. Reg.	Transf. Enc.	BERT	m-BERT	Log. Reg.	Transf. Enc.	BERT	m-BERT
Arabic	zero	0.422	0.585	0.599	**0.672**	0.547	0.615	0.558	**0.638**
	few50	0.727	0.69	0.675	**0.775**	0.676	0.647	0.657	**0.76**
	few100	0.743	0.686	0.692	**0.824**	0.698	0.734	0.662	**0.753**
	few150	0.718	0.689	0.698	**0.791**	0.726	0.688	0.652	**0.775**
	full	0.747	0.74	0.712	**0.787**	0.708	0.716	0.679	**0.764**
	trg	0.649	0.684	0.735	**0.738**	0.649	0.684	0.735	**0.738**

Table 3: Cross-lingual (source language → target language) results (F1 score) on the development set. *fewx* setup denotes that only x samples in the target language are used for training.

rate linear layers to produce the logits corresponding to the 7 tasks. The loss is computed as the sum of the cross entropy loss for each task.

3.1 Post-processing

The multitask learning models produce outputs which may not satisfy the required constraint that if the prediction for Q1 is No, then the predictions for Q2, Q3, Q4 and Q5 should all be "nan". To make sure that this constraint is satisfied, we apply post-processing to the output. The post-processing involves overwriting the prediction for Q2, Q3, Q4, Q5 to "nan" if the prediction for Q1 is No. The post-processing does not have any impact if the prediction to Q1 is Yes.

4 Experiments

We performed cross lingual experiments in different setups as outlined below. We are interested in gauging the cross-lingual ability of prediction models when trained on data from one language (source language) and tested on data from another language (target language). We compare 4 experimental conditions, varying the amount of source language and target language data that is used for training. The four conditions are described below.

Zero shot In this condition, we only used the source language training data to train the model. The model does not see any training data in the target language and we only evaluated the model on the target language dev set. The advantage of the zero shot setup is that it enables us to evaluate the prediction models in conditions when no training data is available in the target language.

Few shot In this setup, we considered all the source language training data combined with x training samples from the target language. We set x to 50, 100, 150 and 200. We select x samples from the complete target language training data uniformly at random to simulate the few shot setup. For Arabic, the number of training data samples is 198 (without using additional data, see Table 1). So we set x to 50, 100, and 150. The advantage of the few shot setup is that it enables us to gauge the performance when only a handful of training samples are available in the target language.

Full shot In this setup, we used all the available training data from the source and target languages for training the model. This setup is useful to see the impact of the source language training data when combined to the target language training data.

Target In this setup, we used only the target language training data for training. This setup enables us to evaluate the models when there is availability of training data in the target language, and compare monolingual with cross-lingual classification.

4.1 Training

We implemented the models, training and evaluation pipelines using PyTorch (Paszke et al., 2019).[2] For the logistic regression and the transformer en-

[2]The code is available in `https://github.com/subhadarship/nlp4if-2021`.

coder models, we first tokenized the tweets and normalized the emojis, urls and usernames.[3] We tuned the hidden layer size {128, 256, 512} and the maximum vocabulary size {8k, 16k, 32k} by considering only the most frequent set of tokens. We set the dropout to 0.1 and used the Adam optimizer setting the learning rate to 0.0005. For the transformer encoder model, we used 3 encoder layers and 8 heads.

For the BERT based models, we used the Transformers library (Wolf et al., 2020) and loaded the `bert-base-uncased` model for English BERT and `bert-base-multilingual-cased` model for m-BERT, and also the corresponding tokenizers. We tuned the hidden layer size {128, 256, 512} of the added linear layer and the learning rate {0.0005, 0.005, 0.05}. The optimizer used was Adam. We also experimented with two variants: training the BERT pre-trained weights or freezing them. We found that freezing them resulted in better results overall. For training all the models, we used early stopping, that is, we stopped training when the dev F1 score does not improve for 10 consecutive epochs.

5 Results

Lang.	Model	Dev F1		Test F1
		No add. data	Add. data	
En	BERT	**0.745**	0.729	0.736
Bg	m-BERT	**0.843**	-	0.817
Ar	m-BERT	0.556	**0.688**	0.741

Table 4: Best scores on the dev set and final score on the test set. Best scores were obtained when trained in the target setup. For Arabic the dev set used for evaluation contains the additional data also (see Table 1).

For most experiments, we evaluate on the target language dev sets, since those labels are available for evaluation. We also report the final test set evaluation, which was conducted by the organizers based on our submitted predicted labels for the blind test set. We used the initial data release for most of our reported experiments (i.e. without the additional data released by the shared task organizers closer to the deadline) unless otherwise noted. Table 3 shows the results for different source-target language pairs, comparing the 4 multitask learning models in the multiple experimental conditions (zero shot, few shot, target). The results indicate that out of all the four models considered, fine-tuning multilingual BERT generalizes best across languages. Remarkably, for the target language Bulgarian, even without using any Bulgarian training data, multilingual BERT obtains 0.81 F1 score when trained on English only and 0.808 F1 score when trained on Arabic only. As we increase the target language training samples in the few shot setup, the performance increases, as one would expect. For each model, the best scores are usually obtained by using all the target language training data, either in the full shot setup or in the target-only setup. Overall, multilingual BERT achieves the best F1 scores.

We identified the best systems based on the dev set scores and predicted the test set labels using them. Table 4 shows the top performing models that we submitted for test evaluation, along with their dev and test F1 scores. In addition, the table shows a comparison between the dev F1 scores with and without the additional training data. Surprisingly, the additional English training data did not improve the English F1 score. However, using the additional Arabic training data resulted in a substantial improvement in Arabic F1 score.

6 Conclusion

In this paper, we described Hunter SpeechLab's submission to the shared task, NLP4IF 2021: Fighting the COVID-19 Infodemic. We explored the cross-lingual generalization ability of multitask models trained from scratch (logistic regression, transformer encoder) and pre-trained models (English BERT, m-BERT) for deception detection. We found that even without using any training samples in Bulgarian and Arabic (zero shot), m-BERT achieves impressive scores when evaluating on those languages. In some cases, using just a few training samples in the target language achieves results equal or better than using all the training data in the target language. Our best systems are based on English BERT for English and multilingual BERT for Bulgarian and Arabic. We obtained competitive evaluation test scores on all the three languages, especially Bulgarian and Arabic for which we obtained second best scores among all participating teams. In future work we will further explore the cross-lingual generalization ability of BERT based models in detecting false or deceptive information.

[3]We used the script from `https://github.com/VinAIResearch/BERTweet/blob/master/TweetNormalizer.py` for tokenization and normalization of tweets.

References

Pasquale Capuozzo, Ivano Lauriola, Carlo Strapparava, Fabio Aiolli, and Giuseppe Sartori. 2020a. Automatic detection of cross-language verbal deception.

Pasquale Capuozzo, Ivano Lauriola, Carlo Strapparava, Fabio Aiolli, and Giuseppe Sartori. 2020b. DecOp: A multilingual and multi-domain corpus for detecting deception in typed text. In *Proceedings of the 12th Language Resources and Evaluation Conference*, pages 1423–1430, Marseille, France. European Language Resources Association.

Jacob Devlin, Ming-Wei Chang, Kenton Lee, and Kristina Toutanova. 2019. BERT: Pre-training of deep bidirectional transformers for language understanding. In *Proceedings of the 2019 Conference of the North American Chapter of the Association for Computational Linguistics: Human Language Technologies, Volume 1 (Long and Short Papers)*, pages 4171–4186, Minneapolis, Minnesota. Association for Computational Linguistics.

Sepp Hochreiter and Jürgen Schmidhuber. 1997. Long short-term memory. *Neural Computation*, 9(8):1735–1780.

Tamanna Hossain, Robert L Logan IV, Arjuna Ugarte, Yoshitomo Matsubara, Sean Young, and Sameer Singh. 2020. Covidlies: Detecting covid-19 misinformation on social media. In *Proceedings of the 1st Workshop on NLP for COVID-19 (Part 2) at EMNLP 2020*.

Karthikeyan K, Zihan Wang, Stephen Mayhew, and Dan Roth. 2020. Cross-lingual ability of multilingual bert: An empirical study. In *International Conference on Learning Representations*.

Tanushree Mitra, Graham P Wright, and Eric Gilbert. 2017. A parsimonious language model of social media credibility across disparate events. In *Proceedings of the 2017 ACM conference on computer supported cooperative work and social computing*, pages 126–145.

Adam Paszke, Sam Gross, Francisco Massa, Adam Lerer, James Bradbury, Gregory Chanan, Trevor Killeen, Zeming Lin, Natalia Gimelshein, Luca Antiga, Alban Desmaison, Andreas Kopf, Edward Yang, Zachary DeVito, Martin Raison, Alykhan Tejani, Sasank Chilamkurthy, Benoit Steiner, Lu Fang, Junjie Bai, and Soumith Chintala. 2019. Pytorch: An imperative style, high-performance deep learning library. In H. Wallach, H. Larochelle, A. Beygelzimer, F. d'Alché-Buc, E. Fox, and R. Garnett, editors, *Advances in Neural Information Processing Systems 32*, pages 8024–8035. Curran Associates, Inc.

Verónica Pérez-Rosas and Rada Mihalcea. 2014. Cross-cultural deception detection. In *Proceedings of the 52nd Annual Meeting of the Association for Computational Linguistics (Volume 2: Short Papers)*, pages 440–445, Baltimore, Maryland. Association for Computational Linguistics.

Telmo Pires, Eva Schlinger, and Dan Garrette. 2019. How multilingual is multilingual BERT? In *Proceedings of the 57th Annual Meeting of the Association for Computational Linguistics*, pages 4996–5001, Florence, Italy. Association for Computational Linguistics.

Shaden Shaar, Firoj Alam, Giovanni Da San Martino, Alex Nikolov, Wajdi Zaghouani, Preslav Nakov, and Anna Feldman. 2021. Findings of the NLP4IF-2021 shared task on fighting the COVID-19 infodemic and censorship detection. In *Proceedings of the Fourth Workshop on Natural Language Processing for Internet Freedom: Censorship, Disinformation, and Propaganda*, NLP4IF@NAACL' 21, Online. Association for Computational Linguistics.

Kai Shu, Amy Sliva, Suhang Wang, Jiliang Tang, and Huan Liu. 2017. Fake news detection on social media: A data mining perspective. *ACM SIGKDD explorations newsletter*, 19(1):22–36.

Ashish Vaswani, Noam Shazeer, Niki Parmar, Jakob Uszkoreit, Llion Jones, Aidan N Gomez, Ł ukasz Kaiser, and Illia Polosukhin. 2017. Attention is all you need. In *Advances in Neural Information Processing Systems*, volume 30. Curran Associates, Inc.

Thomas Wolf, Lysandre Debut, Victor Sanh, Julien Chaumond, Clement Delangue, Anthony Moi, Pierric Cistac, Tim Rault, Rémi Louf, Morgan Funtowicz, Joe Davison, Sam Shleifer, Patrick von Platen, Clara Ma, Yacine Jernite, Julien Plu, Canwen Xu, Teven Le Scao, Sylvain Gugger, Mariama Drame, Quentin Lhoest, and Alexander M. Rush. 2020. Transformers: State-of-the-art natural language processing. In *Proceedings of the 2020 Conference on Empirical Methods in Natural Language Processing: System Demonstrations*, pages 38–45, Online. Association for Computational Linguistics.

Y. Zhu, R. Kiros, R. Zemel, R. Salakhutdinov, R. Urtasun, A. Torralba, and S. Fidler. 2015. Aligning books and movies: Towards story-like visual explanations by watching movies and reading books. In *2015 IEEE International Conference on Computer Vision (ICCV)*, pages 19–27.

Transformers to Fight the COVID-19 Infodemic

Lasitha Uyangodage[‡], **Tharindu Ranasinghe**[§], **Hansi Hettiarachchi**[♡],
[‡]Department of Information Systems, University of Münster, Germany
[§]Research Group in Computational Linguistics, University of Wolverhampton, UK
[♡]School of Computing and Digital Technology, Birmingham City University, UK
luyangod@uni-muenster.de

Abstract

The massive spread of false information on social media has become a global risk especially in a global pandemic situation like COVID-19. False information detection has thus become a surging research topic in recent months. NLP4IF-2021 shared task on fighting the COVID-19 infodemic has been organised to strengthen the research in false information detection where the participants are asked to predict seven different binary labels regarding false information in a tweet. The shared task has been organised in three languages; Arabic, Bulgarian and English. In this paper, we present our approach to tackle the task objective using transformers. Overall, our approach achieves a 0.707 mean F1 score in Arabic, 0.578 mean F1 score in Bulgarian and 0.864 mean F1 score in English ranking 4th place in all the languages.

1 Introduction

By April 2021, coronavirus(COVID-19) pandemic has affected 219 nations around the world with 136 million total cases and 2.94 million deaths. With this pandemic situation, a rapid increase in social media usage was noticed. In measures, during 2020, 490 million new users joined indicating a more than 13% year-on-year growth (Kemp, 2021). This growth is mainly resulted due to the impacts on day-to-day activities and information sharing and gathering requirements related to the pandemic.

As a drawback of these exponential growths, the dark side of social media is further revealed during this COVID-19 infodemic (Mourad et al., 2020). The spreading of false and harmful information resulted in panic and confusions which make the pandemic situation worse. Also, the inclusion of false information reduced the usability of a huge volume of data which is generated via social media platforms with the capability of fast propagation. To handle these issues and utilise social media data effectively, accurate identification of false information is crucial. Considering the high data generation in social media, manual approaches to filter false information require significant human efforts. Therefore an automated technique to tackle this problem will be invaluable to the community.

Targeting the infodemic that occurred with COVID-19, NLP4IF-2021 shared task was designed to predict several properties of a tweet including harmfulness, falseness, verifiability, interest to the general public and required attention. The participants of this task were required to predict the binary aspect of the given properties for the test sets in three languages: Arabic, Bulgarian and English provided by the organisers. Our team used recently released transformer models with the text classification architecture to make the predictions and achieved the 4th place in all the languages while maintaining the simplicity and universality of the method. In this paper, we mainly present our approach, with more details about the architecture including an experimental study. We also provide our code to the community which will be freely available to everyone interested in working in this area using the same methodology[1].

2 Related Work

Identifying false information in social media has been a major research topic in recent years. False information detection methods can be mainly categorised into two main areas; Content-based methods and Social Context-based methods (Guo et al., 2020).

Content-based methods are mainly based on the different features in the content of the tweet. For example, Castillo et al. (2011) find that highly credible tweets have more URLs, and the textual content length is usually longer than that of lower credibility tweets. Many studies utilize the lexical and

[1]The GitHub repository is publicly available on https://github.com/tharindudr/infominer

Proceedings of the 4th NLP4IF Workshop on NLP for Internet Freedom, pages 130–135
June 6, 2021. ©2021 Association for Computational Linguistics

syntactic features to detect false information. For instance, Qazvinian et al. (2011) find that the part of speech (POS) is a distinguishable feature for false information detection. Kwon et al. (2013) find that some types of sentiments are apparent features of machine learning classifiers, including positive sentiments words (e.g., love, nice, sweet), negating words (e.g., no, not, never), cognitive action words (e.g., cause, know), and inferring action words (e.g., maybe, perhaps). Then they propose a periodic time-series model to identify key linguistic differences between true tweets and fake tweets. With the word embeddings and deep learning getting popular in natural language processing, most of the fake information detection methods were based on embeddings of the content fed into a deep learning network to perform the classification (Ma et al., 2016).

Traditional content-based methods analyse the credibility of the single microblog or claim in isolation, ignoring the high correlation between different tweets and events. However, Social Context-based methods take different tweets in a user profile or an event to identify false information. Many studies detect false information by analyzing users' credibility (Li et al., 2019) or stances (Mohammad et al., 2017). Since this shared task is mainly focused on the content of the tweet to detect false information, we can identify our method as a content-based false information identification approach.

3 Data

The task is about predicting several binary properties of a tweet on COVID-19: whether it is harmful, whether it contains a verifiable claim, whether it may be of interest to the general public, whether it appears to contain false information, etc. (Shaar et al., 2021). The data has been released for three languages; English, Arabic and Bulgarian [2]. Following are the binary properties that the participants should predict for a tweet.

I **Verifiable Factual Claim**: Does the tweet contain a verifiable factual claim?

II **False Information**: To what extent does the tweet appear to contain false information?

III **Interest to General Public**: Will the tweet have an effect on or be of interest to the general public?

IV **Harmfulness**: To what extent is the tweet harmful to the society?

V **Need of Verification**: Do you think that a professional fact-checker should verify the claim in the tweet?

VI **Harmful to Society**: Is the tweet harmful for the society?

VII **Require attention**: Do you think that this tweet should get the attention of government entities?

4 Architecture

The main motivation for our architecture is the recent success that the transformer models had in various natural language processing tasks like sequence classification (Ranasinghe and Hettiarachchi, 2020; Ranasinghe et al., 2019; Pitenis et al., 2020), token classification (Ranasinghe and Zampieri, 2021a; Ranasinghe et al., 2021), language detection (Jauhiainen et al., 2021), word context prediction (Hettiarachchi and Ranasinghe, 2020a, 2021) question answering (Yang et al., 2019) etc. Apart from providing strong results compared to RNN based architectures (Hettiarachchi and Ranasinghe, 2019; Ranasinghe et al., 2019), transformer models like BERT (Devlin et al., 2019) provide pretrained multilingual language models that support more than 100 languages which will solve the multilingual issues of these tasks (Ranasinghe et al., 2020; Ranasinghe and Zampieri, 2021b, 2020).

Transformer models take an input of a sequence and outputs the representations of the sequence. There can be one or two segments in a sequence which are separated by a special token [SEP] (Devlin et al., 2019). In this approach we considered a tweet as a sequence and no [SEP] token is used. Another special token [CLS] is used as the first token of the sequence which contains a special classification embedding. For text classification tasks, transformer models take the final hidden state **h** of the [CLS] token as the representation of the whole sequence (Sun et al., 2019). A simple softmax classifier is added to the top of the transformer model to predict the probability of a class c as shown in Equation 1 where W is the task-specific parameter matrix. In the classification task all the parameters from transformer as well as W are fine tuned jointly by maximising the log-probability of the correct label. The architecture of transformer-based sequence classifier is shown in Figure 1.

[2]The dataset can be downloaded from `https://gitlab.com/NLP4IF/nlp4if-2021`

$$p(c|\mathbf{h}) = softmax(W\mathbf{h}) \quad (1)$$

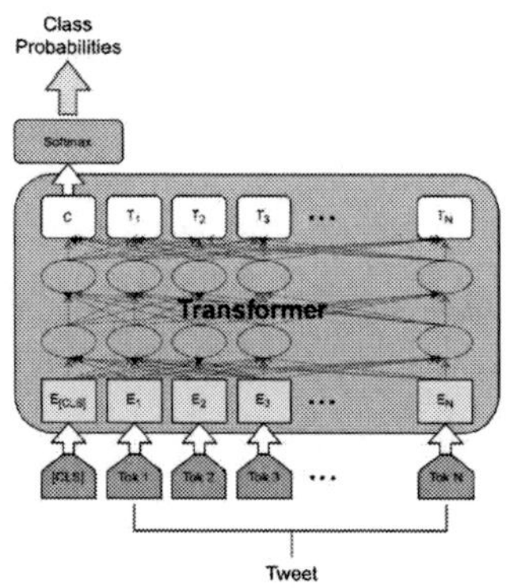

Figure 1: Text Classification Architecture

5 Experimental Setup

We considered the whole task as seven different classification problems. We trained a transformer model for each label mentioned in Section 3. This gave us the flexibility to fine-tune the classification model in to the specific label rather than the whole task. Given the very unbalanced nature of the dataset, the transformer models tend to overfit and predict only the majority class. Therefore, for each label we took the number of instances in the training set for the minority class and undersampled the majority class to have the same number of instances as the minority class.

We then divided this undersampled dataset into a training set and a validation set using 0.8:0.2 split. We mainly fine tuned the learning rate and number of epochs of the classification model manually to obtain the best results for the development set provided by organisers in each language. We obtained $1e^{-5}$ as the best value for learning rate and 3 as the best value for number of epochs for all the languages in all the labels. The other configurations of the transformer model were set to a constant value over all the languages in order to ensure consistency between the languages. We used a batch-size of eight, Adam optimiser (Kingma and Ba, 2014) and a linear learning rate warm-up over 10% of the training data. The models were trained using only training data. We performed early stopping if the evaluation loss did not improve over ten evaluation rounds. A summary of hyperparameters and their values used to obtain the reported results are mentioned in Appendix - Table 3. The optimized hyperparameters are marked with ‡ and their optimal values are reported. The rest of the hyperparameter values are kept as constants. We did not use any language specific preprocessing techniques in order to have a flexible solution between the languages. We used a Nvidia Tesla K80 GPU to train the models. All the experiments were run for five different random seeds and as the final result, we took the majority class predicted by these different random seeds as mention in Hettiarachchi and Ranasinghe (2020b). We used the following pretrained transformer models for the experiments.

bert-base-cased - Introduced in Devlin et al. (2019), the model has been trained on a Wikipedia dump of English using Masked Language Modelling (MLM) objective. There are two variants in English BERT, base model and the large model. Considering the fact that we built seven different models for each label, we decided to use the base model considering the resources and time.

roberta-base - Introduced in Liu et al. (2019), RoBERTa builds on BERT and modifies key hyperparameters, removing the next-sentence pretraining objective and training with much larger mini-batches and learning rates. RoBERTa has outperformed BERT in many NLP tasks and it motivated us to use RoBERTa in this research too. Again we only considered the base model.

bert-nultilingual-cased - Introduced in Devlin et al. (2019), the model has been trained on a Wikipedia dump of 104 languages using MLM objective. This model has shown good performance in variety of languages and tasks. Therefore, we used this model in Arabic and Bulgarian.

AraBERT Recently language-specific BERT based models have proven to be very efficient at language understanding. AraBERT (Antoun et al., 2020) is such a model built for Arabic with BERT using scraped Arabic news websites and two publicly available Arabic corpora; 1.5 billion words Arabic Corpus (El-khair, 2016) and OSIAN: the Open Source International Arabic News Corpus (Zeroual et al., 2019). Since AraBERT has outperformed multilingual bert in many NLP tasks in Arabic (Antoun et al., 2020) we used this model for Arabic in this task. There are two version in AraBERT; AraBERTv0.1 and AraBERTv1, with the difference being that AraBERTv1 uses pre-segmented text where prefixes and suffixes were

	Model	I	II	III	IV	V	VI	VII	Mean
English	roberta-base	0.822	0.393	0.821	0.681	0.461	0.235	0.251	0.523
	bert-base-cased	0.866	0.461	0.893	0.740	0.562	0.285	0.303	0.587
Arabic	bert-multilingual-cased	0.866	0.172	0.724	0.400	0.557	0.411	0.625	0.536
	arabert-v2	0.917	0.196	0.782	0.469	0.601	0.433	0.686	0.583
	arabert-v2-tokenized	0.960	0.136	0.873	0.571	0.598	0.424	0.678	0.606
Bulgarian	bert-multilingual-cased	0.845	0.098	0.516	0.199	0.467	0.303	0.196	0.375

Table 1: Macro F1 between the algorithm predictions and human annotations for development set in all the languages. Results are sorted from Mean F1 score for each language.

	Model	I	II	III	IV	V	VI	VII	Mean
English	Best System	0.835	0.913	0.978	0.873	0.882	0.908	0.889	0.897
	InfoMiner	0.819	0.886	0.946	0.841	0.803	0.884	0.867	0.864
	Random Baseline	0.552	0.480	0.457	0.473	0.423	0.563	0.526	0.496
Arabic	Best System	0.843	0.762	0.890	0.799	0.596	0.912	0.663	0.781
	InfoMiner	0.852	0.704	0.774	0.743	0.593	0.698	0.588	0.707
	Random Baseline	0.510	0.444	0.487	0.442	0.476	0.584	0.533	0.496
Bulgarian	Best System	0.887	0.955	0.980	0.834	0.819	0.678	0.706	0.837
	InfoMiner	0.786	0.749	0.419	0.599	0.556	0.303	0.631	0.578
	Random Baseline	0.594	0.502	0.470	0.480	0.399	0.498	0.528	0.496

Table 2: Macro F1 between the InfoMiner submission and human annotations for test set in all the languages. Best System is the results of the best model submitted for each language as reported by the task organisers (Shaar et al., 2021).

splitted using the Farasa Segmenter (Abdelali et al., 2016).

6 Results

When it comes to selecting the best model for each language, highest F1 score out of the evaluated models was chosen. Due to the fact that our approach uses a single model for each label, our main goal was to achieve good F1 scores using light weight models. The limitation of available resources to train several models for all seven labels itself was a very challenging task to the team but we managed to evaluate several.

As depicted in Table 1, for English, bert-base-cased model performed better than roberta-base model. For Arabic, arabert-v2-tokenized performed better than the other two models we considered. For Bulgarian, with the limited time, we could only train bert-multilingual model, therefore, we submitted the predictions from that for Bulgarian.

As shown in Table 2, our submission is very competitive with the best system submitted in each language and well above the random baseline. Our team was ranked 4th in all the languages.

7 Conclusion

We have presented the system by InfoMiner team for NLP4IF-2021-Fighting the COVID-19 Infodemic. We have shown that multiple transformer models trained on different labels can be successfully applied to this task. Furthermore, we have shown that undersampling can be used to prevent the overfitting of the transformer models to the majority class in an unbalanced dataset like this. Overall, our approach is simple but can be considered as effective since it achieved 4th place in the leader-board for all three languages.

One limitation in our approach is that it requires maintaining seven transformer models for the seven binary properties of this task which can be costly in a practical scenario which also restricted us from experimenting with different transformer types due to the limited time and resources. Therefore, in future work, we are interested in remodeling the task as a multilabel classification problem, where a single transformer model can be used to predict all seven labels.

Acknowledgments

We would like to thank the shared task organizers for making this interesting dataset available. We further thank the anonymous reviewers for their insightful feedback.

References

Ahmed Abdelali, Kareem Darwish, Nadir Durrani, and Hamdy Mubarak. 2016. Farasa: A fast and furious segmenter for Arabic. In *Proceedings of the 2016 Conference of the North American Chapter of the Association for Computational Linguistics: Demonstrations*, pages 11–16, San Diego, California. Association for Computational Linguistics.

Wissam Antoun, Fady Baly, and Hazem Hajj. 2020. AraBERT: Transformer-based model for Arabic language understanding. In *Proceedings of the 4th Workshop on Open-Source Arabic Corpora and Processing Tools, with a Shared Task on Offensive Language Detection*, pages 9–15, Marseille, France. European Language Resource Association.

Carlos Castillo, Marcelo Mendoza, and Barbara Poblete. 2011. Information credibility on twitter. In *Proceedings of the 20th International Conference on World Wide Web*, WWW '11, page 675–684, New York, NY, USA. Association for Computing Machinery.

Jacob Devlin, Ming-Wei Chang, Kenton Lee, and Kristina Toutanova. 2019. BERT: Pre-training of deep bidirectional transformers for language understanding. In *Proceedings of the 2019 Conference of the North American Chapter of the Association for Computational Linguistics: Human Language Technologies, Volume 1 (Long and Short Papers)*, pages 4171–4186, Minneapolis, Minnesota. Association for Computational Linguistics.

Ibrahim Abu El-khair. 2016. 1.5 billion words arabic corpus. In *arXiv preprint arXiv:1611.04033*.

Bin Guo, Yasan Ding, Lina Yao, Yunji Liang, and Zhiwen Yu. 2020. The future of false information detection on social media: New perspectives and trends. *ACM Comput. Surv.*, 53(4).

Hansi Hettiarachchi and Tharindu Ranasinghe. 2019. Emoji powered capsule network to detect type and target of offensive posts in social media. In *Proceedings of the International Conference on Recent Advances in Natural Language Processing (RANLP 2019)*, pages 474–480, Varna, Bulgaria. INCOMA Ltd.

Hansi Hettiarachchi and Tharindu Ranasinghe. 2020a. BRUMS at SemEval-2020 task 3: Contextualised embeddings for predicting the (graded) effect of context in word similarity. In *Proceedings of the Fourteenth Workshop on Semantic Evaluation*, pages 142–149, Barcelona (online). International Committee for Computational Linguistics.

Hansi Hettiarachchi and Tharindu Ranasinghe. 2020b. InfoMiner at WNUT-2020 task 2: Transformer-based covid-19 informative tweet extraction. In *Proceedings of the Sixth Workshop on Noisy User-generated Text (W-NUT 2020)*, pages 359–365, Online. Association for Computational Linguistics.

Hansi Hettiarachchi and Tharindu Ranasinghe. 2021. TransWiC at SemEval-2021 Task 2: Transformer-based Multilingual and Cross-lingual Word-in-Context Disambiguation. In *Proceedings of the Fifteenth Workshop on Semantic Evaluation*.

Tommi Jauhiainen, Tharindu Ranasinghe, and Marcos Zampieri. 2021. Comparing approaches to Dravidian language identification. In *Proceedings of the Eighth Workshop on NLP for Similar Languages, Varieties and Dialects*, pages 120–127, Kiyv, Ukraine. Association for Computational Linguistics.

Simon Kemp. 2021. 15.5 users join social every second (and other key stats to know). `https://blog.hootsuite.com/simon-kemp-social-media/`.

Diederik P. Kingma and Jimmy Ba. 2014. Adam: A method for stochastic optimization. In *arXiv preprint arXiv:1412.6980*.

S. Kwon, M. Cha, K. Jung, W. Chen, and Y. Wang. 2013. Prominent features of rumor propagation in online social media. In *2013 IEEE 13th International Conference on Data Mining*, pages 1103–1108.

Quanzhi Li, Qiong Zhang, and Luo Si. 2019. Rumor detection by exploiting user credibility information, attention and multi-task learning. In *Proceedings of the 57th Annual Meeting of the Association for Computational Linguistics*, pages 1173–1179, Florence, Italy. Association for Computational Linguistics.

Yinhan Liu, Myle Ott, Naman Goyal, Jingfei Du, Mandar Joshi, Danqi Chen, Omer Levy, Mike Lewis, Luke Zettlemoyer, and Veselin Stoyanov. 2019. Roberta: A robustly optimized bert pretraining approach. In *arXiv preprint arXiv:1907.11692*.

Jing Ma, Wei Gao, Prasenjit Mitra, Sejeong Kwon, Bernard J. Jansen, Kam-Fai Wong, and Meeyoung Cha. 2016. Detecting rumors from microblogs with recurrent neural networks. In *Proceedings of the Twenty-Fifth International Joint Conference on Artificial Intelligence*, IJCAI'16, page 3818–3824. AAAI Press.

Saif M. Mohammad, Parinaz Sobhani, and Svetlana Kiritchenko. 2017. Stance and sentiment in tweets. *ACM Trans. Internet Technol.*, 17(3).

Azzam Mourad, Ali Srour, Haidar Harmanai, Cathia Jenainati, and Mohamad Arafeh. 2020. Critical impact of social networks infodemic on defeating coronavirus covid-19 pandemic: Twitter-based study and research directions. *IEEE Transactions on Network and Service Management*, 17(4):2145–2155.

Zesis Pitenis, Marcos Zampieri, and Tharindu Ranasinghe. 2020. Offensive language identification in Greek. In *Proceedings of the 12th Language Resources and Evaluation Conference*, pages 5113–5119, Marseille, France. European Language Resources Association.

Vahed Qazvinian, Emily Rosengren, Dragomir R. Radev, and Qiaozhu Mei. 2011. Rumor has it: Identifying misinformation in microblogs. In *Proceedings of the 2011 Conference on Empirical Methods in Natural Language Processing*, pages 1589–1599, Edinburgh, Scotland, UK. Association for Computational Linguistics.

Tharindu Ranasinghe, Sarthak Gupte, Marcos Zampieri, and Ifeoma Nwogu. 2020. WLV-RIT at HASOC-Dravidian-CodeMix-FIRE2020: Offensive Language Identification in Code-switched YouTube Comments. In *Proceedings of the 12th annual meeting of the Forum for Information Retrieval Evaluation*.

Tharindu Ranasinghe and Hansi Hettiarachchi. 2020. BRUMS at SemEval-2020 task 12: Transformer based multilingual offensive language identification in social media. In *Proceedings of the Fourteenth Workshop on Semantic Evaluation*, pages 1906–1915, Barcelona (online). International Committee for Computational Linguistics.

Tharindu Ranasinghe, Diptanu Sarkar, Marcos Zampieri, and Alex Ororbia. 2021. WLV-RIT at SemEval-2021 Task 5: A Neural Transformer Framework for Detecting Toxic Spans. In *Proceedings of the Fifteenth Workshop on Semantic Evaluation*.

Tharindu Ranasinghe and Marcos Zampieri. 2020. Multilingual offensive language identification with cross-lingual embeddings. In *Proceedings of the 2020 Conference on Empirical Methods in Natural Language Processing (EMNLP)*, pages 5838–5844, Online. Association for Computational Linguistics.

Tharindu Ranasinghe and Marcos Zampieri. 2021a. MUDES: Multilingual Detection of Offensive Spans. In *Proceedings of the 2021 Conference of the North American Chapter of the Association for Computational Linguistics (Demonstrations)*.

Tharindu Ranasinghe and Marcos Zampieri. 2021b. Multilingual Offensive Language Identification for Low-resource Languages. *ACM Transactions on Asian and Low-Resource Language Information Processing (TALLIP)*.

Tharindu Ranasinghe, Marcos Zampieri, and Hansi Hettiarachchi. 2019. BRUMS at HASOC 2019: Deep learning models for multilingual hate speech and offensive language identification. In *Proceedings of the 11th annual meeting of the Forum for Information Retrieval Evaluation*.

Shaden Shaar, Firoj Alam, Giovanni Da San Martino, Alex Nikolov, Wajdi Zaghouani, Preslav Nakov, and Anna Feldman. 2021. Findings of the NLP4IF-2021 shared task on fighting the COVID-19 infodemic and censorship detection. In *Proceedings of the Fourth Workshop on Natural Language Processing for Internet Freedom: Censorship, Disinformation, and Propaganda*, NLP4IF@NAACL' 21, Online. Association for Computational Linguistics.

Chi Sun, Xipeng Qiu, Yige Xu, and Xuanjing Huang. 2019. How to fine-tune bert for text classification? In *Chinese Computational Linguistics*, pages 194–206, Cham. Springer International Publishing.

Wei Yang, Yuqing Xie, Aileen Lin, Xingyu Li, Luchen Tan, Kun Xiong, Ming Li, and Jimmy Lin. 2019. End-to-end open-domain question answering with BERTserini. In *Proceedings of the 2019 Conference of the North American Chapter of the Association for Computational Linguistics (Demonstrations)*, pages 72–77, Minneapolis, Minnesota. Association for Computational Linguistics.

Imad Zeroual, Dirk Goldhahn, Thomas Eckart, and Abdelhak Lakhouaja. 2019. OSIAN: Open source international Arabic news corpus - preparation and integration into the CLARIN-infrastructure. In *Proceedings of the Fourth Arabic Natural Language Processing Workshop*, pages 175–182, Florence, Italy. Association for Computational Linguistics.

A Appendix

A summary of hyperparameters and their values used to obtain the reported results are mentioned in Table 3. The optimised hyperparameters are marked with ‡ and their optimal values are reported. The rest of the hyperparameter values are kept as constants.

Parameter	**Value**
learning rate‡	$1e^{-5}$
number of epochs‡	3
adam epsilon	$1e^{-8}$
warmup ration	0.1
warmup steps	0
max grad norm	1.0
max seq. length	120
gradient accumulation steps	1

Table 3: Hyperparameter specifications

Classification of Censored Tweets in Chinese Language using XLNet

Shaikh Sahil Ahmed and Anand Kumar M.
Department of Information Technology,
National Institute of Technology Karnataka,
Surathkal, Mangalore, India
sahilahmed786001@gmail.com m_anandkumar@nitk.edu.in

Abstract

In the growth of today's world and advanced technology, social media networks play a significant role in impacting human lives. Censorship is the overthrowing of speech, public transmission, or other details that play a vast role in social media. The content may be considered harmful, sensitive, or inconvenient. Authorities like institutes, governments, and other organizations conduct Censorship. This paper has implemented a model that helps classify censored and uncensored tweets as a binary classification. The paper describes submission to the Censorship shared task of the NLP4IF 2021 workshop. We used various transformer-based pre-trained models, and XLNet outputs a better accuracy among all. We fine-tuned the model for better performance and achieved a reasonable accuracy, and calculated other performance metrics.

1 Introduction

The suppression of words, images, and ideas is known as Censorship. The government or the private organization can carry Censorship based on objectionable, harmful, sensitive, or inconvenient material. There are different types of Censorship; for example, when a person uses Censorship for their work or speech, this type of Censorship is known as self-censorship. Censorship is used for many things like books, music, videos, movies, etc., for various reasons like hate speech, national security, etc. (Khurana et al., 2017). Many countries in their law provide protections against Censorship, but there is much uncertainty in determining what could be censored and what could not be censored.

However, nowadays, we know that most of the data and the information are available on the internet, so many governments strictly monitor the disturbing or objectionable content on the internet. We could not use any method other than the software like fraud censorship detection and disturbing and objectionable content monitor, which works continuously and maintains the same accuracy for monitoring this vast data size.

This paper examines the methodologies and various machine learning domains that classify the censored and uncensored tweets associated with the workshop (Shaar et al., 2021). We used multiple models such as BERT (Bidirectional Encoder Representations from Transformers) (Devlin et al., 2018), DeBERTa (Decoding- enhanced BERT with disentangled attention) (He et al., 2020), ELECTRA (Clark et al., 2020), and XLNet (a generic autoregressive pre-training procedure) for binary classification of the tweets. "0" says that the tweet is uncensored, and "1" says that the tweet is censored. Also, we have experimented with various phases, such as data preprocessing, tokenization, and fine-tuning for model prediction. Further, we will go through various performance metrics such as accuracy, precision, and recall. We achieved a reasonable accuracy using XLNet as compared to other models.

2 Relevant Work

(Aceto and Pescapè, 2015) proposed a source for censoring procedures and a characterization of censoring systems and studied the tools and various censorship detection platforms. They also presented a characterization plan to analyze and examine multiple censored and uncensored data. They used their results to understand current hurdles and suggested new directions in the area of censorship detection.

(Ben Jones and Gill, 2014) presented an automated system that permits continuous measurements of block pages and filters them from generated. They claimed that their system detects 95% of the block pages, recognized five filtering tools, and evaluated performance metrics and various fingerprinting methods.

(Athanasopoulos et al., 2011) presented the idea and implementation of a web-based censorship monitor named "CensMon". CensMon works automatically and does not depends on Internet users to inform censored websites. Possible censorship is distinguished from access network breakdowns, and various input streams are utilized to define the type of censored data. They showed that their model detects the censored data favourably and points filtering methodologies efficiently used by the censor.

(Niaki et al., 2019) presented ICLab used for censorship research that is known to be an internet measurement platform. It can recognize DNS manipulation where the browser initially purposes its IP address with a DNS query and TCP-packed injection. ICLabs attempts to reduce false positives and manual validation

Proceedings of the 4th NLP4IF Workshop on NLP for Internet Freedom, pages 136–139
June 6, 2021.

through performing operations and going through all the processing levels. They plotted various graphs, planned, and calculated metrics and concluded that ICLab detects different censorship mechanisms.

3 Dataset Description

The dataset of the shared task has been built using a web scraper (Kei Yin Ng and Peng, 2020) that contains censored and uncensored tweets gathered for a duration of 4 months (August 29, 2018, to December 29, 2018). The dataset attributes contain tweets (represented by the text in the dataset) and label, where the "text" field contains the information collected in the Chinese language, and "label" contains 0's and 1's where '0' signifies the tweet as uncensored and '1' signifies as a censored tweet. The first few lines and format of the dataset is shown in Fig. 1.

text	label
据说 卡塔尔 要 退出 石油输出国组织 ， 这是 川普 退群潮 的 连锁反应 ， 也 是 世...	0
早上 没 起床 先 各 渠道 看看 与 川普 在 阿根廷 的 会面 。 留给 中国 国家足球...	1
面对 加拿大 及 美国 的 无理 行为 ， 中国 也 可以 （ 无 任何理由 ） 把 加拿大...	0
如果 特朗普 宣布 美国 对 2000 亿 中国 出口 美国 商品 征收 10% 的 关税 ...	1
两个 白日梦 什么 时候 能 像 宣传 禁毒 一样 宣传 反 强奸 什么 时候 防空警报 能...	0

Figure 1: First few lines of dataset.

The dataset comprises three sets, i.e. train, validation and test set. The train set comprises 1512 tweets, and the validation set comprises 189 tweets. The test set only comprises 189 tweets with no labels.

4 Methodology

The XLNet (Yang et al., 2019) is a transformer-based machine learning method for Natural Language Processing tasks. It is famous for a generalized autoregressive pretraining method which is one of the most significant emerging models of NLP. The XLNet consists of the recent innovations in NLP, stating the solutions and other approaches regarding language modelling. XLNet is also known for the auto-regressive language model that promotes joint predictions over a sequence of tokens on transformer design. It aims to find the possibility of a word token's overall alterations of word tokens in a sentence.

The language model comprises two stages, the pre-train phase and fine-tune phase. XLNet mainly concentrates on the pre-train phase. Permutation Language Modeling is one of the new objectives which is implemented in the pre-train phase. We used "hfl/chinese-xlnet-base" as a pre-trained model (Cui et al., 2020) for Chinese data that targets enhancing Chinese NLP resources and contributes a broad category of Chinese pre-trained model selection.

Initially, the dataset is preprocessed, and the generated tokens are given input to XLNet pre-trained model. The model trains the data over 20 epochs and further

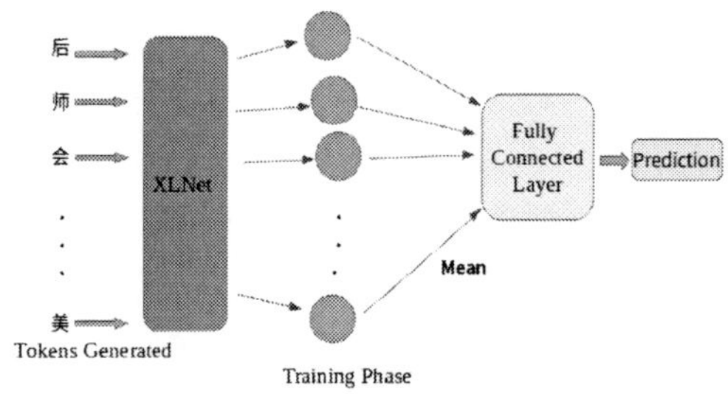

Figure 2: Architecture of XLNet.

goes through a mean pool, passing through a fully connected layer for fine-tuning and classification, and predicts the data over a given test set. Fig. 2 shows the architecture of the XLNet model.

4.1 Data Preprocessing

The dataset contains fields like "text" and "label" only, extra attribute "id" is added to the dataset for better preprocessing. Also, the noisy information from the dataset has been filtered out by using the "tweet-preprocessor" library. After preprocessing the dataset with the first few lines is shown in Fig. 3.

text	label	id
据说 卡塔尔 要 退出 石油输出国组织 ， 这是 川普 退群潮 的 连锁反应 ， 也 是 世...	0	1
早上 没 起床 先 各 渠道 看看 与 川普 在 阿根廷 的 会面 。 留给 中国 国家足球...	1	2
面对 加拿大 及 美国 的 无理 行为 ， 中国 也 可以 （ 无 任何理由 ） 把 加拿大...	0	3
如果 特朗普 宣布 美国 对 2000 亿 中国 出口 美国 商品 征收 10% 的 关税 ...	1	4
两个 白日梦 什么 时候 能 像 宣传 禁毒 一样 宣传 反 强奸 什么 时候 防空警报 能...	0	5

Figure 3: First few lines of dataset after preprocessing.

4.2 Tokenization

Tokenization breaks down a text document into a phrase, sentence, paragraph, or smaller units, such as single words. Those smaller units are said to be tokens. All this breakdown happens with the help of a tokenizer before feeding it to the model. We used "XLNetTokenizer" on the pre-trained model, as the models need tokens to be in an orderly fashion. The tokenizer imports from the "transformers" library. So, word segmentation can be said to break down a sentence into component words that are to be feed into the model.

4.3 Fine-Tuning

A pre-trained model is used to classify the text, where an encoder subnetwork is combined with a fully connected layer for prediction. Further, the tokenized training data is used to fine-tune the model weights. We have used "XLNetForSequenceClassification" for sequence classification. It consists of a linear layer on the pooled output peak. The model targets to do binary classification on the test data.

5 Experiments and Results

We have used Adam optimizer to fine-tune the pre-trained model and performed label encoding for output labels. The softmax over the logits used for prediction and the learning rate is initialized with 2e-5, and twenty epochs were used for training. After training the data with XLNet, we achieved a training accuracy of 0.99.

Models	Validation Set		
	Precision	Recall	F1-measure
BERT	0.544	0.544	0.544
DeBERTa	0.476	0.476	0.476
ELECTRA	0.624	0.624	0.624
XLNET	**0.634**	**0.634**	**0.634**

Table 1: Performance of the system on validation data.

We calculated precision, recall and F1-measure for the validation set with all the four models used in our investigation, as shown in Table 1. We got a precision of 0.634 and a recall of 0.634, which is far better than other models. Fig. 4 shows the plot for different epochs vs. validation accuracy during the training phase.

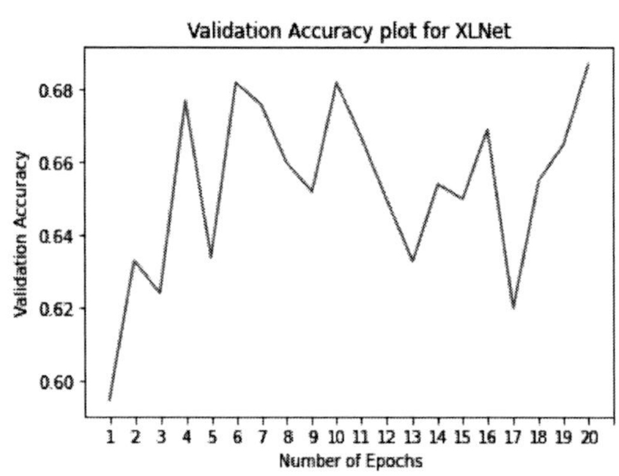

Figure 4: Validation Accuracy plot.

Class	Test Set		
	Precision	Recall	F1-Measure
0	0.61	0.73	0.66
1	0.69	0.56	0.62

Table 2: Performance of the system on test data using XLNet.

Class	Accuracy
Majority baseline	49.98
Human baseline	23.83
XLNet	0.64

Table 3: Accuracy.

Moving ahead with test data, we achieved a precision of 0.65 and recall of 0.64 using XLNet. Table 2. shows the precision, recall, and F1-Measure for test set using XLNet. Also, we found majority class baseline as 49.98 and human baseline as 23.83 as shown in Table 3.

Finally, we made one CSV file where the file contains test data tweet with label attribute. Fig. 5 shows the test data prediction, where the tweets are classified as censored and uncensored tweets.

Tweet id	Tweet	label
1	20.一位机械工程专家讲过这样一件事："文革"中，他在某地...	0
2	警惕看不到内心的人，虚荣的人，心狠的人，没有是非观的人，...	1
3	这个国在计划生育的时候对人都能下杀手，何况现在杭州政策杀狗...	1
4	罗伯特.所罗门《大问题——简明哲学导论》在我们这样一个多元的...	0
5	特朗普，输了！O特朗普，输了！	1

Figure 5: First few lines of test data after prediction.

6 Conclusion and Future Work

In the paper, we investigated various pre-trained models and achieved a reasonable accuracy for XLNET. We cleaned the dataset during preprocessing, which is further given input to the model. XLNet seems to be influential in the classification problem moving deep into censorship detection. XLNet performs better than BERT, DeBERTa, and ELECTRA having its improved training methodology, where it uses permutation language modelling predicting the tokens randomly. The future work is to examine other NLP models and fine-tune them censorship detection in other languages.

References

Giuseppe Aceto and Antonio Pescapè. 2015. Internet censorship detection: A survey. *Computer Networks*, 83.

Elias Athanasopoulos, Sotiris Ioannidis, and Andreas Sfakianakis. 2011. Censmon: A web censorship monitor. In *USENIX Workshop on Free and Open Communications on the Internet (FOCI 11)*, San Francisco, CA. USENIX Association.

Nick Feamster Ben Jones, Tzu-Wen Lee and Phillipa Gill. 2014. Automated detection and fingerprinting of censorship block pages. *Stony Brook University*.

Kevin Clark, Minh-Thang Luong, Quoc Le, and Christopher Manning. 2020. Electra: Pre-training text encoders as discriminators rather than generators.

Yiming Cui, Wanxiang Che, Ting Liu, Bing Qin, Shijin Wang, and Guoping Hu. 2020. Revisiting pre-trained models for Chinese natural language processing. In *Proceedings of the 2020 Conference on Empirical Methods in Natural Language Processing: Findings*, pages 657–668, Online. Association for Computational Linguistics.

Jacob Devlin, Ming-Wei Chang, Kenton Lee, and Kristina Toutanova. 2018. Bert: Pre-training of deep bidirectional transformers for language understanding.

Pengcheng He, Xiaodong Liu, Jianfeng Gao, and Weizhu Chen. 2020. Deberta: Decoding-enhanced bert with disentangled attention.

Anna Feldman Kei Yin Ng and Jing Peng. 2020. Linguistic fingerprints of internet censorship: The case of sina weibo. volume 34, pages 446–453. Proceedings of the AAAI Conference on Artificial Intelligence.

Diksha Khurana, Aditya Koli, Kiran Khatter, and Sukhdev Singh. 2017. Natural language processing: State of the art, current trends and challenges.

Arian Akhavan Niaki, Shinyoung Cho, Zachary Weinberg, Nguyen Phong Hoang, Abbas Razaghpanah, Nicolas Christin, and Phillipa Gill. 2019. Iclab: A global, longitudinal internet censorship measurement platform.

Shaden Shaar, Firoj Alam, Giovanni Da San Martino, Alex Nikolov, Wajdi Zaghouani, Preslav Nakov, and Anna Feldman. 2021. Findings of the NLP4IF-2021 shared task on fighting the COVID-19 infodemic and censorship detection. In *Proceedings of the Fourth Workshop on Natural Language Processing for Internet Freedom: Censorship, Disinformation, and Propaganda*, NLP4IF@NAACL' 21, Online. Association for Computational Linguistics.

Zhilin Yang, Zihang Dai, Yiming Yang, Jaime Carbonell, Ruslan Salakhutdinov, and Quoc Le. 2019. Xlnet: Generalized autoregressive pretraining for language understanding.

Author Index

Abdul-Mageed, Muhammad, 57
Abdullah, Malak Abdullah, 104
Abujaber, Dia, 104
Agarwal, Raksha, 99
Ahmed, Shaikh Sahil, 136
Al-Qarqaz, Ahmed, 104
Alabdulkarim, Amal, 57
Alam, Firoj, 82
Alhindi, Tariq, 57
Alnajjar, Khalid, 39
Alshehri, Ali, 57
Althoff, Tim, 29
Ayton, Ellyn, 29

Banerjee, Ritwik, 76
Bekoulis, Giannis, 23
Bose, Tulika, 51

Caselli, Tommaso, 119
Chatterjee, Niladri, 99

Da San Martino, Giovanni, 82
Daelemans, Walter, 7, 17
Deligiannis, Nikos, 23

Feldman, Anna, 82
Fohr, Dominique, 51
Fourati, Chayma, 115

Ghneim, Nada, 93
Glenski, Maria, 29
Goldwasser, Dan, 66

Haddad, Hatem, 115
Hämäläinen, Mika, 39
Henia, Wassim, 115
Hettiarachchi, Hansi, 130
Hussein, Ahmad, 93

Illina, Irina, 51

Jhunjhunwala, Naman, 99
Joukhadar, Ammar, 93

Kazemi, Ashkan, 45
Kogkalidis, Konstantinos, 119
Kowshik, Shreyas, 110
Kumar M., Anand, 136
Kumar, Ankit, 99

Lemmens, Jens, 7
Levitan, Sarah Ita, 125
Li, Chang, 66
Li, Zehua, 45

Markov, Ilia, 7, 17
Maronikolakis, Antonis, 1
Mihalcea, Rada, 45

Nakov, Preslav, 57, 82
Nikolov, Alex, 82

Panda, Subhadarshi, 125
Papagiannopoulou, Christina, 23
Partanen, Niko, 39
Pérez-Rosas, Verónica, 45

Ranasinghe, Tharindu, 130
Rjab, Oumayma, 115
Rueter, Jack, 39

Schütze, Hinrich, 1
Shaar, Shaden, 82
Stevenson, Mark, 1
Suhane, Ayush, 110

Tziafas, Georgios, 119

Uyangodage, Lasitha, 130

Weld, Galen, 29

Zaghouani, Wajdi, 82
Zhang, Qi, 76
Zuo, Chaoyuan, 76

Association for Computational Linguistics
209 N. Eighth Street
Stroudsburg, Pennsylvania 18360

ISBN 978-1-7138-3025-2

9 781713 830252

CURRAN ASSOCIATES INC.
proceedings.com